SCOTTISH FAMILY HISTORIES
HELD IN SCOTTISH LIBRARIES

Scottish Family Histories

held in

Scottish Libraries

Compiled by

JOAN P. S. FERGUSON, M.A., A.L.A.

Chief Assistant, Scottish Central Library

With an Introduction by

SIR THOMAS INNES OF LEARNEY,

K.C.V.O., LL.D., F.S.A.Scot.

Lord Lyon King of Arms

Published by

THE SCOTTISH CENTRAL LIBRARY

LAWNMARKET EDINBURGH

1960

© The Scottish Central Library, 1960

First printed	1960
Reprinted	1964
Reprinted	1968
Reprinted	1970
Reprinted	1973

CONTENTS

INTRODUCTION

SIR THOMAS INNES OF LEARNEY, K.C.V.O., LL.D., F.S.A.Scot.

Lord Lyon King of Arms

IT is now just on thirty years since the publication of Margaret Stuart and Sir James Balfour Paul's *Scottish Family History*. This has been a source of great assistance to every genealogist and enquirer, and has also, from its introduction, been of immense help to those starting to write a family history of their own. One only wishes that some of those who have compiled such *without* having read that introduction had done so! I cannot on this point do better than say that everyone who aspires to writing a genealogical work should carefully study that useful guide—and the structure of the articles in the *Scots Peerage*, 1904-1910 edition—before they start. Such articles can be expanded to include much additional matter, and yet maintain the same form—which is after all that also used (with great condensation) in those admirable works, Burke's *Peerage* and Burke's *Landed Gentry*.

I do not think that quarto can be bettered as the size for serious family history, because it enables just the right amount to be got upon a single page, and enough of children and grandchildren to be readily grasped at a glance, and thus makes the most of the material and probably the maximum use also of the printed area.

Nevertheless, the size used in the *Scots Peerage* itself, and in books such as those of the *Scottish History Society* format, can indeed be used for family history, but they will take longer to consult. One point certainly to bear in mind is that if the book is to be welcome on modern bookshelves and serve its purpose in modern life, it should be on thin paper, and so take the minimum space on bookshelves. The edges should, moreover, be clean-trimmed so that they turn rapidly and the index should follow the style of those in the *Scots Peerage*, or the *Registrum Magni Sigilli*—and of these the older are particularly well constructed. There is no excuse nowadays for single-sided sized paper illustrations—both sides should be employed—likewise for space-saving needs. For appendix purposes, the type and fully occupied page of *Scottish Record Society* publications are a guide on how to make a family history accessible.

So much, then, for the volumes for which demand steadily increases, for as time passes in a world which often pays less and less attention to The Family in daily life, people all over both the Old

World and the New are paying more and more attention to The Family which, in a recent case, Lord President Clyde observed, is the foundation of human society.

The Court of the Lord Lyon is more widely invoked nowadays than it has ever been in the past; the Scots Ancestry Research Society furnishes enquirers with the skilled reports of a staff of qualified searchers, and literary and historical societies are again, after the difficulties of post-war years, taking up the thread of local history.

During the past generation—the thirty years since Stuart and Paul's valuable list of Scottish family histories—many further volumes of public records have been printed, many works of learned societies have also emerged, and many new family histories have been printed, so that today, Stuart and Paul are no longer a fully up-to-date source for the latest information on family history.

A new compendium of such published works has become necessary for both historians, students, tourists and local, and indeed national, historians. This the Scottish Central Library has now furnished and has moreover added the useful information *where* the listed family histories can be consulted—information which will be a boon to many searchers and save much valuable time. I must congratulate all concerned in thus making available a fresh and important reference book to all interested in Scottish history, and in Scottish families, whose vicissitudes and activities have made such an imprint on the general history of a tribally organised nation such as Scotland.

NOTE ON SCOPE AND ARRANGEMENT

THIS Catalogue has been compiled from lists sent in to the Scottish Central Library in response to a circular enquiry, and the result is impressive evidence of the harmonious spirit of co-operation prevailing among Scottish libraries. This compilation records the whereabouts of some 2,000 Scottish family histories held in 76 urban, county, university and institutional libraries.

Users of the Catalogue are asked to note the following:

(1) Biographies of individuals have not been included, except where they contain sufficient information about the families to justify inclusion as family histories.

(2) The arrangement of the works is alphabetically by *family name*, subdivided by branches, and with references from titles, e.g.

Campbell
Campbell, Earl of, Marquess of, Duke of Argyll
Campbell of Auchinbreck

Argyll, Earl of, Marquess of, Duke of, *see* **Campbell**, Earl of, Marquess of, Duke of Argyll

(3) An exception to the foregoing rule is made for *peerage cases*, where titles were disputed, and the works are more conveniently entered under the title, e.g.

Mar, Earldom of

(4) Where ascertainable, the place and date of publication are given. The abbreviations "n.p." and "n.d." mean that the place or date, respectively, of the work have not been ascertained from the work itself.

(5) This compilation does not include the very extensive holdings of the National Library of Scotland, since the task of preparing a comprehensive catalogue of all its Scottish family history material would be quite beyond its resources in staff. Those who are able to visit the National Library, however, will there find a wealth of material, both printed and in manuscript.

The holdings of Edinburgh University Library are limited to Scottish family histories added to stock since the publication of the printed catalogue of the University Library in three volumes, 1918-23.

(6) With a few exceptions, this Catalogue is restricted to printed books and pamphlets. At a future date it may be found possible to collect and publish details of all the manuscript material on Scottish family history held in the libraries which have co-operated in the present venture.

(7) The inclusion of any work in this list does not necessarily imply that it is available for loan. Readers are asked to approach their local Librarian in the first instance, with the request that he should communicate with the Librarian of the Scottish Central Library if the required work is not available locally.

Where works are too valuable or too rare to be lent in the original, it should in many cases be possible for the Scottish Central Library Photographic Department to supply microfilms or photographic prints.

M. C. POTTINGER
Librarian, Scottish Central Library

KEY TO LIBRARY SYMBOLS

Ab. C.	. .	Aberdeen County Library
Ab. P. .	. .	Aberdeen Public Library
Ab. U. .	. .	Aberdeen University Library
Air. P.	. .	Airdrie Public Library
Ang. C.	. .	Angus & Kincardine County Library
Arb. P.	. .	Arbroath Public Library
Arg. C.	. .	Argyll County Library
Ayr C.	. .	Ayr County Library
Ayr P. .	. .	Ayr Public Library
Banff C.	. .	Banff County Library
Ber. C.	. .	Berwickshire County Library
Bo'n. P.	. .	Bo'ness Public Library
Bre. P.	. .	Brechin Public Library
Buck. P.	. .	Buckhaven & Methil Public Library
Burnt. P.	. .	Burntisland Public Library
Bute C.	. .	Bute County Library
Cai. C.	. .	Caithness County Library
Camp. P.	. .	Campbeltown Public Library
Clack. C.	. .	Clackmannan County Library
Cly. P.	. .	Clydebank Public Library
Coat. P.	. .	Coatbridge Public Library
Dun. P.	. .	Dunoon Public Library
Dumb. P.	. .	Dumbarton Public Library
Dumf. C.	. .	Dumfries County Library
Dund. C.	. .	Dunbarton County Library
Dund. P.	. .	Dundee Public Library
Dund. Q.	. .	Dundee, Queen's College
Dunf. P.	. .	Dunfermline Public Library
Edin. Ant.	. .	Edinburgh, Society of Antiquaries
Edin. L.L.	. .	Edinburgh, Lyon Office
Edin. P.	. .	Edinburgh Public Library
Edin. Port.	. .	Edinburgh, Scottish National Portrait Gallery
Edin. S.	. .	Edinburgh, Signet Library
Edin. U.	. .	Edinburgh University Library
Elg. P.	. .	Elgin Public Library
Falk. P.	. .	Falkirk Public Library
Fife C.	. .	Fife County Library
Forf. P.	. .	Forfar Public Library
Fras. P.	. .	Fraserburgh Public Library
Gala. P.	. .	Galashiels Public Library

Glas. Mit.	. .	Glasgow, Mitchell Library
Glas. U.	. .	Glasgow University Library
Gra. P.	. .	Grangemouth Public Library
Gree. P.	. .	Greenock Public Library
Ham. P.	. .	Hamilton Public Library
Haw. P.	. .	Hawick Public Library
Inv. C.	. .	Inverness County Library
Inv. P.	. .	Inverness Public Library
Kil. P.	. .	Kilmarnock Public Library
Kir. P.	. .	Kirkcaldy Public Library
Kirkcud. Bro.	.	Kirkcudbright, Broughton House
Kirkcud. C.	. .	Kirkcudbright County Library
Lan. C.	. .	Lanark County Library
Mid. C.	. .	Midlothian County Library
Mont. P.	. .	Montrose Public Library
Mor. C.	. .	Moray County Library
Nai. C.	. .	Nairn County Library
Ork. C.	. .	Orkney County Library
Pai. P.	. .	Paisley Public Library
Pee. C.	. .	Peebles County Library
Per. C.	. .	Perth County Library
Per. P.	. .	Perth Public Library
Pet. P.	. .	Peterhead Public Library
Ren. C.	. .	Renfrew County Library
Ross C.	. .	Ross & Cromarty County Library
Rox. C.	. .	Roxburgh County Library
Ruth. P.	. .	Rutherglen Public Library
S.C.L.	. .	Scottish Central Library
St.A. U.	. .	St. Andrews University Library
Sel. P.	. .	Selkirk Public Library
Sti. C.	. .	Stirling County Library
Sti. P.	. .	Stirling Public Library
Stor. P.	. .	Stornoway Public Library
Suth. C.	. .	Sutherland County Library
West L. C.	. .	West Lothian County Library
Wig. C.	. .	Wigtown County Library
Zet. C.	. .	Shetland County Library

SCOTTISH FAMILY HISTORIES
HELD IN SCOTTISH LIBRARIES

Abercorn, Marquess of, Duke of, *see* **Hamilton,** Marquess, Duke of Abercorn

Abercrombie of Abercrombie

ROSE (David Murray): The Tragic history of the Abercrombies. [Banff, 1902.] (Repr. from *Banffshire Journal,* Oct.-Nov. 1902.) *S.C.L.; Banff C.; Edin. Ant.*

Abercromby

ABERCROMBY (Cavendish Douglas): The Family of Abercromby. Aberdeen, 1927. *Ab. P.; Banff C.; Ab. U.; St.A. U.; Glas. U.; Edin. P.; Edin. S.; Glas. Mit.; Edin. L.L.*

Abernethy

ACCOUNT of the family of Abernethy. n.p., n.d. *Edin. S.*

Adair of Kinhilt

ROSE (David Murray): Adairs of Kinhilt. n.p., n.d. *Ab. U.*

Adam of Blairadam

ADAM (Sir Charles Elphinstone), Bt.: Sir Charles Elphinstone Adam, bart., of Blair-Adam: [lineage]. Blair-Adam, 1925. *Edin. P.; Edin. S.*

PEDIGREE of the Adam family, as certified by the Provost and Bailies of Forfar in 1776. (*Typescript copy.*) *Edin. P.*

Adam in Glasgow

BULLOCH (John Malcolm): The Adam family of Glasgow, more particularly Frank Adam . . . [1937]. (*Press cuttings & misc. letters*). *Glas. Mit.*

Agnew

AGNEW (Sir Andrew): The Agnews of Lochnaw. A history of the hereditary Sheriffs of Galloway, etc. Edinburgh, 1864. *Kil. P.; Dumf. P.; Wig. C.; Kirkcud. C.; St.A. U.; Glas. U.; Edin. P.; Edin. S.; Glas. Mit.; Edin. L.L.*

— The Hereditary Sheriffs of Galloway. 2 v. 2nd ed. Edinburgh, 1893. *Haw. P.; Wig. C.; St.A. U.; Glas. U.; Edin. P.; Edin. S.; Glas. Mit.; Edin. L.L.*

Ailsa, Marquess of, *see* **Kennedy,** Marquess of Ailsa

Ainslie

FOULIS (William Ainslie), *comp.*: Ainslie family charts. n.p., n.d. (*MS.*) *Edin. P.*

— Ainslie family: miscellaneous papers. n.p., n.d. (*MS. & typescript papers.*) *Edin. P.*

— The Ainslies of Dolphinston, Falla, Ulliston, etc. in Roxburghshire, and Pilton, Pentland, Hillend, etc. in Midlothian. n.p., n.d. (*MS.*) *Edin. P.*

— Ainslie papers. [Binder's title.] 4 v. n.p., n.d. (*MS. & typescript papers.*) *Edin. P.*

— [Genealogical chart of the families of Ainslie.] n.p., n.d. (*MS.*) *Edin. P.*

Airlie, Earldom of

OGILVIE (Walter): Case of Walter Ogilvie . . . *Edin. L.L.*

— Additional case of Walter Ogilvie . . . *Edin. L.L.*

OGILVY (David): Case of David Ogilvy, Esq., claiming the titles etc. of Earl of Airlie and Lord Ogilvy of Alith and Lintrathen. *Edin. L.L.*

see also **Ogilvy,** Earl of Airlie

Airth, Earldom of

AIRTH papers. n.p., n.d. *S.C.L.; Edin. S.; Edin. L.L.*

ALLARDICE (Robert Barclay): Case of Robert Barclay Allardice of Urie & Allardice with two appendixes of evidences. 1838. *Edin. L.L.*

MINUTES of evidence . . . 1839. *Edin. L.L.*

NICOLAS (Sir Nicholas Harris): History of the earldoms of Strathern, Monteith and Airth; with a report of the proceedings before the House of Lords on the claim of Robert Barclay Allardice to the earldom of Airth. London, 1842. *Dund.P.; Per.C.; Per.P.; St.A. U.; Ab. U.; Glas. U.; Edin. P.; Edin. S.; Glas. Mit.; Edin. L.L.*

Aitken of Thornton

RUVIGNY & RAINEVAL (M. A. H. D. H. de la C. Massue de Ruvigny), *9th Marquis de:* Aitken of Thornton. London, 1901. *Dunf. P.; Edin. L.L.*

Aiton, *see* **Ayton**

Albany, Duke of, *see* **Stewart,** Duke of Albany

Alexander, Earl of Stirling

. . . AN ACCOUNT of the resumption of the titles by the present Earl of Stirling . . . with an epitome of the genealogy of . . . Alexander. London, 1826. *Edin. P.*

HUMPHRYS (Alexander): Narrative . . . also a genealogical account of the family of Alexander . . . Edinburgh, 1836. *Glas. U.; Edin. P.; Edin. S.; Glas. Mit.*

2

MACAULAY (Joseph Babington): The Life of the last Earl of Stirling ... Paignton, 1906. *Edin. P.*

ROGERS (Charles): Memorials of the Earl of Stirling and of the house of Alexander. 2 v. Edinburgh, 1877. *Dunf. P.; Sti. P.; Ab. U.; St.A. U.; Glas. U.; Air. P.; Edin. P.; Edin. S.; Glas. Mit.; Edin. L.L.; Edin. Ant.*

see also **Stirling,** Earldom of

Allan of Easter Crombie

ROSE (P.): The Allans, formerly of Easter Crombie, Banffshire. 1806. (In *Proc. Banffshire Field Club,* 1903-4). *Edin. L.L.*

Allan in Kirkcaldy

McCALL (Hardy Bertram): Some old families: a contribution to the genealogical history of Scotland. Birmingham, 1890. *S.C.L.; Edin. P.; Edin. S.; Sel. P.; Edin. L.L.; Edin. Ant.*

Allardice of Allardice

NICOLAS (Sir Nicholas Harris): History of the earldoms of Strathern, Monteith & Airth: with a report of the proceedings before the House of Lords on the claim of Robert Barclay Allardice to the earldom of Airth. London, 1842. *Dund. P.; Per. P.; Per. C.; Glas. Mit.; St.A. U.; Ab. U.; Glas. U.; Edin. P.; Edin. S.*

see also **Airth,** Earldom of

Ancram, Earl of, see **Ker,** Earl of Ancram

Anderson

ANDERSON (William): The Croft House Andersons; with memories of Ceres in the sixties and seventies of last century, by one of themselves. Cupar, 1933. *Fife C.; St.A. U.; Kir. P.; Edin. P.*

Anderson of Ardbrake

ANDERSON (F. J.): Anderson of Wester Ardbrake, Banffshire. [Chart]. n.p., 1911. *Ab. U.*

Anderson in Inverness

ANDERSON (Isabel Harriet): An Inverness lawyer and his sons, 1796-1878. (*With genealogical table.*) Aberdeen, 1900 *Inv. P.; Glas. Mit.*

Anderson in Peterhead

ANDERSON (John): Records of a family of "Andersons" of Peterhead and their connections. n.p., 1936. *Ab. U.; Edin. P.; Edin. L.L.*

Anderson of Phingask

WOOD (James Mackenzie Anderson): The Andersons in Phingask and their descendants. Aberdeen, 1910. *Ab. P.; Edin. P.; Edin. S.*

Angus

WATSON (Angus): The Angus clan (years 1588 to 1950). Gateshead, 1955. *Edin. P.*

see also **Douglas**

Annand of Sauchie

BROWN-MORISON (John Brown): Genealogical notes anent some ancient Scottish families. Perth, 1884. *Clack. C.; Dumf. C.; Edin. S.*

Annandale, Earldom of

CASES . . . *Edin. L.L.*

[MACDONALD (J. A. D. J.)]: The Annandale peerage. Enquiry concerning the alleged extinction of Captn. the Hon. John Johnstone of Stapleton, brother of William, Earl & Marquis of Annandale, 1655-1721 and uncle of George, last Marquis of Annandale, 1720-1792. [1925.] *Edin. Port.*

MINUTES of evidence . . . petition of John James Hope Johnstone of Annandale, Esq., . . . claiming the earldom of Annandale and Hartfell. 1825-1838. *Edin. L.L.; Edin. Ant.*

SPEECHES and judgments. 4 v. *Edin. L.L.*

see also **Johnstone, Earl of Annandale**

Anstruther

ANSTRUTHER (Arthur Wellesley): History of the family of Anstruther. Edinburgh, 1923. *Fife C.; St.A. U.; Edin. P.; Edin. S.; Edin. L.L.*

Anstruther-Thomson of Charleton

[ANSTRUTHER-THOMSON of Charleton, Fife. (*MS.*) 18—.] *Glas. U.*

Arbuthnot

ARBUTHNOT (Ada Jane P. Stewart-Mackenzie), *Mrs. Arbuthnot*: Memories of the Arbuthnots of Kincardineshire and Aberdeenshire. London, 1920. *Ab. P.; Mont. P.; Edin. U.; St.A. U.; Edin. P.; Edin. S.; Glas. Mit.*

Archer

[ARCHER (James H. L.)]: Memorials of families of the surname of Archer. London, 1861. *S.C.L.; Glas. Mit.*

Argyll, Earl of, Marquess of, Duke of, *see* **Campbell, Earl of,** Marquess of, Duke of Argyll

Armstrong
> ARMSTRONG (James Lewis): Chronicles of the Armstrongs. Jamaica, N.Y., 1902. *Edin. P.; Edin. S.; Glas. Mit.*

Arnot
> ARNOTT (James): The House of Arnot and some of its branches. Edinburgh, 1918. *Dund. P.; St.A. U.; Edin. P.; Edin. S.; Glas. Mit.; Dumf. C.; Edin. L.L.; Edin. Ant.*

Arnot of Orkney
> CRAVEN (James Brown): Sir John Arnot of Barswick and the family of Arnot in South Ronaldshay. Kirkwall, 1913. *Edin. P.; Edin. S.*

Atholl, Earldom of
> COWAN (Samuel): Three Celtic earldoms: Atholl, Strathearn, Menteith. Edinburgh, 1909. *Sti. P.; Per. C.; Per P.; Ab. P.; Dund. P.; Glas. Mit.*
>
> PATON (Sir Joseph Noel): Genealogy of the Celtic earls of Atholl, with chart of the descendants of Conan. n.p., 1873. *Dunf. P.; Glas. Mit.; Ab. U.; Edin. L.L.*

Atholl, Earl of, Marquess of, Duke of, *see* **Murray, Earl of,** Marquess of, Duke of Atholl

Auchinleck
> MAIDMENT (James): Genealogical fragments relating to the families of . . . Auchenleck . . . Berwick, 1855. *Inv. P.; Glas. U.; Edin. P.; Edin. S.; Glas. Mit.; Edin. Ant.*

Ayton, Aytoun, Aiton of Ayton
> AITON (William): Enquiry into the origin, pedigree and history of the family, or clan, of Aitons in Scotland. Hamilton, 1830. *Edin. P.; Glas. Mit.*
>
> AYTOUN (A.): The Aytons of Ayton in the Merse: an old chapter of family history derived from the charters of Coldingham Priory . . . n.p., 1887. *S.C.L.; Edin. P.; Edin. S.; Edin. L.L.*

Baikie of Burness
> [ORIGINAL family papers.] *Ork. C.*

5

Baikie of Tankerness

MARWICK (Hugh): The Baikies of Tankerness. (In *Orkney Miscellany*, v. 4, 1957, pp. 27-48.) *Ork. C.; Glas. Mit.*

[ORIGINAL family papers.] *Ork. C.*

Baillie

BAILLIE (James William): Lives of the Baillies. Edinburgh, 1872. *Inv. P.; St.A. U.; Glas. U.; Edin. P.; Edin. S.; Glas. Mit.; Edin. L.L.*

BULLOCH (Joseph Gaston Baillie): The Family of Baillie of Dunain, Dochfour and Lamington . . . Green Bay, Wisc., 1898. *Inv. P.; Ab. U.; Edin. S.; Edin. L.L.*

— Genealogical and historical records of the Baillies of Inverness, Scotland and some of their descendants in the United States of America. Washington, D.C., 1923. *Inv. P.*

Baillie of Jerviswood

MURRAY (Lady Grisell): Memoirs of the Rt. Hon. George Baillie of Jerviswood and of Lady Grisell Baillie. Edinburgh, 1822. *Edin. S.*

Bain

ROGERS (Charles): Genealogical chart of the family of Bain, co. Haddington. [Edinburgh, 1871.] *Dunf. P.; St.A. U.; Edin. P.; Edin. S.; Glas. Mit.; Edin. L.L.; Edin. Ant.*

Baird

BAIRD (Allan Fullarton): Annals of a Scots family, [Baird], 1691-1936. Glasgow, 1936. *St.A. U.; Edin. P.*

BAIRD (William): Dominus fecit: genealogical collections concerning the sir-name of Baird, and the families of Auchmedden, Newbyth and Sauchtonhall. London, 1870. *Ab. P.; Inv. P.; St.A. U.; Ab. U.; Pai. P.; Edin. P.; Edin. S.; Glas. Mit.; Edin. Ant.*

BULLOCH (John Malcolm): The Last Baird laird of Auchmedden and Strichen: the case of "Mr. Abington". Aberdeen, 1934. *Ab. P.; Edin. P.*

FRASER (William N.), *ed.*: Account of the surname of Baird— particularly of the families of Auchmedden, Newbyth, and Sauchtonhall. Edinburgh, 1857. *S.C.L.; Ab. P.; Ab. U.; St.A. U.; Glas. U.; Glas. Mit.; Edin. L.L.*

SHAND (Eliza): God is in the generation of the righteous [a brief account of the Baird family, by E. Shand] . . . London, 1864. *St.A. U.*

6

Baird of Gartsherrie

MACGEORGE (Andrew): The Bairds of Gartsherrie: some notices of their origin and history. Glasgow, 1875. *Ayr P.; Glas. U.; Air. P.; Glas. Mit.*

Baird of Saughton Hall

[WOOD (John Philip)]: Some notes about Baird of Saughton Hall . . . (In his *Memorials of various families* . . . c. 1830. (*MS.*).) *Edin. P.*

Balfour, Lord Balfour of Burleigh

BALFOUR (Francis Walter): Case on behalf of Francis Walter Balfour of Fernie . . . *Edin. L.L.*

— Supplemental case . . . *Edin. L.L.*

BRUCE (Alexander Hugh): Case on behalf of Alexander Hugh Bruce of Kennet . . . *Edin. L.L.*

BRUCE (Robert): Case on behalf of Robert Bruce of Kennet, in the co. of Clackmannan, Esq., claiming the dignities of Lord Balfour of Burley and Lord Kilwinning in the peerage of Scotland. [1860.] *Edin. L.L.*

EGLINTON (Archibald William Montgomerie), *14th Earl of*: Case . . . Archibald Wm. Montgomerie, Earl of Eglinton and Winton, Lord Montgomerie & Kilwinning & Baron Ardrossan . . . in opposition to . . . *Edin. L.L.*

MINUTES of evidence . . . etc. 1860-64. *Edin. L.L.*

Balfour of Denmilne

MACKIE (John Duncan): The Denmilne MSS. in the National Library of Scotland. Edinburgh, 1928. *Dunf. P.; Glas. Mit.; Edin. L.L.*

Balfour of Pilrig

BALFOUR-MELVILLE (Barbara): The Balfours of Pilrig: a history for the family. Edinburgh, 1907. *St.A. U.; Ab. U.; Glas. U.; Edin. P.; Edin. S.; Glas. Mit.; Edin. L.L.; Edin. Ant.*

Baliol, Balliol

HUYSHE (Wentworth): The Royal manor of Hitchin and its lords; Harold and the Balliols. London, 1906. *Dumf. C.*

[SINCLAIR (Alexander)]: Heirs of the royal house of Baliol. Edinburgh, [1870?]. *Edin. U.*

SINCLAIR (Alexander): Remarks on the tables of the Heirs of the royal house of Baliol. Edinburgh, [1870?]. *Edin. U.; Edin. L.L.; Edin. Ant.; Dumf. C.*

Baliol le Scot

BAIN (Joseph): The Baliol le Scot family and their heart stone. (In *Collection of miscellaneous papers.* n.d.) *Glas. Mit.*

Balmerino, Lord, *see* **Elphinstone,** Lord Balmerino

Bannerman of Elsick

ROSE (David Murray): The Bannermans of Elsick and Watertown. [Aberdeen, 1900?] (Also in *Scottish Notes & Queries*, 2nd ser., v. 3, pp. 17-18.) *Ab. P.*

SOME account of the family of Bannerman of Elsick. Aberdeen, 1812. *Ab. P.; Dund. Q.; Edin. L.L.*

Barclay

BARCLAY (Charles W.) & BARCLAY (Hubert F.): A history of the Barclay family, 1067-1933. 3 v. London, 1924-34. *S.C.L.; Ab. P.; Ang. C.; St.A. U.; Glas. U.; Edin. P.* (v. 2, 3); *Edin. S.* (v. 2, 3); *Glas. Mit.; Dund. P.* (v. 2); *Edin. L.L.* (v. 2).

BARCLAY (Leslie George de Rune): History of the Scottish Barclays. Folkestone, 1915. *S.C.L.; St.A. U.; Ab. U.; Glas. U.; Edin. P.; Edin. S.; Edin. L.L.*

MAULE (Hon. Harry): Registrum de Panmure. 2 v. Edinburgh, 1874. *Arb. P.; Glas. Mit.; Per. P.; St.A. U.; Ab. U.; Forf. P.; Glas. U.; Edin. P.; Edin. S.; Dund. P.; Edin. L.L.*

Barclay of Barclay

WIMBERLEY (Douglas): The Barclays of Barclay of Grantully or Gartly and of Towie Barclay. Aberdeen, 1903. *Edin. P.; Edin. S.; Edin. L.L.*

Barclay of Tollie

PETER (John): The Barclays of Tollie [genealogical chart] . . . down to 1877. Edinburgh, 1878. *Edin. P.; Edin. L.L.*

Barclay of Urie

BARCLAY (Robert), *the younger*: A genealogical account of the Barclays of Urie . . . London, 1812. *St.A. U.; Glas. U.; Edin. P.; Glas. Mit.; Edin. L.L.; Edin. Ant.*

BUDGE (Frances Anne): The Barclays of Ury, and other sketches of the early Friends. London, 1881. *Ab. P.; Glas. Mit.*

Barclay in U.S.A.

MOFFAT (R. Burnham): The Barclays of New York: who they are and who they are not—and some other Barclays. New York, 1904. *Edin. L.L.*

Bean

PEDIGREE of Bean of Portsoy. n.p., n.d. *Edin. P.*

Beaton, *see* **Bethune**

Beaton of Islay

MACKINNON (Donald): Genealogy of the Macbeths or Beatons of Islay and Mull. Glasgow, 1902. (In *Journal of Caledonian Medical Society*, v. 5, 1902.) *Edin. L.L.*

Beatson

BEATSON (Alexander John): Genealogical account of the families of Beatson. 2nd ed. Edinburgh, 1860. *Dunf. P.; Edin. P.; Edin. S.; Glas. Mit.* (n.d.); *Edin. L.L.* (n.d.).

BEATSON (William Burns): Story of the surname of Beatson . . . London, 1900. (Repr. from *Genealogical Magazine*, rev. & corrected.) *St.A. U.; Edin. P.*

Belhaven & Stenton, Lord

HAMILTON (James): Case on behalf of James Hamilton . . . claiming . . . Lord of Belhaven & Stenton in the peerage of Scotland. 1874. *Edin. L.L.*

— Supplementary case . . . 1875. *Edin. L.L.*

HAMILTON (Robert William): Case . . . *Edin. L.L.*

MINUTES and proceedings . . . 1875. *Edin. L.L.*

Bell

BELL (Charles Davidson): Memorial of the clan of the Bells, more particularly of the Bells of Kirkconnel and Bells of Blackethouse. Cape Town, 1864. *Dumf. C.; Edin. S.; Edin. L.L.*

BELL (Robin), *comp.*: The Bell family of Arkinholm [Langholm]. [Family tree.] [1958.] (*Typescript.*) *Dumf. C.*

STEUART (James): The Bell family in Dumfriesshire. (Records of the Western Marches, v. II.) Dumfries, 1932. *Haw. P.; Dumf. C.; St.A. U.; Dund. Q.; Edin. P.; Edin. S.; Glas. Mit.; Edin. L.L.; Edin. Ant.*

Bell of Blacket House

WATSON (Charles Brodie Boog): Alexander Cowan of Moray House and Valleyfield, his kinsfolk and connections. (And Appendix.) 2 v. Perth, 1915-17. *Ab. P.; St.A. U.; Edin. P.; Edin. S.*

Bellenden

LEITH (Peter): The Bellendens and the Palace of Steness. (In *Proceedings Orkney Antiq. Soc.*, v. 14, 1937, pp. 41-44.) *Ork. C.*

9

Bellenden-Ker, *see* **Roxburghe,** Duke of

Bethune

WEISSE (Mrs. John Adam): A history of the Bethune family. Tr. from the French of Andrè du Chesne, with additions from family records and other available sources . . . New York, 1884. *St.A. U.*

Bethune of Creich

OGILVY-BETHUNE marriage contract, 1566. [Facsimile.] n.p., n.d. *Glas. Mit.*

Bethune in Skye

WHYTE (Thomas): Historical and genealogical account of the Bethunes of the island of Sky. Edinburgh, 1778. *Ab. U.; Glas. U.; Edin. P.; Edin. S.; Glas. Mit.*

—— London, 1893. *Inv. P.; Inv. C.; Ab. U.; St.A. U.; Dund. Q.; Edin. L.L.*

Beveridge

BEVERIDGE (Erskine): A Beveridge family pedigree and letter. 1918. (*MS.*) *Edin. P.*

BEVERIDGE (Sydney A.): The Story of the Beveridge families of England and Scotland. Melbourne, 1923. *Kir. P.; Edin. P.; Glas. Mit.*

HALLEN (Arthur Washington Cornelius): An account of the family of Beveridge in Dunfermline. Edinburgh, 1890. *Clack. C.; Dunf. P.; Edin. P.; Edin. S.*

Biggar

SHIRLEY (George William): The Family of Biggar, Stewartry of Kirkcudbright . . . 1614-1912: genealogical tables with notes. Dumfries, 1912. *Dumf. C.; Wig. C.*

Binning of Binning

[WOOD (John Philip)]: Binning of Binning. (In his *Memorials of various families* . . . c. 1830. (*MS.*).) *Edin. P.*

Birnie

BIRNIE (John): Account of the families of Birnie and Hamilton of Broomhill; ed. by W. B. D. D. Turnbull. Edinburgh, 1838. *S.C.L.; St.A. U.; Ab. U.; Glas. U.; Edin. P.; Edin. S.; Edin. L.L.*

Bisset

BATTEN (Edmund Chisholm): The Charters of the priory of Beauly, with notices of the Priories of Pluscardine and

10

Ardchattan and of the family of the founder, John Byset. Edinburgh, 1877. (Grampian Club, 12.) *Edin. S.; Edin. L.L.*

Bisset of Lessendrum

BULLOCH (John Malcolm): Maurice George Bisset of Lessendrum, 1757-1821. [Aberdeen], 1929. *Edin. P.*

Bisset of Lovat

MACDONALD (Archibald): The Old lords of Lovat and Beaufort. Inverness, 1934. *Ab. P.; Fife C.; Glas. Mit.*

Black

BLACK (Adam & Charles), *Ltd.*: Adam and Charles Black, 1807-1957: some chapters in the history of a publishing house. [Comp. by J. D. N.] London, 1957. *Per. C.; Glas. Mit.*

Black of Breich Water

BLACK (John) of Breich: Melodies and memories with a history of the Blacks of Breich Water district. Glasgow, 1909. *Glas. Mit.*

Black of Over Abington

BLACK (William George): A note on the family of Black of Over Abington, 1694-1924. With memoranda on . . . Willison of Redshaw . . ., Steel of Annathill, and Blackie of Glasgow. [2nd ed.] Glasgow, 1924. *Ab. P.; Edin. P.; Edin. S.; Glas. Mit.; Glas. U.* (+1908); *Edin. L.L.* (+1908); *Edin. Ant.*

Blackader of Tulliallan

BLACKADER (John): The Life and diary of Colonel John Blackader. Edinburgh, 1824. *Dunf. P.; Glas. Mit.*

CRICHTON (Andrew): Memoirs of the Rev. John Blackader. Edinburgh, 1823. *Dunf. P.; Glas. Mit.*

Blackhall

MORISON (Alexander): The Blackhalls of that ilk and Barra, hereditary coroners and foresters of the Garioch. Aberdeen, 1905. (New Spalding Club, 29.) *S.C.L.; Elg. P.; Inv. P.; Ab. C.; Ang. C.; Edin. U.; Ab. P.; Dund. Q.; Glas. U.; Dund. P.; Edin. P.; Edin. S.; Glas. Mit.; Edin. L.L.*

Blackie

BLACK (William George): A note on the family of Black of Over Abington . . . with memoranda on . . . Blackie of Glasgow. [2nd ed.] Glasgow, 1924. *Glas. Mit.; Ab. P.; Glas. U.* (+1908); *Edin. P.; Edin. S.; Edin. L.L.* (+1908); *Edin. Ant.*

11

Blackwood

OLIPHANT (Margaret Oliphant Wilson), *Mrs. Oliphant*: Annals of a publishing house: Wm. Blackwood and his sons . . . 3 v. Edinburgh, 1897-8. (Vol. 3: John Blackwood by Mrs. Gerald Porter.) *S.C.L.; Glas. Mit.*

TREDREY (Frank D.): The House of Blackwood, 1804-1954: the history of a publishing house. Edinburgh, 1954. *Per. C.; Glas. Mit.*

Blackwood of West Fife

BLACKWOOD (Isabella C.): The Early house of Blackwood. Edinburgh, 1900. *Dunf. P.; Edin. P.; Ab. P.; Glas. Mit.; Edin. L.L.*

Blair

MICHELL (Arthur T.): Five generations of the family of Blair, from the counties of Perth and Forfar. Exeter, 1895. *Edin. P.; Edin. S.*

MURRAY (Archibald): William Scott Blair *v.* Hamilton Blair . . . appellants case and respondents case to be heard at the Bar of the House of Lords . . . 4th April, 1739. [Edinburgh, 1739.] *Edin. P.*

Blair of Balthayock

ANDERSON (William): The Family of Blair of Balthayock, Perthshire. n.p., n.d. *Per. P.*

BAETCKE (Adolph Julius): Die Schottische Abstammung der Lothringer de Blair. Hamburg, n.d. *Edin. L.L.*

Blaw of Castlehill

JOHNSTON (Christopher Nicholson), *Lord Sands*: Blaw of Castlehill, Jacobite and criminal. Edinburgh, 1916. *Glas. Mit.*

Bogue

BOGUE (Virgil T.): Bogue and allied families. Geneva, Ohio, 1944. *Ber. C.; Glas. Mit.*

Boog

WATSON (Charles Brodie Boog): Traditions and genealogies of some members of the families of Boog, Heron, Leishman, Ross, Watson. Perth, 1908. *St.A. U.; Edin. P.; Edin. S.; Edin. L.L.; Edin. Ant.*

Borthwick, Lord Borthwick

BORTHWICK (Archibald): Case of Archibald Borthwick, Esq., claiming the title of Lord Borthwick. [1808.] *Edin. L.L.*

— Case . . . with reference to the objection to that claim made by John Borthwick of Crookston. *Edin. L.L.*

BORTHWICK (Cunninghame): Case on behalf of Cunninghame Borthwick, Esq., on his claim to . . . Lord Borthwick in the peerage of Scotland. 1868. *Edin. L.L.*

BORTHWICK (Henry): Case of Henry Borthwick . . . claiming . . . Lord Borthwick . . . 1762. *Repr.* 1868. *Edin. L.L.*

BORTHWICK (John): Case of John Borthwick of Crookston . . . 1764. *Repr.* 1868. *Edin. L.L.*

— Case of John Borthwick of Crookston objecting to the claim of Mr. Archd. Borthwick to the title of Lord Borthwick. 1809. *Edin. L.L.*

— Additional case of above . . . 1774. *Repr.* 1868. *Edin. L.L.*

— Case of John Borthwick . . . 181-. *Repr.* 1868. *Edin. L.L.*

— Additional case of above . . . *Edin.* L.L.

MINUTES of Evidence . . . 1812-1814. *Edin. L.L.; Edin. Ant.* (+ appendix).

PEDIGREE of the family of Borthwick. *Edin. L.L.*

Boston

BOSTON (Thomas): A general account of my life . . . ed. by G. D. Low. Edinburgh, 1908. (*Appendix cont. account of the Boston family.*) *Glas. Mit.*

Boswell

BOSWELL (Jaspar John): History and genealogical tables of the Boswells. London, [1906]. *Edin. P.*

[CAMPBELL (Jane) & CAMPBELL (Mary)]: A family chronicle: [the family of Robert Campbell of Alloway]. Edinburgh, 1925. *Ayr P.; Edin. P.; Glas. Mit.*

Bower

[BOWER (Sir Alfred Louis)]: History of the Bower family, 1066-1930. n.p. [c. 1935]. *Edin. L.L.*

Bowes (-Lyon), Earl of Strathmore

EWING (William) *v.* EARL OF STRATHMORE; answers for William Ewing. [Edinburgh, 1825.] *Edin. P.*

LAING (William) *v.* CALLANDAR (George); summons of maills and duties, Laing against Callandar. 1826. *Edin. P.*

LAING (William) *v.* EARL OF STRATHMORE; answers for Wm. Laing . . . to the petition . . . of the Rt. Hon. Thomas Bowes designing himself Earl of Strathmore & Kinghorn. 1821. *Edin. P.*

see also **Strathmore,** Earldom of

Boyd

PEDIGREE of the House of Boyd. Compiled from authentic documents. [n.p., 1904.] *S.C.L.; St.A. U.*

CLARKE (Seymour): Dean Castle, Kilmarnock, and the family of Boyd (1263-1746). 1918. (*MS.*) *Edin. P.*

Boyd, Earl of Kilmarnock

[CORBETT (Cunningham)], *comp.*: Boyds of Kilmarnock, Porterfields of Porterfield and Corbetts of Tolcross. n.p., n.d. *Edin. S.*

MAIDMENT (James), *ed.*: Selection from papers of the family of Boyd of Kilmarnock, 1468-1590. Edinburgh, 1837. (Bannatyne Club, 11.) *Ab. U.*

MEMOIRS of the lives and families of the Lords Kilmarnock, Cromartie and Balmerino. London, 1746. *Ayr P.*

Boyd of Penkill and Trochrig

CLARKE (Seymour): The Boyds of Penkill and Trochrig. Edinburgh, 1909. *S.C.L.; Ayr P.; St.A. U.; Ab. U.; Glas. U.; Edin. P.; Edin. S.; Glas. Mit.*

Boyle of Kelburne, Earl of Glasgow

BOYLE (Hon. Robert Elphinstone): Genealogical account of the Boyles of Kelburne, Earls of Glasgow. n.p., 1904. *S.C.L.; St.A. U.; Glas. U.; Edin. P.; Edin. S.; Glas. Mit.; Edin. L.L.*

ROBERTSON (William): An account of the family of Boyle of Kelburn, adapted and abridged by Wm. Robertson from an unpublished memoir by Col. the Hon. Robert Boyle, and inc. in vol. II of his "History of Ayrshire". Kilmarnock, 1908. *Edin. Port.*

Breadalbane, Earldom of

BREADALBANE (John), *Earl of*: Case of John, Earl of Breadalbane in the peerage of Scotland. 1872. *Edin. L.L.*

CAMPBELL (Gavin): Case on behalf of Gavin Campbell claiming to be Earl of Breadalbane etc., on his claim to . . . Earl of Breadalbane, etc. in the peerage of Scotland. *Edin. L.L.*

CAMPBELL (John): Case on behalf of John Campbell, Esq., claiming . . . Earl of Breadalbane, etc. [1867.] *Edin. L.L.*

CAMPBELL (John Alexander Gavin): Petition of John Alexander Gavin Campbell of Glenfalloch claiming the title . . . etc. [1867.] *Edin. L.L.*

MINUTES of evidence . . . 1872. *Edin. L.L.*

14

PATERSON (James): The Breadalbane case. Edinburgh, 1863. *Per. P.*

PROCEEDINGS ... 1867. *Edin. L.L.*

SINCLAIR (Alexander): Statement of the Breadalbane case. Glasgow, 1866. *Glas. U.; Glas. Mit.; Edin. P.*

Brechin

MAULE (Hon. Harry): Registrum de Panmure. 2 v. Edinburgh, 1874. *Arb. P.; Glas. U.; Ab. U.; Dund. P.; Edin. P.; Per. P.; Edin. S.; Glas. Mit.; St.A. U.; Forf. P.; Edin. L.L.*

Brisbane of Bishoptoun

FRASER (Sir William): Genealogical table of the families of Brisbane of Bishoptoun and Brisbane; Makdougall of Makerstoun; and Hay of Alderstoun, etc. Edinburgh, 1840. *(Photocopy.) S.C.L.*

Brisbane of Brisbane

BRISBANE (Sir Thomas Makdougall), Bt.: Reminiscences of General Sir Thomas Makdougall Brisbane. Edinburgh, 1860. *Edin. Ant.*

see also **Brisbane** of Bishoptoun

Brodie

LAWRANCE (Robert Murdoch): Brodie family history. Glasgow, 1915. *Ab. P.; Edin. P.*

Brodie of Brodie

BRODIE (William): The Genealogy of the Brodie family from Malcolm Thane of Brodie, 1249-85, to 1862. Eastbourne, 1862. *Edin. L.L.*

HISTORY of the family of Brodie of Brodie. n.p., [c. 1881]. *Edin. P.*

INNES (Sir Thomas), of Learney: The Brodie family: Alexander Brodie of Brodie, 1697-1754. 1930. (From *Trans. Banffshire Field Club*.) *Ab. P.*

Broun of Colstoun.

BROWN-MORISON (John Brown): Genealogical notes anent some ancient Scottish families. Perth, 1884. *Clack. C.; Dumf. C.; Edin. S.; Edin. L.L.*

— A monograph on the notice of the ancient family of Broun of Colstoun in Crawford's MS. Baronage. n.p., 1881. *Edin. L.L.; Per. P.; Edin. Ant.*

15

Broun of Sauchie, Balquarne & Finderlie

BROWN-MORISON (John Brown): Genealogical notes anent some ancient Scottish families. Perth, 1884. *Clack. C.; Dumf. C.; Edin. S.; Edin. L.L.*

Broun-Morison of Finderlie & Murie

BROWN-MORISON (John Brown) & BROWN (James), *eds.*: The Progress of titles of Finderlie during the 16th century. n.p., n.d. *Edin. P.*

Brown

BROWN (Alexander Taylor): Genealogical tree of the Browns of Newmilns, Ayrshire, and their descendants . . . n.p., 1930. *Edin. P.*

BROWN (Rachel) & NOBBS (E.A.), *comps.*: The Family tree of the Rev. John Brown of Haddington. [1952-54.] (*Typescript.*) *Edin. P.*

Brown of Dolphinton

MACKENZIE (Alice Ann), *comp.*: Dolphinton. n.p., 1888. *Edin. L.L.*

Brown of Fordell

STODART (Robert Riddle): Memorials of the Browns of Fordell, Finmount and Vicarsgrange. Edinburgh, 1887. *Sel. P.; St.A. U.; Ab. U.; Kirk. P.; Glas. U.; Edin. P.; Edin. S.; Glas. Mit.; Edin. L.L.; Edin. Ant.*

Bruce

ADAM (Abbé J.-L.): Le Chateau d'Adam Bruce à Brix berceau de la famille royale des Bruces d'Ecosse et d'Angleterre. Cherbourg, 1897. *Edin. Ant.*

ARMSTRONG (William Bruce), *comp.*: Collectanea Bruceana: two . . . MS. volumes presented . . . by the compiler. 1898. *Edin. L.L.*

BRUCE (Mary Elizabeth Cumming): Family records of the Bruces and the Cumyns. Edinburgh, 1870. *S.C.L.; Ab. P.; Haw. P.; Inv. P.; Dumf. C.; Ab. U.; Sti. P.; Nai. C.; Dumb. P.; St.A. U.; Glas. U.; Edin. P.; Edin. S.; Glas. Mit.; Edin. L.L.; Edin. Ant.*

DRUMMOND (Henry): Bruce family. (In his *Histories of noble British Families.* Vol. 1. 1846.) *Edin. P.; Glas. U.; Glas. Mit.; Edin. S.*

SINCLAIR (Alexander): Genealogical descent of the royal line of Bruce. Edinburgh, 1860. *Dunf. P.; Edin. L.L.*

Surenne (Gabriel): Prospectus of the History of the Royal Scottish House of Bruce, in three volumes. [Edinburgh?], 1856. *Glas. Mit.; Edin. L.L.*

Bruce of Airth

Armstrong (William Bruce): The Bruces of Airth and their cadets. Edinburgh, 1892. *S.C.L.; Clack. C.; Dumf. C.; St.A. U.; Ab. P.; Falk. P.; Edin. P.; Edin. S.; Glas. Mit.; Edin. L.L.; Edin. Ant.*

—Notes on the origin of the baronial house of Bruce of Airth. London, 1888. *Edin. Ant.*

M'Grouther (Thomas): The Bruces of Airth and their barony. Stirling, 1928. *Ab. U.*

Bruce, Earl of Carrick, *see* **Carrick,** Earldom of

Bruce of Clackmannan

MS. volume of copies of charters relating to the Bruces from 1330 to 1829. *Edin. S.*

Bruce of Cultmalundie

Armstrong (William Bruce): Bruces of Cultmalundie in Perthshire; of Muness, Sumburgh, Symbister in Shetland. n.p., n.d. *Edin. Ant.*

Bruce of Earlshall

Stodart (Robert Riddle): Bruce of Earlshall in the parish of Leuchars, co. Fife. [1883.] (Repr. from *Genealogist,* v. 7, 1883.) *Edin. S.*

Bruce of Kennet, *see* **Balfour,** Lord Balfour of Burleigh

Bruce, Baron Bruce of Kinloss

Bruce (James Ernest Brudenell): Remarks on Scottish peerages: their limitations by patent or otherwise, particularly with reference to the barony of Bruce, of Kinloss, now enjoyed by the Earl of Elgin & Kincardine, but claimed by the Duke of Buckingham & Chandos. London, 1868. *St.A. U.; Dunf. P.*

Pedigree of the Bruces, Barons Bruce of Kinloss, showing the heirs of line and the collateral heirs male. n.p., [1867]. *Ab. P.; Edin. P.* (1867).

Bruce of Muness, *see* **Bruce** of Cultmalundie

Bruce of Newtown

An account of the Bruces of Newtoune and of the Irish branch of that house and now representing it in the male line. n.p., n.d. *Edin. L.L.*

Bruce of Sumburgh, *see* **Bruce** of Cultmalundie

Bruce of Symbister, *see* **Bruce** of Cultmalundie

Bruce of Uyeasound, Shetland

    CLARK (John): Genealogy, records and intermarriages of the Fordyce, Bruce and Clark families at Uyeasound, Unst, Shetland. 2nd ed. Falkirk, 1902. *Zet. C.; Edin. P.; Ork. C.;* (Falkirk, 1899).

Buchan, Earldom of

    MACKENZIE (Sir Colin) of Kilcoy: Case of Sir Colin Mackenzie of Kilcoy, Bt., on his claim to the title and dignity of Earl of Buchan and Lord Auchterhouse. [n.p., 18—.] *St.A. U.; Glas. Mit.* ([c. 1840]); *Edin. L.L.*

Buchan of Auchmacoy

    [WOOD (John Philip)]: Buchan of Auchmacoy. (In his *Memorials of various families* . . . c. 1830. (*MS.*).) *Edin. P.*

Buchanan

    BUCHANAN (Alice Lilian), *aft. Mrs. A. L. Smith*: A memoir of the Buchanan family, and in particular of George Buchanan, Kt., 1831-1895. Aberdeen, 1941. *Edin. P.*

    BUCHANAN (Arthur William Patrick): The Buchanan book: the life of Alex. Buchanan, Q.C., of Montreal, followed by an account of the family of Buchanan. Montreal, 1911. *Edin. P.; Edin. S.; Edin. L.L.*

    BUCHANAN (Barbara Isabella), *comp.*: Buchanan family records; James Buchanan and his descendants. Capetown, 1923. *Glas. Mit.*

    BUCHANAN (Patrick): Later leaves of the Buchanan book. Montreal, 1929. *Edin. P.; Edin. L.L.*

    BUCHANAN (R[obert?] M[acNeil?]), *comp.*: Notes on the members of the Buchanan Society, nos. 1-366 (1725-1829); comp. by R. M. Buchanan. Glasgow, 1931. *Glas. Mit.*

    BUCHANAN (William) of Auchmar: The History of the ancient surname of Buchanan, and of ancient Scottish surnames. Glasgow, 1723. *Glas. U.; Edin. S.; Glas. Mit.*

    — — Edinburgh, 1775. *Edin. L.L.*

    — — Glasgow, 1793. *Dumb. P.; Ayr P.; Arg. C.*

    — — Glasgow, 1820. *S.C.L.; Glas. U.; Edin. P.; Edin. S.; Glas. Mit.*

    SMITH (John Guthrie): Strathendrick and its inhabitants. Glasgow, 1896. *S.C.L.; Glas. Mit.*

Buchanan of Ardoch

PARKES-BUCHANAN (John): The Family book of the Buchanans of Ardoch, commonly called the Ardoch Register. Glasgow, 1894. *Dumb. P.; Glas. Mit.; Edin. L.L.*

Buchanan of Spittal

HAMILTON (Francis), *formerly Buchanan* (*Francis*): Claim of Dr. Francis Hamilton Buchanan of Spittal [to be considered chief of the name]. Edinburgh, 1826. *Glas. Mit.; Edin. S.*

Bulloch

BULLOCH (Joseph Gaston Baillie): The Family of Baillie of Dunain, etc. Green Bay, Wisc., 1898. *Inv. P.; Ab. U.; Edin. S.*

— History and genealogy of the families of Bulloch and Stobo and Irvine of Cults. Washington, D.C., 1911. *Ab. P.; Edin. S.; Edin. L.L.*

Burn-Murdoch

FORSYTH (Dorothea): A Family memoir. Malton, 1939. *Edin. S.*

Burnes

BURNES (James): Notes on the name and family of James Burnes, K.H., F.R.S. Edinburgh, 1851. *Ab. P.; Edin. P.; Edin. S.; Glas. Mit.*

Burnett

BURNETT (Charles Howard): The Burnett family, with collateral branches. Also historical and genealogical notes on allied families, and biographical sketches of various eminent Burnetts. Los Angeles, Calif., 1950. *Ab. U.; Edin. P.*

Burnett of Burnetland and Barns

BURNETT (Montgomery): Genealogical account of the family of Burnett of Burnetland and Barns. 2nd ed. Edinburgh, 1880. *Ab. U.; Edin. P.* (+1882); *Edin. S.* (+1882); *Edin. L.L.* (1882).

Burnett of Gadgirth

THE CHALMERSES and Burnetts of Gadgirth. n.p., n.d. *Ayr P.*

Burnett of Leys

BURNETT (George): The Family of Burnett of Leys, with collateral branches; from the MS. of the late G. Burnett; ed. by J. Allardyce. (New Spalding Club, 22.) Aberdeen, 1901. *S.C.L.; Inv. P.; Ab. C.; Elg. P.; Dund. Q.; Ab. P.; Glas. U.; Dund. P.; Edin. P.; Edin. S.; Glas. Mit.; Edin. L.L.*

BURNETT (William Kendall): Genealogical tree of the family of Burnett of Leys. Aberdeen, 1893. *Inv. P.; Ab. C.; Edin. P.; Glas. Mit.*

RAMSAY (Elizabeth Maule): Legends of Leys; collected from oral traditions of the Burnett family, etc. Aberdeen, 1856. *Edin. P.*

Burns

BALLANTINE (James), *ed.*: Chronicle of the hundredth birthday of Robert Burns. Edinburgh, 1859. *Ab. P.; Dund. P.; Edin. P.; Glas. Mit.; Glas. U.*

ROBERTSON (James) of Aberdeen: A history of Burn's forefathers, his travels in Scotland and his masonic affairs. Aberdeen, 1950. *Lan. C.*

ROGERS (Charles): Book of Robert Burns: genealogical and historical memoirs of the poet, his associates, etc. 3 v. Edinburgh, 1889-91. (Grampian Club, 23.) *Dumf. C.; Dunf. P.; Dund. P.; Glas. U.; Edin. P.; Edin. S.; Glas. Mit.*

— Genealogical memoirs of the family of Robert Burns and of the Scottish house of Burnes. London, 1877. *Dunf. P.; Ab. P.; Inv. P.; Sti. P.; Gree. P.; Fife C.; St.A. U.; Ab. U.; Glas. U.; Edin. P.; Edin. S.; Glas. Mit.; Edin. L.L.*

SMITH (Grant F. O.): The Man Robert Burns. [With genealogical tables.] Toronto, 1940. *Edin. P.*

WATSON (James): Genealogical sketch of the descendants of Robert Burns in Kincardineshire. Aberdeen, n.d. (*Typescript.*) *Ab. P.*

Byres

GILL (Andrew J. Mitchell): The Families of Moir and Byres. Edinburgh, 1885. *S.C.L.; Ab. P.; Glas. U.; Dund. P.; Edin. P.; Edin. S.; Glas. Mit.; St.A. U.; Edin. L.L.*

Byres of Coates

MEMOIR of the family of Sir John Byres of Coates, now of Tonley in the county of Aberdeen. n.p., n.d. *Edin. S.*

Byset, Bysset, *see* Bisset

Cadell

STEVENSON (John Horne): The Cadells of Banton, Grange, Tranent and Cockenzie, etc., 1668-1890. Edinburgh, 1890. *Edin. P.; Edin. S.*

Cadenhead

CADENHEAD (George): The Family of Cadenhead. Aberdeen, 1887. *Ab. P.; Ab. C.; St.A. U.; Edin. P.; Edin. S.; Glas. Mit.*

Caird

CAIRD (Rennie Alexander): A history of (or notes upon) family of Caird (Scotland). Surname from very early times. [Pt. 1.] Leicester, 1913. *Glas. Mit.*

— — The Clan from very early times. [Pt. 2.] Leicester, 1915. *Glas. Mit.*

Cairns

LAWLOR (Henry Cairnes): A history of the family of Cairnes or Cairns and its connections. London, 1906. *Dund. P.; Dumf. C.; Ab. U.; Wig. C.; St.A. U.; Edin. P.; Edin. S.; Glas. Mit.; Edin. L.L.; Edin. Ant.*

Caithness, Earldom of

SINCLAIR (James): Information for James Sinclair in Reiss against William Sinclair of Ratter. n.p., 1769. *Edin. P.*

Calder

THE ANCIENT and honourable family of Calder. The Book of Calder. n.d. (*MS. with watercolour illus.*) *Inv. P.*

DEUCHAR (A.): Genealogical collections relative to the family of Calder. n.d. (*MS.*) *Glas. Mit.*

GENEALOGICAL tree of the family of Calder. n.d. (*MS.*) *Inv. P.*

[SHAW (Rev. Lauchlan)]: A succinct account of the family of Calder. [c. 17—.] (In *Highland Papers*, ed. by J. R. N. Macphail, v. I, Scottish History Soc., 2nd ser. v. V.) *S.C.L.; Arg. C.*

see also **Campbell** of Cawdor or Calder

Cameron

[ARBUTHNOT (Archibald)]: A brief account of the life and family of Miss Jenny Cameron, the reputed mistress of the Pretender's eldest son. London, 1746. *Inv. P.*

CAMERON (George Henry): John Cameron, non-juror, his ancestors and descendants; with special reference to the Camerons of Worcester. 4 pts. Oxford, 1919-23. *Glas. Mit.; Edin. L.L.*

CAMERON (John): The Clan Cameron . . . with short notices of eminent clansmen. Kirkintilloch, 1894. *Ab. P.; Inv. P.; St.A. U.; Edin. U.; Ab. U.; Edin. P.; Edin. S.; Glas. Mit.*

21

FRASER (Charles Ian) of Reelig: Clan Cameron: a patriarchy beset. Edinburgh, 1953. *Inv. P.; Inv. C.; Ayr P.; Edin. U.; Cly. P.; Lan. C.; Ab. P.; Ren. C.; Per. C.; Dund. P.; Pai. P.; Arg. C.; Edin. P.; Edin. S.; Glas. Mit.; Cai. C.; Ber. C.; Edin. L.L.; Edin. Ant.*

MACKENZIE (Alexander): History of the Camerons; with genealogies of the principal families of the name. Inverness, 1884. *S.C.L.; Dund. P.; Ab. P.; Inv. P.; Sti. P.; Ab. U.; St.A. U.; Glas. U.; Edin. P.; Edin. S.; Glas. Mit.; Edin. L.L.*

Cameron of Lochiel

CAMERON (John), *20th of Lochiel*: Answers for His Majesty's Advocate, in behalf of His Majesty; to the claim of John Cameron, son of the deceased Donald Cameron of Lochiel [to his father's forfeited estate. (Dec. 12, 1749)]. [Edinburgh, 1749.] *Glas. Mit.*

[DRUMMOND (John)]: Memoirs of Sir Ewen Cameron of Lochiel, with an introductory account of the history and antiquities of that family and the neighbouring clans. Edinburgh, 1842. (Maitland Club, 59.) *Inv. P.; Glas. U.; Dund. P.; Edin. P.; Edin. S.; Glas. Mit.* (Abbotsford Club, 24).

Campbell

ANE accompt of the genealogie of the Campbells. (From a MS. in the Advocate's Library in *Highland Papers*, ed. by J. R. N. Macphail, v. II, Scottish History Soc., 2nd ser. v. XII). *S.C.L.*

BALFOUR (Lady Frances): Lady Victoria Campbell, etc. 2nd ed. London, [1911]. *Edin. P.*

BEDE (Cuthbert), *pseud.* [*i.e. Edward Bradley*]: Argyll's High-landers, or MacCailein Mor and the Lords of Lorne. Glasgow, 1902. *S.C.L.; Inv. P.; Glas. Mit.*

CAMPBELL (Sir Duncan): Records of the Clan Campbell in the military service of the Hon. East India Co., 1600-1858. London, 1925. *Dund. P.; Ren. C.; Edin. U.; Ab. U.; Ab. P.; Glas. U.; Edin. P.; Edin. S.; Glas. Mit.*

CAMPBELL ASSOCIATION OF AMERICA. The Highlander, No. 1, 1930. *Edin. P.; Glas. Mit.* (no. 2, 1937-39).

CHRISTIE (John), [*of Aberfeldy*]: The Lairds and lands of Loch Tayside. Aberfeldy, 1892. *Per. C.; Ab. P.; Dund. Q ; Glas. U.; Edin. P.; Edin. S.; Glas. Mit.; Edin. L.L.*

DESCENT of Campbell of Shian from Egbert, King of England; Malcolm, King of Scotland and Gillespie Campbell. n.p., n.d. (*Typescript.*) *Edin. P.*

GILLIES (William A.): In famed Breadalbane. Perth, 1938. *S.C.L.; Glas. Mit.*

JOHNSTON (George Harvey): The Heraldry of the Campbells, with notes on all males of the family, etc. 2 v. Edinburgh, 1920-21. *Dun. P.; Arg. C.; Edin. P.; Edin. S.; Glas. Mit.*

MCKERRAL (Andrew): Clan Campbell (clan Diarmid): a record of service by a race of statesmen. Edinburgh, 1953. *Cai. C.; Ber. C.; Inv. P.; Inv. C.; Sti. C.; Ayr P.; Cly. P.; Lan. C.; Dunf. P.; Ren. C.; Per. C.; Dund. P.; Pai. P.; Arg. C.; Edin. P.; Edin. S.; Glas. Mit.; Ab. P.; Edin. U.; Edin. L.L.; Edin. Ant.*

PATON (Henry): The Clan Campbell . . . from the Campbell collection formed by Sir D. Campbell of Barcaldine and Glenure, . . . Ed. by . . . H. Paton, . . . 8 v. Edinburgh, 1913-22. *S.C.L.* (v. 1, 2, 3, 5); *St.A. U.; Ab. U.; Edin. U.; Glas. U.; Glas. Mit.; Inv. C.* (v. 3); *Camp. P.* (v. 1, 4); *Edin. P.* (v. 1-6, 8); *Edin. S.* (v. 1-6, 8); *Edin. L.L.* (v. 1, 2).

SINTON (Rev. Thomas): The MacPhails or Campbells. (In *Family and genealogical sketches*, 1911.) *Inv. P.; Ab. U.; Ab. P.; Dund. Q.; Edin. P.; Edin. S.*

Campbell, Earl of, Marquess of, Duke of Argyll

ARGYLL (John G. E. H. D. S. Campbell), *9th Duke of*: Joint print of documents in causa His Grace the Duke of Argyll, against Angus John Campbell of Dunstaffnage and another. Edinburgh, 1910. *Edin. P.*

CAMPBELL (Robert): Life of the most illustrious Prince John, Duke of Argyle & Greenwich, containing a . . . genealogical account of His Grace's family and ancestors. London, 1745. *Ab. P.; Glas. U.; Dund. P.; Edin. P.; Glas. Mit.*

A HISTORY of the Campbells, dukes of Argyle . . . to 1776. [1776.] (*MS.*) *Edin. P.*

[HOGG (John)]; The Clan Campbell and the Marquis of Lorne: an epitome of the story of the house of Argyle. London, [1871]. *Cai. C.; Inv. P.; Glas. Mit.*

THE HOUSE of Argyll and the collateral branches of Clan Campbell. Glasgow, 1871. *Inv. P.; Gree. P.; Per. C.; Edin. U.; Ab. U.; Camp. P.; Glas. U.; Pai. P.; Arg. C.; Edin. P.; Edin. S.; Glas. Mit.; Edin. L.L.*

LETTERS to the Argyll family from Elizabeth, Queen of England, Mary, Queen of Scots, King James VI, King Charles I, King Charles II and others. Edinburgh, 1839. (Maitland Club, 50.) *Arg. C.; Glas. U.; Dund. P.; Edin. P.; Edin. S.; Glas. Mit.*

MAIDMENT (James), *ed.*: The Argyle papers, 1640-1723. Edinburgh, 1834. *Edin. P.; Edin. S.; Glas. Mit.; Edin. L.L.; Edin. Ant.; St.A. U.*

SKAE (Hilda T.): The Campbells of Argyll. London, [1913]. *Edin. P.*

SMITH (Hely Hutchinson Augusta): The MacCallum-More: a history of the Argyll family. London, 1871. *S.C.L.; Ab. U.; Edin. P.; Ab. P.; Inv. P.; St.A. U.; Edin. S.; Glas. Mit.; Camp. P.*

STUART (Lady Louisa): Some account of John, Duke of Argyll, and his family, by his great-niece . . . London, 1863. *Rox. C.; Edin. L.L.*

Campbell of Asknish

ALLARDICE (W. P.): Observations on a publication by Duncan Campbell-MacIver of Asknish entitled "Remarks on writings of the Rev. P. C. Campbell, etc." Edinburgh, 1870. *Edin. L.L.*

Campbell of Auchinbreck

THE CAMPBELLS of Auchinbreck. (In *Highland Papers*, ed. by J. R. N. Macphail, v. IV, Scottish History Soc., 3rd ser. v. XXII.) *S.C.L.; Arg. C.*

Campbell, Ayrshire

[CAMPBELL (Jane) & CAMPBELL (Mary)]: A family chronicle: the family of Robert Campbell of Alloway. Edinburgh, 1925. *Ayr P.; Edin. P.; Glas. Mit.*

Campbell of Barcaldine

FRASER (Alexander Campbell): The Book of Barcaldine: three centuries in the West Highlands. London, 1936. *Ren. C.; Dunb. C.; Ab. C.; Arg. C.; Gra. P.; Rox. C.; Ab. U.; Ab. P.; Dund. Q.; Pai. P.; Edin. P.; Edin. S.; Glas. Mit.*

Campbell of Blythswood

EASTON (W. J.): Family of Blythswood. Paisley, 1876. *Pai. P.*

Campbell, Baron, Viscount, etc. Breadalbane

THE BLACK book of Taymouth; ed. by Cosmo Innes. Edinburgh, 1855. (Bannatyne Club, 100.) *Per. C.; Inv. P.; Glas. U.; Dund. P.; Edin. P.; Edin. S.; Glas. Mit.; Edin. L.L.*

see also **Breadalbane**, Earldom of

Campbell of Cawdor or Calder

INNES (Cosmo), *ed.*: The Book of the thanes of Cawdor: a series of papers selected from the Charter Room, Cawdor, 1236-1742. Edinburgh, 1859. (Spalding Club, 30.) *S.C.L.; Glas. U.; Dund. P.; Elg. P.; Inv. P.; Inv. C.; Edin. P.; Edin. S.; Glas. Mit.; Edin. L.L.*

Campbell of Craignish & Lagganlochan

CAMPBELL (Alexander): The Manuscript history of Craignish; ed. by Herbert Campbell. (In *Scottish History Soc., Miscellany*, 3rd ser. v. IX, 1926). *S.C.L.; Edin. L.L.*

CAMPBELL (T. Hay): Craignish and Lagganlochan: a genealogical sketch. n.p., 1890. *Edin. S.; Edin. L.L.*

GENEALOGICAL and historical account of the family of Craignish, with genealogical chart and other MS. papers. 2 pts. n.p., n.d. (*Typescript.*) *Glas. Mit.*

Campbell of Duntroon

CAMPBELL (Herbert): The Campbells of Duntroon and their cadets. 2 pts. Exeter, 1913-21. (Repr. from *Genealogist.*) *Edin. S.; Edin. L.L.*

Campbell in Garth

CAMPBELL (Duncan): The Book of Garth and Fortingall. Inverness, 1888. *S.C.L.; Per. C.; Edin. P.; Edin. S.*

Campbell of Glenfalloch, *see* **Breadalbane,** Earldom of

Campbell of Glenlyon

CAMPBELL (Duncan): The Lairds of Glenlyon: historical sketches of Appin, Glenlyon and Breadalbane. Perth, 1886. *S.C.L.; Per. C.; Edin. P.; Edin. S.; Glas. Mit.*

Campbell of Glenorchy

THE BLACK book of Taymouth; ed. by Cosmo Innes. Edinburgh, 1855. (Bannatyne Club, 100.) *Per. C.; Inv. P.; Glas. U.; Dund. P.; Edin. P.; Edin. S.; Glas. Mit.*

Campbell of Inverardine

GIBB (Sir George Duncan): Pedigree of James Reid Campbell of Inverardine, Cornwall, Canada. London, 1872. *Glas. U.*

Campbell of Inverawe

CAMPBELL (Ian MacLeod): Notes on the Campbells of Inverawe. Edinburgh, 1951. *S.C.L.; Edin. P.; Edin. S.; Edin. Ant.*

Campbell, of Kilmartin

WIMBERLEY (Douglas): Memorials of four old families. 1894. *Ab. P.; Inv. P.; Dund. Q.; Edin. P.; Edin. S.; Glas. Mit.*

— Memorials of the family of Campbell of Kilmartin, and some notes on the family of Campbell of Inverawe. Inverness, 1894. *St.A. U.; Ab. U.*

Campbell of Kiltearn

MACGREGOR (Rev. Duncan): Campbell of Kiltearn. Edinburgh, 1874. *Inv. P.*

Campbell of Kinloch

LOGIN (Edith Dalhousie): The Story of the Campbells of Kinloch. London, 1924. *S.C.L.; Ab. P.; Per. P.; St.A. U.; Ab. U.; Per. C.; Edin. P.; Edin. S.; Glas. Mit.; Edin. L.L.*

Campbell of Lagganlochan

CAMPBELL (Thomas Fraser): The Campbells of Lagganlochan: a chapter in Scottish family history. [Edinburgh, 1930.] *Edin. P.; Edin. S.; Glas. Mit.; Edin. L.L.* (*Typescript,* 1929).

Campbell of Lochdochart

PATERSON (James): Scottish surnames: a contribution to genealogy. Edinburgh, 1866. *Arb. P.; Glas. Mit.; Ab. P.; Dund. Q.*

Campbell of Melfort

CAMPBELL (Margaret Olympia): A memorial history of the Campbells of Melfort, Argyllshire; which includes records of the different Highland and other families with whom they have intermarried. London, 1882. *S.C.L.; Glas. U.; Glas. Mit.; Edin. U.; Edin. L.L.*

— — Supplement. London, 1894. *S.C.L.; Glas. U.; Glas. Mit.; Edin. L.L.*

Campbell-Maclachlan

CAMPBELL-MACLACHLAN (A. N.): Memorial history of the family of Campbell Maclachlan. London, 1883. *Edin. S.*

Cannan in Galloway

CANNON (D. V.): The Cannan family in Galloway. [Typed notes & extracts from official sources collected . . . in connection with the article on the family in vol. XXXI of the *Trans. of the Dumfriesshire & Galloway Nat. Hist. & Antiq. Society.*] *Dumf. C.*

CANNON (D. V.) & REID (R. C.): The Cannan family in Galloway. (In *Trans. Dumfriesshire & Galloway Nat. Hist. & Antiq. Soc.*, v. XXXI, 1952-53.) *Edin. L.L.; Dumf. C.*

Cargill

CARGILL (John): Cargill of Haltoun of Rattray. Notes, on the history of the family, with 3 vol. of references. 4 v. [c. 1930]. (*MS.*) *St.A. U.*

Carlisle

[CARLILE (J. W.), & *others.*]: History of the Paisley branch of the Carlisle or Carlile family. By some of its members. Winchester, 1909. *Dumf. C.; Edin. P.; Pai. P.; Edin. L.L.*

CARLYLE (T. J.): Review of N. Carlisle's "History of the family of Carlisle". Dumfries, 1881. *Edin. L.L.; Edin. Ant.*

[WOOD (John Philip)]: Extracts from collections regarding the ancient family of Carlisle. (In his *Memorials of various families.* c. 1830. (*MS.*).) *Edin. P.*

Carlyle of Waterbeck

The Carlyles of Waterbeck. 1914. (Comp. from obituary notices in local papers.) *Dumf. C.*

Carnegie

CORMACK (Alexander A.): The Carnegie family in Gothenburg. Montrose, 1947. *Arb. P.* (1942)*; Ab. P.; Mont. P.*

Carnegie of Skibo

GRAY (Peter): Skibo: its lairds, and history. Edinburgh, 1906. *S.C.L.; Dunf. P.; Ab. U.; Ab. P.; Dund. P.; Suth. C.; Edin. P.; Edin. S.; Glas. Mit.; Edin. L.L.*

Carnegie, Earl of Southesk

FRASER (Sir William): History of the Carnegies, Earls of Southesk, and of their kindred. 2 v. Edinburgh, 1867. *Arb. P.; Ab. U.; Forf. P.; Glas. U.; Dund. P.; Edin. P.; Edin. S.; Glas. Mit.; Edin. L.L.; Edin. Ant.*

see also **Southesk,** Earldom of

Carrick, Earldom of

CARRICK (Andrew): Some account of the ancient earldom of Carric . . . ed. by J. Maidment. Edinburgh, 1857. *Glas. U.; Ayr P.; Edin. P.; Edin. S.; Glas. Mit.; Edin. L.L.*

Carruthers

CARRUTHERS (Arthur Stanley), *comp.*: A collection of records setting forth the history of the Carruthers family. Purley, Surrey, 1925. *Dumf. C.; Edin. Ant.*

CARRUTHERS (Arthur Stanley) & REID (R. C.): Records of the Carruthers family. London, 1934. *Dumf. C.; Edin. P.; Edin. S.; Glas. Mit.; Edin. L.L.; Edin. Ant.*

GILLESPIE (John) of Mouswald: The Carruthers family: an interesting record. n.p., n.d. *Dumf. C.*

Cassells

CASSELLS (Robert): Records of the family of Cassells and connexions. Edinburgh, 1870. *Edin. P.; Edin. S.; Glas. Mit., Edin. L.L.*

Cassie

CASSIE (R. L.): The Cassies. Banff, 1932. *Ab. P.; Dund. Q.; Edin. P.; Edin. S.*

Cassillis, Earldom of

KENNEDY (Sir Thomas): The Case of Sir Thomas Kennedy, (claiming the title, honour and dignity of) Earl of Cassillis. 1761. *Glas. Mit.*

MAIDMENT (James), *ed.*: The Cassillis peerage, 1760-64, with folding pedigree by W. B. Turnbull. [Edinburgh, 1840.] *Ab. U.*

— Reports of claims . . . to the House of Lords . . . of the Cassillis, Sutherland, Spynie and Glencairn peerages, 1760-1797. Edinburgh, 1882. *Glas. U.; Dund. P.* (1840); *Edin. P.; Edin. S.; Glas. Mit.; Edin. Ant.; Edin. L.L.* (1840).

MARCH & RUGLEN (William), *Earl of*: The Case of William, Earl of Ruglen and March (claiming the titles and dignities of) Earl of Cassillis and Lord Kennedy. 1762. *Glas. Mit.*

Cathcart, Earl Cathcart

GRAHAM (Ethel Maxtone): The Beautiful Mrs. Graham and the Cathcart circle. London, 1927. *S.C.L.; Glas. Mit.*

Cawdor, *see* **Campbell** of Cawdor or Calder

Chalmers

[CHALMERS (Patrick H.)]: Memorandum as to branch of family from which Principal George Chalmers, D.D., was descended. [Aberdeen, 1885.] *Edin. L.L.*

CHALMERS and Burns Roll of Honour. Edinburgh, 1915 [Contains names of 96 descendants of James Chalmers. printer . . . Aberdeen, 1741-1810 . . . and John Burns . . , H.M. Customs, Borrowstounness, 1730-1817, etc.] *Edin. Port.*

[CORMACK (Alexander Allan)]: The Chalmers family and Aberdeen newspapers: links between Aberdeen and Gothenburg. [Aberdeen], 1958. *Edin. P.*

GRANT (Rev. A. Thomson): MSS. notes on family of Chalmers. n.d. *Forf. P.*

GUTHRIE (Charles John), *Lord Guthrie, comp.*: Genealogy of the descendants of the Rev. Thomas Guthrie . . . connected chiefly with the families of Chalmers and Trail . . . Edinburgh, 1902. *Edin. S.; Glas. Mit.; Arb. P.; Ab. P.; St.A. U.; Glas. U.; Edin. P.*

Chalmers of Gadgirth
THE CHALMERSES and Burnetts of Gadgirth. n.p., n.d. *Ayr P.*

Charles in East Lothian
CHARLES (J. H.): Our family history. Bournemouth, 1935. *Edin. P.*

Charteris of Amisfield
REID (Robert Corsane): The Family of Charteris of Amisfield. Dumfries, 1938. *Dumf. C.; St.A. U.; Ab. U.; Edin. P.; Edin. S.; Edin. L.L.* (1921).

Charters

WATSON (Charles Brodie Boog): Traditions and genealogies of some members of the families of Boog, Heron, Leishman, Ross and Watson. Perth, 1908. *St.A. U.; Edin. P.; Edin. S.*

Chatelherault, Duke of

ABERCORN (James Hamilton), *2nd Duke of*: Consultation pour J. H., Marquis d'Abercorn . . . contre le Duc d'Hamilton. (Maintien et confirmation du titre héréditaire de Duc de Chatellerault concédé à James Hamilton par Henri II, Roi de France, en 1548.) Paris, 1865. *S.C.L.; Glas. Mit.; Edin. L.L.; Edin. Ant.*

DEFENSE pour S. A. Mme. Marie Cardine de Bade Duchesse d'Hamilton . . . contre M. James Hamilton, Marquis d'Abercorn, etc. [1864.] *Edin. L.L.*

TEULET (Jean Baptiste Alex. Theodore): Mémoire justificatif du droit qui appartient à M. le duc d'Hamilton de porter le titre de Duc de Chatellerault. Paris, [1864]. *Glas. U.; Edin. P.; Edin. S.*

TITRES et pieces justificatives des legitimes pretentions de la maison de Hamilton. 1713. *Edin. L.L.*

[TURNBULL (William Barclay David Donald)]: Factum of the Earl of Arran touching the restitution of the Duchy of Chatelherault, 1685. Edinburgh, 1843. *S.C.L.; Edin. P.; Edin. S.; Glas. Mit.; Edin. L.L.; Edin. Ant.*

Chattan, Clan, *see* Mackintosh

Chene

ROSE (David Murray): Knightly Chenes. n.p., n.d. *Ab. U.*

Cheyne

CHEYNE (Archibald Ythan): The Cheyne family in Scotland. Eastbourne, 1931. *Kir. P.; Arb. P.; Burnt. P.; Ayr P.; Zet. C.; Dunf. P.; Dund. P.; Ren. C.; Fal. P.; Cai. C.; Ab. P.; Haw. P.; Bo'n. P.; Inv. P.; Sti. P.; Nai. C.; Ruth. P.; Ham. P.; Kil. P.; Fras. P.; Gala. P.; Pee. C.; Per. P.; Dumb. P.; Edin. U.; St.A. U.; Ab. U.; Forf. P.; Ork. C.; Glas. U.; Pet. P.; Edin. P.; Edin. S.; Glas. Mit.; Edin. L.L.*

CHEYNE-MACPHERSON (W. D.): Cheynes of Inverugie, Esslemont and Arnage, and their descendants. Kirkwall, 1943. *Inv. P.; St.A. U.; Ab. U.; Edin. P.; Edin. L.L.; Edin. Ant.*

Chisholm

ANDERSON (James Stuart Murray): Memoir of the Chisholm, late M.P. for Inverness-shire. London, 1842. *Inv. P.; Glas. U.; Edin. P.; Edin. S.; Glas. Mit.; Edin. L.L.*

DUNLOP (Jean): The Clan Chisholm. Edinburgh, 1953. *Inv. P.; Inv. C.; Lan. C.; Ren. C.; Dund. P.; Edin. P.; Edin. S.; Glas. Mit.; Edin. L.L.*

MACKENZIE (Alexander): History of the Chisholms, with genealogies of the principal families of that name. Inverness, 1891. *S.C.L.; Ab. P.; Haw. P.; Inv. P.; Sel. P.; Inv. C.; St.A. U.; Ab. U.; Glas. U.; Edin. U.; Edin. S.; Glas. Mit.; Edin. L.L.*

STIRTON (John): A day that is dead. [Memoir of Mrs. Chisholm, Glassburn House, Strathglass.] 2nd ed. London, [1929]. *Ab. P.; Inv. P.; Dund. P.; Per. C.; Edin. P.; Glas. Mit.; Edin. L.L.; Edin. Ant.*

Christie

BROWN (Elisabeth Christie): The Kildrummy Christies. Aberdeen, 1948. *Ab. C.; Banff C.; Ab. P.; Edin. P.; Edin. S.; Glas. Mit.*

RICHARDSON (Ralph): Family tree of Christie of Ferrybank, Fifeshire. [Edinburgh, 1902.] *St.A. U.*

30

ROGERS (Charles): Genealogical memoirs of the Scottish house of Christie. London, 1878. *Dunf. P.; Sti. P.; Ab. U.; St.A. U.; Edin. P.; Edin. S.; Glas. Mit.; Edin. Ant.*

Clark of Uyeasound, Shetland

CLARK (John): Genealogy, records and intermarriages of the Fordyce, Bruce and Clark families at Uyeasound, Unst, Shetland. 2nd ed. Falkirk, 1902. *Zet. C.; Edin. P.; Ork. C.* (Falkirk, 1899).

Cleland

CLELAND (John Burton): The ancient family of Cleland: an account of the Clelands of that ilk, in the county of Lanark; of the branches of Faskine, Monkland, etc., and of others of the name. London, 1905. *Air. P.; Glas. Mit.*

Clouston

CLOUSTON (J. Storer): The Family of Clouston. Kirkwall, 1948. *Edin. L.L.*

Coats

COATS (A.): From the cottage to the castle. n.d. (*MS.*) *Pai. P.*

Cochran

CALLENDER (James Hodge), *comp.*: History and genealogy of the Cochran family of Kirkcudbright and New York. [New York], 1932. *Kirkcud. Bro.*

HAUGHTON (Ida Clara Cochran), *Mrs. Haughton*: Chronicles of the Cochrans, etc. Columbus, Ohio, 1915. *Glas. Mit.*

Cochrane of Cochrane

GRANT (Sir Francis James), *ed.*: Inventory of the charter chest of the earldom of Dundonald, 1219-1672. Edinburgh, 1910. (Scottish Record Soc. 36.) *S.C.L.; Edin. P.*

PARKER (Katherine), *comp.*: Pedigree of the Cochranes of Cochrane, Lord Cochrane of Dundonald; Earls of Dundonald, Lords Cochrane of Paisley and Ochiltree . . . comp. between . . . 1888-1908 . . . by K. Parker, and rev. by J. Anderson . . . London, [1908]. *St.A. U.; Ab. U.; Dund. P.; Edin. U.; Edin. P.; Glas. Mit.; Edin. L.L.*

Cochrane, Earl of Dundonald, *see* **Cochrane** of Cochrane

Cochrane, U.S.A.

WATKINS (Walter Kendall): The Cochranes of Renfrewshire, Scotland: the ancestry of Alex. Cochrane of Billerica & Malden, Mass., U.S.A. Boston, Mass., 1904. *Edin. P.; Edin. L.L.*

31

Cockburn

COCKBURN (Sir Robert) & COCKBURN (Henry A.): The Records of the Cockburn family . . . etc. Edinburgh, 1913. *Sel. P.; Ab. U.; Edin. P.; Edin. S.; Glas. Mit.; Edin. L.L.*

COCKBURN-HOOD (Thomas H.): House of Cockburn of that ilk, and the cadets thereof . . . Edinburgh, 1888. *Ber. C.; Glas. Mit.; Edin. P.; St.A. U.; Ab. U.; Dund. Q.; Glas. U.; Edin. S.; Edin. L.L.*

Collie

COLLIE (George F.): The Collie family tree. Cults, 1957. *Ab. P.*

Collins

COLLINS (Edward), *comp.*: An account of the information gained in the course of research regarding the pedigree of the family of Collins of Glasgow. n.p., 1928. *Glas. Mit.; Edin. Ant.*

KEIR (David): The House of Collins: the story of a Scottish family of publishers from 1789. London, 1952. *S.C.L.; Per. C.; Mid. C.; Ab. P.; Glas. U.; Edin. P.; Edin. S.; Glas. Mit.*

Colquhoun

COLQUHOUN (F. Mary) & COLQUHOUN (Neil Campbell): The Clan Colquhoun society, constitution, office-bearers . . .; also traditions . . . of the clan, etc. etc. [Glasgow, 1897.] *Dumb. P.; Glas. Mit.*

FRASER (Sir William): Cartulary of Colquhoun of Colquhoun and Luss. Edinburgh, 1873. *S.C.L.; Dumb. P.; Edin. P.; Edin. S.; Glas. Mit.; Edin. Ant.*

— The Chiefs of Colquhoun and their country. 2 v. Edinburgh, 1869. *S.C.L.; Dumb. P.; Cly. P.; Moth. P.; St.A. U.; Ab. U.; Glas. U.; Edin. P.; Edin. S.; Glas. Mit.; Edin. L.L.; Edin. Ant.*

[PAMPHLET relating to Colquhouns and their connection with the Falconers, etc.] Bath, [c. late 19th cent.]. *Edin. L.L.*

Colquhoun of Luss

GENEALOGICAL tree of family of Colquhoun of Luss. n.p., 1873. (Comp. from *Chiefs of Colquhoun* by Wm. Fraser, and from other sources.) *Inv. P.*

Colt

COLT (George Frederick Russell): History and genealogy of the Colts of that ilk and Gartsherrie. Edinburgh, 1887. *Glas. U.; Air. P.; Edin. P.; Edin. S.; Glas. Mit.; Edin. L.L.*

ROGERS (Charles): Genealogical memoirs of the families of Colt and Coutts. London, 1879. (Cottonian Soc.) *Arb. P.; Kil. P.; Dunf. P.; Dumf. C.; Ab. P.; Inv. P.; Sti. P.; Per. C.; Sti. C.; Per. P.; St.A. U.; Ab. U.; Forf. P.; Mid. C.; Pai. P.; Dund. Q.; Dund. P.; Edin. P.; Edin. S.; Glas. Mit.; Edin. Ant.*

Colville, Lord, Viscount Colville of Culross

COLVILLE (Georgiana M.): The Ancestry of Lord Colville of Culross. London, 1887. *Dunf. P.; Edin. L.L.*

Colyer-Fergusson, *see* **Fergusson**

Coningsburgh

REID (Robert Corsane): Family of Coningsburgh. (In *Trans. Dumfriesshire & Galloway Nat. Hist. &. Antiq. Soc.,* v. XX, 1938.) *Edin. L.L.; Dumf. C.*

Connal

OAKLEY (Charles Allen): Connal & Co., Ltd. [of Glasgow], 1722-1946. [Glasgow, 1947.] *Ayr P.; Glas. Mit.*

Constable

ROGERS (Charles): Four Perthshire families: Roger, Playfair, Constable and Haldane of Barmony. Edinburgh, 1887. *Sti. P.; Glas. U.; Per. P.; Dunf. P.; St.A. U.; Dund. P.; Edin. S.; Edin. Ant.; Edin. L.L.*

Constable-Maxwell, Lord Herries, *see* **Herries,** Lord of Teregles

Cook

COOK (George Milne): A family history. Aberdeen, 1951. (*Typescript.*) *Ab. P.*

Copland

KING (Norman): The Copland family in Galloway and Dumfriesshire. 1954. (*Typescript.*) *Dumf. C.*

Cornwall of Bonhard

STODART (Robert Riddle): Genealogy of the family of Cornwall of Bonhard, co. Linlithgow. Edinburgh, 1877. *Ab. U.; Edin. S.; Edin. L.L.*

Corrie

CORRIE (Jessie Elizabeth): Records of the Corrie family, 802-1899. 2 v. London, 1899. *S.C.L.; Dumf. C.; St.A. U.; Edin. P.; Edin. S.; Glas. Mit.*

Coulthart

KNOWLES (George Parker): A genealogical and heraldic account of the Coultharts of Coulthart and Collyn, chiefs of the name . . . London, 1855. *S.C.L.; Wig. C.; Edin. P.; Edin. L.L.*

Couper

OSLER (James Couper): Osler tree. [Chart pedigree] with some supplementary notes on . . . Coupers . . . [Dundee,] 1924. *Edin. L.L.; Edin. Ant.*

THOMSON (D. C.): Thomson, Couper, Yule, Sinclair genealogical chart. Dundee, 1936. *Dund. P.*

Coutts

FORBES (Sir William): Memoirs of a banking house. London, 1860. *S.C.L.; Ab. P.; Dund. P.; Edin. P.; Edin. S.; Glas. U.* (Edinburgh, 1859)*; Glas. Mit.*

RICHARDSON (Ralph): Coutts and Co., Bankers, Edinburgh and London: memoirs of a family distinguished for its public services in England and Scotland. London, 1900. *Ab. P.; Glas. Mit.*

—— 2nd ed. London, 1901. *Mont. P.; Dund. P.*

ROBINSON (Ralph Mosley): Coutts': the history of a banking house. London, 1929. *S.C.L.; Mont. P.; Glas. Mit.*

ROGERS (Charles): Genealogical memoirs of the families of Colt and Coutts. London, 1879. (Cottonian Soc.) *Arb. P.; Kil. P.; Dunf. P.; Ab. P.; Inv. P.; Sti. P.; Glas. Mit.; Per. C.; Sti. C.; Per. P.; St.A. U.; Ab. U.; Forf. P.; Mid. C.; Pai. P.; Dund. Q.; Dund. P.; Edin. P.; Edin. S.; Edin. L.L.*

Coutts in Montrose

LOW (James G.): John Coutts, or, Notes on an eminent Montrose family. Montrose, 1892. *Ab. P.; Edin. P.; Edin. Ant.*

Cowan

BIRRELL (James): Annals of the Cowan family. 1896. *(Typescript.) Edin. P.*

FORSYTH (Mary): The Cowans at Moray House. Edinburgh, 1932. *Edin. S.*

JOURNALS of the family of Cowan, 1830-44. Edinburgh, 1845. *Edin. P.*

WATSON (Charles Brodie Boog): Alexander Cowan of Moray House and Valleyfield, his kinsfolk and connections. (And Appendix.) 2 v. Perth, 1915-17. *Ab. P.; St.A. U.; Edin. P.; Edin. S.; Edin. L.L.*

Cowper, Lord Dingwall, *see* **Dingwall,** Lord

Craig

CRAIG (Margaret): Genealogical chart of Craig-Brechin, etc. —Canada—Chicago. Aberdeen, [c. 1925]. *Ab. P.*

LANG (Patrick Sellar), *comp.*: The Langs of Selkirkshire, with some notes on [other families]. Melbourne, 1910. *Edin. P.; Edin. S.*

Craig of Newbattle and New Monkland

CRAIG (R.) & Sons, Ltd.: A century of paper-making, 1820-1920. Edinburgh, 1920. *Mid. C.; Glas. Mit.*

Cranna

CRANNA (William H.): The Surnames of Cranna and Vass. Aberdeen, 1926. (*Typescript.*) *Ab. P.*

Cranstoun

CRANSTOUN papers MSS.: a collection of papers relative to the Cranstoun family, household accounts, receipts, letters, etc. c. 1800. (*MSS.*) *Edin. P.*

Craufurd of Auchenames & Crosbie

FERGUSSON (Sir James): Crosbie and the Craufurds. (In his *Lowland lairds.* 1949.) *S.C.L.; Dund. P.; Falk. P.; Edin. U.; Edin. P.; Glas. Mit.; Per. C.; Dunb. C.*

Craufurd of Kilbirnie

WILLIAMSON (George): Old Cartsburn: a history of the estate from . . . 1669 . . . with notices of the families of Kilbirnie, Jordanhill and Cartsburn. Paisley, 1894. *S.C.L.*

Crawford

[FAMILY papers, documents, letters, etc.] *Gree. P.*

Crawford, Earldom of

[ADAMS (Alexander Maxwell)]: The Crawfurd peerage: with other original genealogical, historical and biographical particulars relating to the illustrious houses of Crawfurd and Kilbirnie; including, also, a succinct account of the persecutions and abuses to which John Lindsay Crawfurd has been subjected . . . Edinburgh, 1829. *Dund. P.; Inv. P.; Ab. P.; Glas. U.; Ayr P.; Edin. P.; Glas. Mit.*

ADAMS (Alexander Maxwell): A sketch of the case of John Lindsay Crawford. Edinburgh, 1834. *Edin. S.*

CRAUFURD (John Lindsay): Sketch of the life of John Lindsay Craufurd, Esq., containing a full . . . account of his claim to the title and estates of George, Earl of Craufurd & Lindsay . . . written by himself. 2nd ed. Dalry, 1812. *Glas. U.; Glas. Mit.*

CRAWFORD & BALCARRES (James Lindsay), *24th/7th Earl of*: Case of James, Earl of Balcarres, etc. claiming titles, honours and dignities of the Earldom of Crawford and older Barony of Lindsay. [Prep. by J. Riddell?] Edinburgh, [1845]. *Edin. P.; Edin. S.; Glas. Mit.; Edin. L.L.*

— Summary or abstract of the chief deeds and evidence founded upon James, Earl of Balcarres, etc. etc. in his claim to the Earldom of Crawfurd and older Barony of Lindsay; . . . n.d. *Glas. Mit.*

DOBIE (James): Examination of the claim of John Lindsay Crawfurd to the titles and estates of Crawfurd and Lindsay. Edinburgh, 1831. *Ayr P.; Glas. U.; Edin. P.; Edin. S.; Glas. Mit.; Edin. L.L.; Edin. Ant.*

MINUTES of evidence taken before the Committee for Privileges . . . the petition of James, Earl of Balcarres . . . and also the petition of Robert Lindsay Crawfurd, Esq. 1845. *Glas. Mit.; Edin. L.L.*

RIDDELL (John): Analysis of objections . . . and of the replies furnished by John Riddell in the matter of the evidence adduced by the Earl of Balcarres, claiming the Earldom of Crawford and Barony of Lindsay. June, 1847. *Ab. P.; Edin. L.L.*

SHORT biographical sketches of the Earls of Crawford from the earliest times to the present. Wigan, 1885. *Ab. P.*

SPEECHES of counsel, and judgement. [1845-1848.] *Glas. Mit.; Edin. L.L.*

Crawfurd of Cartsburn

WILLIAMSON (George): Old Cartsburn: a history of the estate from the year 1669 . . . with notices of the families of Kilbirnie, Jordanhill and Cartsburn . . . Paisley, 1894. *S.C.L.*

Crawfurd of Jordanhill, *see* **Crawfurd of Cartsburn**

Craven

CRAVEN (J. B.): Genealogical collections relating to the family of Cravie or Craven in Scotland, with notes and documents illustrative of their family connections. Kirkwall, 1910. *Ork. C.; Edin. P.; Edin. S.*

Crichton

CRICHTON (Douglas): Sanquhar and the Crichtons. Dumfries, 1907. *Dumf. C.; Ab. U.; Edin. P.; Edin. S.; Glas. Mit.; Edin. L.L.; Edin. Ant.*

SINTON (Rev. T.): The Crichtons. (In his *Family and genealogical sketches.* 1911.) *Inv. P.; Ab. U.; Ab. P.; Dund. Q.; Edin. P.; Edin. S.*

STEELE (John Haughton): Genealogy of the Earls of Erne. Edinburgh, 1910. *St.A. U.; Edin. S.*

Crichton, Lord Frendraught, *see* **Frendraught,** Lord

Crogo

PROOFS of the descent of the family of Crogo in the Stewartry of Kirkcudbright. n.d. *Wig. C.*

Cromartie, Earl of, *see* **Mackenzie,** Earl of Cromartie

Crozier

CROZIER (F. H.): Memorials of the family of Crozier. Lymington, 1881. *Edin. S.*

Cruickshank

CRUICKSHANK (E. G. G.) & GORDON (W.): Cruickshank in Strathspey and of Stracathro. Elgin, 1847. *Ab. P.*

Cuming, Cumming of Culter

[TOMKINS (Henry Barr)]: A table showing the families descended from Sir Alexander Cumming of Coulter, created a Scots baronet in 1695. n.p., [1877]. *Edin. L.L.*

Cuming, Cumming of Lochtervandich

CUMINE (James): History of the Cumins of Lochtervandech. n.p., c. 1900. *Ab. U.*

Cumming

DUNLOP (Annie Isabella Cameron), *Mrs. Dunlop* & POLACZEK (Helena): Diploma of nobility of Thomas Cumming, 1727. 1938. (Repr. from the *Juridical Review*, Mar. 1938.) *Edin. P.*

Cumyn

BRUCE (Mary Elizabeth Cumming): Family records of the Bruces and the Cumyns. Edinburgh, 1870. *S.C.L.; Ab. P.; Haw. P.; Inv. P.; Dumf. C.; Sti. P.; Nai. C.; Glas. U.; Edin. P.; Edin. S.; Glas. Mit.; Dumb. P.; St.A. U.; Ab. U.; Edin. L.L.*

Cuninghame

PATERSON (James): Scottish surnames: a contribution to genealogy. Edinburgh, 1866. *Arb. P.; Glas. Mit.; Ab. P.; Dund. Q.*

Cunningham, Earl of Glencairn, *see* **Glencairn,** Earldom of

Cunninghame of Craigend

McKENZIE (R. D.): Notes on Cunninghames of Craigend. c. 1900. (*MS.*) *Pai. P.*

Cunynghame

CUNYNGHAME (Robert Myrton): Robert Myrton Cunynghame, second son of Sir Wm. Augustus Cunynghame of Livingston, Bt. . . . appellant. David Cunynghame . . . respondent. [n.p., 1777.] *Edin. P.; Edin. S.*

Currie of Howford

LANG (Patrick Sellar), *comp.*: The Langs of Selkirk with some notes on [other families]. Melbourne, 1910. *Edin. P.; Edin. S.*

Cursiter

CLOUSTON (John Storer): A note on an odal family. (In *Viking Soc. Old-lore miscellany of Orkney and Shetland,* v. I, 1907-8, pp. 135-6.) *Ork. C.*

Curwen

CURWEN (John F.): History of the ancient house of Curwen of Workington in Cumberland and its various branches. Kendal, 1928. *Dumf. C.*

Cuthbert

BULLOCH (Joseph Gaston Baillie): The Cuthberts of Castlehill and their descendants in South Carolina and Georgia. Washington, 1908. *Inv. P.; Edin. L.L.*

Dalgleish of Tinnygask

RUVIGNY & RAINEVAL (M. A. H. D. H. de la C. Massue de Ruvigny), *9th Marquis de*: Dalgleish of Tinnygask. London, 1902. *Dunf. P.; Edin. L.L.*

Dallas

DALLAS (James): A history of the family of Dallas; ed. by C. S. Romanes. Edinburgh, 1921. *S.C.L.; Kirkcud. C.; Elg. P.; Inv. P.; Nai. C.; Per. C.; St.A. U.; Ab. U.; Ab. P.; Edin. P.; Edin. S.; Glas. Mit.; Edin. L.L.*

Dalmahoy

> FALCONER (T.): An account of the family of Dalmahoy of that
> ilk and of the family of Falconer. London, n.d. *Edin. S.*

> [FALCONER (Thomas)]: The Family of Dalmahoy of Dalmahoy,
> Ratho, county of Edinburgh. [London, 1870?] *Mid. C.;
> St.A. U.; Edin. P.; Edin. S.; Glas. Mit.; Edin. L.L.* (n.p., n.d.).

Dalrymple

> DALRYMPLE (Christian): Private annals of my own time, 1765-
> 1812. Edinburgh, 1914. *Edin. P.*

> SETON (George): Memoir of Alexander Seton . . . with an
> appendix cont. . . . genealogical tables of the legal families
> of Erskine, Hope, Dalrymple and Dundas. Edinburgh,
> 1882. *Dunf. P.; Glas. Mit.*

Dalrymple of Langlands

> SHAW (John): The Dalrymples of Langlands. Bath, [1868].
> *Edin. P.*

Dalrymple, Earl of Stair

> DALRYMPLE (Hon. Hew Hamilton): Genealogical account of
> the Dalrymples of Stair, Earls of Stair. n.p., 1909. *Wig. C.;
> St.A. U.; Edin. L.L.*

> GRAHAM (John Murray): Annals and correspondence of the
> Viscount and the 1st and 2nd Earls of Stair. 2 v. Edinburgh,
> 1875. *S.C.L.; Haw. P.; Dumf. C.; Mid. C.; Glas. U.; Edin. P.;
> Edin. S.; Glas. Mit.*

Dalrymple of Waterside

> McCALL (Hardy Bertram): Some old families: a contribution
> to the genealogical history of Scotland. Birmingham, 1890.
> *S.C.L.; Edin. P.; Sel. P.; Edin. S.; Edin. L.L.; Edin. Ant.*

Dalyell of Binns

> DALYELL (Sir James Bruce Wilkie) of Binns & BEVERIDGE
> (James), *eds.*: The Binns papers, 1320-1864. Edinburgh,
> 1938. (Scottish Record Soc. 70.) *S.C.L.; Glas. U.; Dund. P.;
> Edin. P.; Edin. S.; Glas. Mit.*

Darnley, Earl of, *see* **Lennox,** Duke of

Davidson of Muirhouse

> PHILIP (Adam): The Ancestry of Randall Thomas Davidson,
> Archbishop of Canterbury. London, 1903. *Ab. P.; Dund.
> O.; Edin. P.; Edin. S.; Glas. Mit.*

Dawson

ADAMS (Percy Walter Lewis): A brief history of a branch of the Dawson family of Dysart and Kirkcaldy, Fife (1690-1840) and their descendants of Madras, Rangoon and Pyapon, Burma and Long Stanton, Cambridgeshire. Stoke-on-Trent, 1952. *S.C.L.; Kirk. P.; Fife C.; Edin. P.; Edin. S.; Glas. Mit.*

De Quincy

IRELAND (William W.): Notes on the Scottish de Quencys of Fawsyde and Leuchars. Edinburgh, 1898. (Repr. from *Proc. Soc. Antiquaries*, 1898-1900.) *Edin. L.L.; Edin. S.*

De Valoniis

MAULE (Hon. Harry): Registrum de Panmure. 2 v. Edinburgh, 1874. *Arb. P.; Glas. Mit.; Per. P.; St.A. U.; Ab. U.; Forf. P.; Glas. U.; Dund. P.; Edin. P.; Edin. S.; Edin. L.L.*

De Veteripont, Vipont

REID (Robert Corsane): De Veteripont. Dumfries, 1956. (Repr. from *Transactions Dumfriesshire & Galloway Nat. Hist. & Antiquarian Soc.*, 3rd ser. v. XXXIII, 1956.) *Edin. L.L.*

Dennistoun of Colgrain

DENNISTOUN (James W.), *ed.*: Some account of the family of Dennistoun and Colgrain. Glasgow, 1906. *Edin. S.; Glas. Mit.*

Dennistoun of Dennistoun

DONALD (Thomas F.): The Dennistouns of Dennistoun. Glasgow, 1918. *Glas. Mit.*

Deuchar

DEUCHAR (J. C. A.): Pedigree of the Deuchar family. n.d. *Glas. Mit.*

Dewar

ANDERSON (Joseph): The Dewars, or hereditary keepers of relics of the Celtic church in Scotland. [1890.] (From the *Highland Monthly*.) *Edin. Ant.*

Dick of Prestonfield

FORBES (Mrs. Atholl), *ed.*: Curiosities of a Scots charta chest, 1600-1800. Edinburgh, 1897. *Ork. C.; Dund. P.; Edin. P.; Edin. S.; Glas. Mit.*

Dick-Lauder

SMITH (Mrs. J. Stewart): The Grange of St. Giles, the Bass and other baronial homes of the Dick-Lauder family. Edinburgh, 1898. *S.C.L.; Elg. P.; Inv. P.; Ork. C.; Ab. P.; Edin. P.; Edin. S.; Glas. Mit.*

Dickson

DIXON (Bernard Homer): The Border, or riding clans . . . a history of the clan Dickson. Albany, N.Y., 1889. *Edin. P.*

— Scotch border clan Dickson, the family of B. Homer Dixon and of the family of De Homere or Homer. Toronto, 1884. *Edin. P.; Edin. Ant.*

Dingwall, Lord

COWPER (Francis Thomas de Grey), *Earl*: Case on behalf of . . . on his claim to . . . Lord Dingwall . . . *Edin. L.L.*

— Supplementary case of above . . . *Edin. L.L.*

MINUTES of evidence . . . to whom were referred the petitions of . . . Francis Thomas de Grey, Earl Cowper, Viscount Fordwich & Baron Cowper, K.G., . . . to declare he is entitled to . . . barony of Dingwall in the peerage of Scotland. 1870. *Edin. L.L.*

Dingwall-Fordyce

FORDYCE (Alexander Dingwall): Family record of the name of Dingwall-Fordyce, including relatives of both names and connections. 2 v. Toronto, 1885-88. *Ab. P.; Ab. C.; Edin. P.; Edin. S.; Glas. Mit.*

Dinwiddie

HOLLADAY (Elizabeth Dinwiddie), *ed.*: Dinwiddie family records; with special attention to the line of William W. Dinwiddie, 1804-1882. Charlottesville, Va., 1957. *Dumf. C.*

Dirom

BULLOCH (John Malcolm): The Dirom family. 1935. *Ab. P.*

Dixon

THE DIXON family and their connection with Glasgow. (Excerpts from *Memoirs and portraits of one hundred Glasgow men* by [J. O. Mitchell & others], 2 v. 1886.) *Glas. Mit.*

Don in Angus

DON (William Gerard): Memoirs of the Don family in Angus: with a general survey of the etymology of the name . . . London, 1897. *St.A. U.; Forf. P.; Edin. P.; Edin. S.*

Donald, *see* MACDONALD

Donaldson

> SKINNER (Robert T.): A notable family of Scots printers.
> Edinburgh, 1927. *Ab. P.; Edin. P.; Edin. S.; Glas. U.* (2nd
> ed. 1928).

Donnachaidh, *see* Robertson

Douglas

> THE BROKEN cross: a legend of Douglas; with chronicles of
> the Black Douglas and an appendix. Glasgow, 1859.
> *Dumf. C.; Haw. P.; Glas. U.; Edin. P.; Glas. Mit.*

> DOUGLAS (Charles Henry James): A collection of family records
> . . . of various families and individuals bearing the name
> Douglas . . . Providence, R.I., 1879. *Glas. Mit.*

> FRASER (Sir William): The Douglas book: memoirs of the
> house of Douglas and Angus. 4 v. Edinburgh, 1885.
> *S.C.L.; Haw. P.; Dumf. C.; Moth. P.; St.A. U.; Ab. U.; Glas.
> U.; Dund. P.; Edin. P.; Edin. S.; Glas. Mit.; Edin. L.L.;
> Edin. Ant.*

> HERD (James): The Martial achievements of the houses of
> Douglas, Angus and Queensberry. Edinburgh, 1769.
> *Edin. L.L.*

> HUME (David), [*of Godscroft*]: The History of the house and race
> of Douglas and Angus. 1643. *Dumf. C.*

> — — Edinburgh, 1644. *Forf. P.*

> — — 1648. *Ab. U.; Edin. Ant.*

> — — 1657. *St.A. U.*

> — — 1743. *Per. P.; Ab. U.; Glas. U.; Edin. P.; Edin. S.;
> Glas. Mit.*

> — — 2 v. 1748. *Edin. L.L.*

> — — Aberdeen, 1820. *Lan. C.; Ber. C.; Ab. P.; Haw. P.;
> Ab. U.* (pt. 1)*; Dund. P.; Edin. P.; Edin. S.*

> JOHNSTON (George Harvey): The Heraldry of the Douglases,
> with notes on all the males of the family. Edinburgh, 1907.
> *Dumf. C.; Glas. Mit.; Edin. P.* (+ 1905)*; Edin. S.* (+ 1905).

> LETTERS etc. relating to the family of Douglas. 1802-05.
> *Glas. Mit.*

> MAXWELL (Sir Herbert Eustace): A history of the house of
> Douglas from the earliest times down to the legislative
> union of England and Scotland. 2 v. London, 1902.
> *S.C.L.; Dumf. C.; Cai. C.; Arb. P.; Kil. P.; Lan. C.; Ab. P.;*

Haw. P.; Inv. P.; Dun. P.; Sti. P.; Gra. P.; Ham. P.; Wig. C.; Sti. C.; Gala. P.; Per. P.; Dumb. P.; Ang. C.; Edin. U.; St.A. U.; Ab. U.; Camp. P.; Forf. P.; Kirkcud. C.; Glas. U.; Dund. P.; Falk. P.; Pai. P.; Edin. P.; Edin. S.; Glas. Mit.; Edin. L.L.; Edin. Ant.

MEMOIRES of my Lord Drunlangrig's and his brother Lord William's travels abroad . . . 1680. n.p., n.d. (*MS. copy.*) *Edin. P.*

MS. notes and press cuttings on the family of Douglas. n.d. *Edin. P.*

PINEDA (Peter): A synopsis of the genealogy . . . of the family of the Brigantes or Douglas. London, 1754. *Edin. P.; Edin. S.; Glas. Mit.; Edin. L.L.*

QUEENSBERRY (Francis Archibald Kelhead Douglas), *10th Marquess of*: The Sporting Queensberrys. London, 1942. *S.C.L.; Dumf. C.; Kil. P.; Lan. C.*

RAMAGE (Craufurd Tait): Drumlanrig Castle and the Douglases. Dumfries, 1876. *S.C.L.; Dumf. C.; Haw. P.; Gala. P.; Ab. P.; Glas. U.; Edin. P.; Edin. S.; Glas. Mit.; Edin. L.L.*

RIACH (Charles C.): Douglas and the Douglas family. Hamilton, 1927. *Fife C.; Edin. P.; Glas. Mit.*

Douglas, Marquess of

ANDERSON (William): Speeches and judgements . . . George James, Duke of Hamilton . . . against Archibald Douglas. Edinburgh, 1768. *Inv. P.; Glas. U.; Edin. P.; Edin. S.; Glas. Mit.*

[BOSWELL (James), *the elder*]: Dorando, a Spanish tale. [A satire on the Douglas cause.] London, 1767. *Glas. Mit.*

— The Essence of the Douglas cause . . . London, 1767. *Glas. Mit.*

[COLVILL (Rev. Robert)]: Fate of Julia, an epic poem in two cantos, sacred to the memory of L - dy J - n D - - g - -s [i.e. Lady Jane Douglas aft. Stewart]. 2nd ed. n.p.,1769. *Glas.Mit.*

— The Merry wives of Douglas; or the Douglas garland . . . written by a young gentleman. Edinburgh, 1769. *Glas. Mit.*

A CONCISE narrative of the proceedings in the Douglas Cause: with remarks upon the memorials; in a letter to a friend. 2nd ed. London, 1767. *Dund. P.; Glas. Mit.*

CONSIDERATIONS on the Douglas Cause, in a letter from a gentleman in Scotland to his friend in London. London, 1767. *Glas. Mit.*

DE LA TORRE (Lillian): The Heir of Douglas. London, 1953. *Inv. P.; Rox. C.; Sti. C.; Arb. P.; Ab. P.; Ren. C.; Edin. P.; Glas. Mit.*

DOUGLAS (Archibald James Edward): Case of Archibald Douglas against the Duke of Hamilton and others. [Edinburgh], 1769. *Inv. P.; Dund. P.; Edin. P.; Glas. Mit.*

— Memorial for Archibald Douglas of Douglas, Esq., and for Margaret Dutchess of Douglas, etc. . . . against George-James, Duke of Hamilton . . . [Signed Ilay Campbell]. [Edinburgh], 1766. *Dund. P.; Edin. P.; Edin. S.; Glas. Mit.*

— Proof for Archibald Douglas of Douglas, Esq., defender; in the reduction, the Duke of Hamilton, Lord Douglas Hamilton, and Sir Hew Dalrymple, against him. [Edinburgh?], 1766. *Glas. Mit.*

[DOUGLAS (Francis)]: A letter to a noble lord; or, A faithful representation of the Douglas Cause. London, 1769. *Dund. P; Glas. Mit.*

FITZGERALD (Percy Hetherington): Lady Jean: the romance of the great Douglas Cause. London, 1904. *Fife C.; St.A. U.; Edin. P.; Edin. S.; Glas. Mit.*

HAMILTON (James George), *7th Duke of*: Archibald James Edward Stewart alias Douglas . . . appellant and George James, Duke of Hamilton, & others, respondents. Case of the Respondents, the Duke of Hamilton, etc. n.p., n.d. *Glas. Mit.*

— Case, George-James, Duke of Hamilton, etc. against the person pretending to be Archibald Douglas. [Signed Alex. Lockhart.] n.p., [June 27, 1766]. *Dund. P.; Glas. Mit.*

— Information for George-James, Duke of Hamilton . . . against Dunbar, Earl of Selkirk, and Archibald Stewart, Esq., [Signed Alex. Lockhart.] [Edinburgh, Apr. 15, 1762.] *Dund. P.*

— Memorial for George-James, Duke of Hamilton, Marquis of Douglas etc. . . . against a person pretending to be Archibald Stewart alias Douglas . . . [Edinburgh], Jan. 1767. *Inv. P.; Dund. P.; Glas. Mit.*

— Proof in the conjoined processes, George-James, Duke of Hamilton . . . against the person pretending to be Archibald Stewart alias Douglas . . . Dec. 19, 1765 & Feb. 5, 1766. [Edinburgh? 1766.] *Dund. P.; Glas. Mit.*

— Trial of George-James, Duke of Hamilton and others and Archibald Douglas. Edinburgh, 1768. *Inv. P.*

HAMILTON (James George), *7th Duke of, & others*: The Cases given to the Court of Session previous to the pleadings in the important cause of *suppositio portus*, George-James, Duke of Hamilton and others, pursuers; against Archibald Douglas, Esq., defender. Edinburgh, 1768. *Glas. Mit.*

[LEGAL papers relating to the Douglas Cause.] 1761-1763. *Glas. Mit.*

PAPERS on the Douglas peerage case. 11 v. *Edin. L.L.*

RICHARDSON (Robert): A state of the evidence in the [Douglas] Cause . . . London, 1769. *Glas. Mit.*

SPEECHES, arguments and determinations of the . . . Lords of Council and Session in Scotland, upon that important cause . . . London, 1767. *Glas. Mit.*

STATE of the facts etc. in the Douglas Cause. 2 v. 1766-67. *Inv. P.*

STEUART (Archibald Francis), *ed.*: The Douglas Cause. Glasgow, 1909. *S.C.L.; Ab. P.; Glas. U.; Dund. P.; Edin. P.; Edin. S.; Glas. Mit.*

STEWART (Lady Jane), *formerly Douglas*: Letters of the Right Hon. Lady Jane Douglas . . . London, 1767. *Glas. Mit.*

STUART (Andrew): Letters to the Rt. Hon. Lord Mansfield from Andrew Stuart. London, 1773. *Glas. U.; Dund. P.; Edin. P.; Edin. S.; Glas. Mit.*

THE WEEKLY MAGAZINE, or, Edinburgh amusement, Thursday, May 25, 1769. *Glas. Mit.; Edin. P.*

Douglas of Kelhead, *see* **Queensberry**, Marquessate of

Douglas of Morton

ADAMS (Percy Walter Lewis): A history of the Douglas family of Morton in Nithsdale and Fingland, and their descendants. Bedford, 1921. *S.C.L.; Dund. P.; Haw. P.; Dumf. C.; Ayr P.; Edin. U.; St.A. U.; Ab. U.; Ab. P.; Glas. U.; Edin. P.; Edin. S.; Glas. Mit.; Edin. L.L.; Edin. Ant.*

REGISTRUM honoris de Morton: a series of ancient charters of the Earldom of Morton with other original papers. 2 v. Edinburgh, 1853. (Bannatyne Club, 94.) *Glas. U.; Dund. P.; Edin. P.; Edin. S.; Glas. Mit.; Edin. L.L.*

Douglas of Mulderg

[AIRD (Gustavus)]: Genealogy of the families of Douglas of Mulderg and Robertson of Kindeace with their descendants. Dingwall, 1895. *Ross C.; Cai. C.; Inv. P.; Nai. C.; St.A. U; Ab. U.; Ork. C.; Ab. P.; Glas. U.; Edin. P.; Edin. S.; Glas. Mit.; Edin. Ant.*

Douglas of Tilquhilly

HISTORY of the family of Douglass of Tilwhilly or Tilliquhilly. Bath, [1874]. *St.A. U.; Ab. U.; Dund. Q.; Ab. P.* ([19—]); *Edin. S.*

PEDIGREE of Douglas of Tilquhilly, or Tilwhilly, co. Kincardine. n.p., [c. 1881]. *Edin. P.*

Douglas of Whiteriggs

MAIDMENT (James): Genealogical fragments relating to the families of . . . Douglas . . . Berwick, 1855. *Inv. P.; Glas. U.; Edin. P.; Edin. S.; Glas. Mit.*

Douglass

WATKINS (Walter Kendall): The Life and ancestry of Francis Douglass, bookseller and author, of Aberdeen and Paisley. Boston, Mass., 1903. *Ab. P.; Edin. P.; Glas. Mit.; Edin. L.L.*

Drummond

DRUMMOND (Henry): Drummond family. (In his *Histories of noble British families.* Vol. 2. 1846.) *Glas. U.; Edin. P.; Edin. S.; Glas. Mit.*

DRUMMOND (Thomas): An interesting statement of the claims of Thomas Drummond . . . to the . . . Earldom of Perth; interspersed with copious memoirs of the most noble house of Drummond . . . Newcastle, 1830. *Edin. P.; Glas. Mit.; Inv. P.* (1831).

MALCOLM (David): A genealogical memoir of the most noble and ancient House of Drummond, and of the several branches . . . Edinburgh, 1808. *Per. P.; St.A. U.; Ab. U.; Dund. Q.; Glas. U.; Edin. P.; Edin. S.; Glas. Mit.; Edin. L.L.*

STRATHALLAN (William Drummond), *1st Viscount*: The Genealogy of the most noble and ancient house of Drummond. Edinburgh, 1831. *Dun. P.; Ab. U.; Glas. U.; Edin. L.L.; Edin. Ant.*

— — Glasgow, 1889. *Dund. P.; St.A. U.; Edin. P.; Glas. Mit.*

Drummond of Logiealmond

ANSWERS and defences for His Majesty's advocate, on behalf of His Majesty; to the claim of Thomas Drummond of Logiealmond to the estate of Drummond and Perth. 1750. *Glas. Mit.*

DRUMMOND (Thomas) of Logy-Almond: Case of Thomas Drummond of Logy-almond, claimant against His Majesty's advocate, in behalf of His Majesty, respondent. 1750. *Glas. Mit.*

INFORMATION for His Majesty's advocate, on behalf of His Majesty, respondent; against Thomas Drummond of Logie-almond, claimant of the estate of Drummond and Perth. 1750. *Glas. Mit.*

FORRESTER (David Marshall): Logiealmond. Edinburgh, 1944. *S.C.L.*

Drummond, Earl of Perth

EARL OF PERTH & MELFORT *v.* the Lord Elphinstone [case in the House of Lords]. 1871. *Glas. U.; Edin. P.*

see also **Perth,** Earldom of

Dudhope, Viscount

G.B. Parliament. House of Lords. Dudhope peerage. Proceedings before the Committee for privileges and judgement. London, 1953. *Dund. P.; Edin. L.L.*

Duff

BAIRD (William) of Auchmeddan: Genealogical memoirs of the Duffs. [Ed. by L. D. G. Duff.] Aberdeen, 1869. *St.A. U.; Edin. L.L.*

BULLOCH (John Malcolm), *comp.*: The Duffs and the Gordons: a table bringing out the literary instincts of the two. n.p., n.d. *(MS.) Edin. P.*

TAYLER (Alistair) & TAYLER (Henrietta): The Book of the Duffs. 2 v. Edinburgh, 1914. *Elg. P.; Ab. P.; Inv. P.; Ab. U.; Edin. P.; Edin. S.; Glas. Mit.; Edin. L.L.; Edin. Ant.*

Duff, Duke of Fife

CRAMOND (William): The Genealogy of the Duke of Fife Edinburgh, [1889]. *Ab. P.*

Duguid

MAIDMENT (James): Genealogical fragments relating to the families of . . . Duguid. Berwick, 1855. *Inv. P.; Glas. U.; Edin. P.; Edin. S.; Glas. Mit.; Edin. Ant.*

Dunbar

DRUMMOND (Henry): Histories of noble British families. Vol. 2: Dunbar, Hume, Dundas. London, 1846. *Edin. P.; Glas. U.; Glas. Mit.; Edin. S.*

JAGGARD (William): Dunbar pedigrees: a biographical chart . . . of the Dunbar family through fourteen centuries. Stratford, 1910. *Ab. U.; Edin. P.; Edin. S.; Glas. Mit.*

MURRAY (Rev. James G.): The Book of Burgie. 1933. *Elg. P.*

Dunbar, Earldom of

[WOOD (John Philip)]: The Claim of Sir John Home of Renton, Bart., to the title . . . of Earl of Dunbar . . . (In his *Memorials of various families.* (*MS.*) c. 1830.) *Edin. P.*

Duncan

DUNCAN (James Alexander) & DUNCAN (Robert), *eds.*: Some family leaves. Edinburgh, 1911. *St.A. U.; Glas. U.; Cly. P.; Edin. P.; Edin. S.; Glas. Mit.*

FORBES (Alexander): Memorials of the family of Forbes of Forbesfield. [With notes on connected . . . Duncans . . .] Aberdeen, 1905. *Ab. P.; Ab. C.; St.A. U.; Glas. U.; Edin. P.; Edin. S.; Glas. Mit.*

Duncan in Sweden

CEDERBERG (A. R.): Some notes about the Duncan family; tr. from the Swedish by Archd. Duncan. (Personhistorisk tidskrift, 1922, XXIII, 3-4.) (*Typescript.*) *Edin. Ant.*

Dundas

DRUMMOND (Henry): Histories of noble British families. Vol. 2: Dunbar, Hume, Dundas. London, 1846. *Edin. P.; Glas. U.; Glas. Mit.; Edin. S.*

[DUNDAS (Francis De Sales)]: The Dundas genealogy. 2nd ed. Staunton, Virginia, [1954]. *Edin. L.L.*

MS. notes and press cuttings on the family of Dundas. n.d. *Edin. P.*

Dundas of Arniston

FORBES (Louisa Lillias): [Genealogy of Dundas of Arniston, 1570-1880.] [n.p., 1880.] *St.A. U.; Mid. C.; Edin. S.; Glas. Mit.; Edin. L.L.*

OMOND (George William Thomson): The Arniston memoirs: three centuries of a Scottish house 1571-1838; ed. from the family papers. Edinburgh, 1887. *S.C.L.; Glas. U.; St.A. U.; Mid. C.; Ab. P.; Edin. P.; Edin. S.; Glas. Mit.; Edin. L.L.; Edin. Ant.*

Dundas of Dundas

MACLEOD (Walter), *ed.*: Royal letters and other historical documents selected from the family papers of Dundas of Dundas. Edinburgh, 1897. *Inv. P.; Ork. C.; Glas. U.; St.A. U.; Edin. P.; Edin. S.; Glas. Mit.; Edin. L.L.; Edin. Ant.*

SETON (George): Memoir of Alexander Seton . . . with an appendix cont. . . . genealogical tables of the legal families of Erskine, Hope, Dalrymple and Dundas. Edinburgh, 1882. *Dunf. P.; Glas. Mit.*

Dundas of Fingask

DUNDAS (Margaret Isabella): Dundas of Fingask: some memorials of the family. Edinburgh, 1891. *S.C.L.; Edin. P.; Edin. S.; Glas. Mit.; Edin. L.L.*

Dundee, Earldom of

G.B. Parliament. House of Lords. Earldom of Dundee. Proceedings before the Committee for privileges and judgement. London, 1953. *Dund. P.; Edin. L.L.*

Dundonald, Earldom of

DUNDONALD (Thomas Barnes), *Earl of*: Case on behalf of Thomas Barnes, Earl of Dundonald . . . [+pedigree]. [1861]. *Edin. L.L.*

MINUTES of evidence taken . . . to whom was referred the petition of Thomas Barnes, Earl of Dundonald, etc. . . . to declare he is of right entitled to titles of Earl of Dundonald and Lord Cochrane & Paisley & Ochiltrie in the peerage of Scotland. 1861-63. *Edin. L.L.*

see also **Cochrane** of Cochrane

Dunfermline, Earl of, *see* **Seton,** Earl of Dunfermline

Dunlop

DUNLOP (Archibald): Dunlop of that ilk. Memorabilia of the families of Dunlop. Glasgow, 1898. *Ayr P.; St.A. U.; Kirkcud. C.; Glas. U.; Pai. P.; Edin. P.; Edin. S.; Glas. Mit.*

DUNLOP (J. G.): Autobiography of John Dunlop. (Dunlop papers, v. 1.) London, 1932. *Ab. U.; Glas. Mit.*

— Dunlops of Dunlop and of Auchenskaith, Keppoch and Gairbraid. (Dunlop papers, v. 2). Frome, 1939. *Gree. P.; Kil. P.; Ayr P.; Edin. U.; St.A. U.; Glas. U.; Pai. P.; Edin. P.; Edin. S.; Glas. Mit.; Edin. L.L.; Edin. Ant.*

— Letters and journals, 1663-1889. Selected and annotated by J. G. Dunlop. (Dunlop papers, v. 3). London, 1953. *St.A. U.; Ab. U.; Edin. U.; Edin. P.; Glas. Mit.*

REID (Robert), *comp.*: Records of the Dunlops of Dunlop. Dunmow, 1900. *St.A. U.; Edin. P.; Glas. U. (2nd ed. 1912).*

Dysart, Earldom of

DYSART (William John Manners), *Earl of*: Case of William John Manners, Earl of Dysart . . . to admit his succession to the dignities of Earl of Dysart & Lord Huntingtower in the peerage of Scotland. 1880. *Edin. L.L.*

MINUTES of evidence . . . 1880-81. *Edin. L.L.*

TOLLEMACHE (Albert Edwin): Case on behalf of Albert Edwin Tollemache in opposition to the claim of William John Manners claiming . . . Earl of Dysart . . . *Edin. L.L.*

Easson

OSLER (James Couper): Osler tree [chart pedigree] with some supplementary notes on . . . Eassons . . . [Dundee], 1924. *Edin. L.L.; Edin. Ant.*

Echlin(e)

CRAWFURD (George): "Memoirs of the ancient familie of the Echlins of Pittadro, in the County of Fyfe, in Scotland, now transplanted to Ireland." Dated, Glasgow, 18th August, 1747. [Ed. by J. R. Echlin.] [n.p., n.d.] *St.A. U.; Edin. L.L.*

ECHLIN (John R.): Genealogical memoirs of the Echlin family, comp. from various authentic sources, with extracts from a MS. memorial composed by George Crawfurd, Esq., in the year, 1747. 2nd ed. rev. and enl. Edinburgh, [n.d.]. *St.A. U.; Edin. P.; Edin. S.; Edin. L.L.*

Edgar

EDGAR (Andrew) & ROGERS (C.): Genealogical collections concerning the Scottish house of Edgar. London, 1873. (Grampian Club, 5.) *Arb. P.; Kil. P.; Ab. P.; Dunf. P.; Haw. P.; Inv. P.; Dumf. C.; Ber. C.; Per. P.; Gala. P.; Pee. P.; Ayr P.; Forf. P.; Glas. U.; Dund. P.; Pai. P.; Edin. P.; Edin. S.; Glas. Mit.; Dumb. P.; Edin. L.L.; Edin. Ant.*

Edgar of Wedderlie

LAWRENCE-ARCHER (James Henry): An account of the sirname Edgar, and particularly of the family of Wedderlie in Berwickshire. London, 1873. *Edin. P.; Edin. S.*

Edmondstone of Ednem and Duntreath

EDMONSTONE (Sir Archibald): Genealogical account of the

family of Edmonstone of Duntreath. Edinburgh, 1875. *S.C.L.; Sti. C.; Ab. U.; St.A. U.; Glas. U.; Edin. P.; Edin. S.; Glas. Mit.; Edin. L.L.; Edin. Ant.*

GENEALOGY of the lairds of Ednem and Duntreath, 1063-1699. Glasgow, 1699. *Inv. P.*

— Ed. by J. Maidment. Edinburgh, 1834. *Edin. P.; Edin. S.; Glas. Mit.; Edin. L.L.*

Eglinton, Earl of, *see* **Montgomerie,** Earl of Eglinton

Elliot

ELLIOT (Hon. Fitzwilliam): Elliot traditions, also family anecdotes, etc., etc. Edinburgh, 1922. *Edin. P.*

ELLIOT (Hon. George Francis Stewart): The Border Elliots and the family of Minto. Edinburgh, 1897. *Haw. P.; Dumf. C.; Sel. P.; Edin. U.; Glas. U.; Edin. P.; Edin. S.; Glas. Mit.; Edin. L.L.; Edin. Ant.*

ELLIOT (William): The Elliots of Brugh and Wells. London, 1925. *Edin. S.; Edin. L.L.*

SCOT (Walter): Metrical history of the honourable families of the name of Scot and Elliot in the shires of Roxburgh and Selkirk. Edinburgh, 1892. *Haw. P.; Glas. U.; Edin. P.; Edin. S.; Glas. Mit.*

Elliot of Binks

GENEALOGY of Elliot of Binks. Edinburgh, 1906. *Haw. P.*

Elliot of Minto.

ELLIOT-MURRAY-KYNYNMOUND (Nina Helen), *aft. Lady Butler*: Notes from Minto manuscripts. [Being a selection from letters written by and to the Elliots of Minto from 1762-1785. . . .] Edinburgh, 1862. *St.A. U.*

Elphinstone

BROWN (John): Historical and genealogical tree of the ancient and noble house of Elphinstone, from John de Elphinstone [1263] . . . until the present time, 1808. Edinburgh, [1808]. *Ab. U.*

FRASER (Sir William): The Elphinstone family book of the Lords Elphinstone, Balmerino and Coupar. 2 v. Edinburgh, 1897. *S.C.L.; Mid. C.; Ab. U.; St.A. U.; Glas. U.; Edin. P.; Edin. S.; Glas. Mit.; Edin. L.L.; Edin. Ant.*

MS. notes and press cuttings on the family of Elphinstone. n.p., n.d. *Edin. P.*

Elphinstone, Lord Balmerino

MEMOIRS of the lives and families of the Lords Kilmarnock, Cromartie and Balmerino. London, 1746. *Ayr P.*

Erskine

THE ERSKINES. [MSS. notes on the Erskine family.] *Forf. P.*

FERGUSSON (Alexander): The Hon. Henry Erskine, Lord Advocate for Scotland, with notices of certain of his kinsfolk. Edinburgh, 1882. *Glas. U.; Dund. P.; Edin. P.; Edin. S.; Glas. Mit.; Edin. L.L.*

KELLIE (   ), *Earl of*: Brief account of the titled family of Erskine of Scotland. [Not pub.] Alloa, n.d. *Edin. L.L.*

MACEWEN (Alexander Robertson): The Erskines. Edinburgh, 1900. *Clack. C.; Mid. C.; Sti. C.; Glas. Mit.*

SETON (George): Memoir of Alexander Seton . . . with an appendix cont. . . . genealogical tables of the legal families of Erskine, Hope, Dalrymple and Dundas. Edinburgh, 1882. *Dunf. P.; Glas. Mit.*

Erskine of Cardross

THE BARONY of Cardross and Summary of the case for the most ancient Earldom of Mar. (Repr. from *Gentleman's Magazine*, 4 s. Apr. 1, 1866.) *Edin. S.*

Erskine of Dun

JACOB (Violet): The Lairds of Dun. London, 1931. *S.C.L.; Kil. P.; Ren. C.; Ab. P.; Inv. P.; Ang. C.; Mont. P.; Per. C.; Arb. P.; Edin. P.; Gala. P.; St.A. U.; Bre. P.; Ab. U.; Forf. P.; Dund. Q.; Glas. U.; Edin. S.; Glas. Mit.*

PAPERS from the charter chest at Dun, 1451-1703. (Spalding Club Miscellany, v. IV, 1849.) *S.C.L.; Forf. P.; Glas. Mit.*

Erskine of Dunfermline

SCOTT (Ebenezer Erskine): The Erskine-Halcro genealogy: the ancestors and descendants of Henry Erskine, minister of Chirnside, his wife, Margaret Halcro of Orkney, & their sons, Ebenezer & Ralph Erskine. London, 1890. *S.C.L.; Dunf. P.; Inv. P.; Ork. C.; Sti. C.; Edin. S.; Glas. Mit.*

— — 2nd ed. Edinburgh, 1895. *Zet. C.; Arb. P.; Ber. C.; Edin. P.; Glas. Mit.; Edin. L.L.; Edin. Ant.; Ork. C.; Inv. P.; St.A. U.; Dunf. P.; Forf. P.; Ab. P.; Glas. U.; Pai. P.*

Erskine, Lord Garioch, *see* **Garioch,** Earldom of

Erskine, Earl of Kellie, *see* **Kellie,** Earldom of; **Mar,** Earldom of

Erskine of Linlathen

Henderson (Henry Frank Hornby): Erskine of Linlathen. Edinburgh, 1899. *Forf. P.; Dund. P.*

Erskine, Earl of Mar, *see* **Mar,** Earldom of

Erskine, Earl of Mar & Kellie

HISTORICAL MSS. COMMISSION. Report of MSS. of the Earl of Mar & Kellie preserved at Alloa House. London, 1904. *Clack. C.*

Erskine of Pittodrie

ERSKINE (Henry William Knight): Royal descent of Henry William Knight Erskine, of Pittodrie, co. Aberdeen . . . from Alfred the Great, King of England. n.p., n.d. *Edin. P.*

Ewan, *see* **MacEwan**

Ewart

[PAMPHLETS and miscellaneous material.] n.d. *Dumf. C.*

Ewing, *see* **Orr-Ewing**

Fairweather

FAIRWEATHER (Alexander): Memorandum regarding the Fairweathers of Menmuir parish, Forfarshire, and others of the surname. Ed. by W. G. Don. London, 1898. *Ab. U.; Edin. P.; Edin. S.*

Falconer

FALCONER (T.): An account of the family of Dalmahoy of that ilk and of the family of Falconer. London, n.d. *Edin. S.; Edin. L.L.*

[PAMPHLET relating to Colquhouns and their connection with the Falconers, etc.] Bath, [c. late 19th cent.]. *Edin. L.L.*

Fall

GRAY (William Forbes): The Falls of Dunbar. Haddington, [1938]. *Edin. P.; Edin. S.*

Farquharson

DONALD Farquharson of Castleton, etc., founder of the Clan Farquharson. (MS. article and cuttings from *Scottish Notes & Queries* relative to the Clan Farquharson.) *Inv. P.*

FARQUHARSON (Francis) of Finzean: Case relating to his son John Farquharson. Glasgow, 1819. *Inv. P.*

MACKINTOSH (A. M.): Farquharson genealogies from the Brouch dearg MSS. of 1773. 3 v. Nairn, 1913-18. *Ab. P.; Inv. P.; Ab. U.; Dund. P.; Edin. P.; Edin. S.; Glas. Mit.; Nai. C.* (2 pts.)*; Edin. L.L.* (1, 3)*; Edin. Ant.* (1, 2).

MICHIE (John Grant), *ed.*: Records of Invercauld, 1547-1828. Aberdeen, 1901. (New Spalding Club, 23.) *S.C.L.; Inv. P.; Ab. P.; Dund. Q.; Glas. U.; Dund. P.; Edin. P.; Edin. S.; Glas. Mit.*

Fasken

FASKEN (William Henry): The Family of Fasken. Stroud, 1931. *Glas. Mit.; Edin. U.; Edin. L.L.*

Fea of Clestrain

FEA (Allan): The Real Captain Cleveland. London, 1912. *Ork. C.; Glas. Mit.*

MARWICK (Hugh): The Feas of Clestran. (In *Proceedings Orkney Antiquarian Soc.*, v. 11, 1933, pp. 31-43.) *Ork. C.; Zet. C.; Glas. Mit.*

Fenton of Baikie

OSLER (James Couper): Osler tree [chart pedigree] with some supplementary notes on . . . Fentons . . . [Dundee,] 1924. *Edin. L.L.; Edin. Ant.*

Fergus, *see* **Fergusson**

Ferguson, *see* **Fergusson**

Fergusson

COOPER (D. Aldred): [Ferguson family tree showing the descendants of Adam Fergusson to 1956]. 1956. (*MS.*) *Ab. P.*

FERGUSON (James): The Clan and name of Ferguson: an address delivered 14 April, 1892. Glasgow, 1892. *Ab. P.; Dumf. C.; Edin. P.; Edin. S.; Glas. Mit.; Edin. L.L.*

FERGUSON (James) & FERGUSSON (Robert Menzies): Records of the clan and name of Fergusson, Ferguson and Fergus. (And Supplement.) 2 v. Edinburgh, 1895-99. *Ab. P.; Inv. P.; Dumf. C.; Sti. P.; St.A. U.* (1895)*; Ab. U.; Glas. U.; Edin. P.; Edin. S.; Glas. Mit.; Edin. L.L.*

FERGUSSON (Sir James): The Fergussons: their lowland and highland branches. Edinburgh, 1956. *Inv. P.; Dunb. C.; Edin. P.; Per C.; Dund. P.; Cai. C.; Glas. Mit.; Ber. C.; Edin. L.L.; Edin. Ant.*

GENEALOGICAL memoranda relating to the families of Fergusson and Colyer-Fergusson. n.p., 1897. *Edin. S.*

THE FERGUSON family and Inverurie. (In *The Royal burgh of Inverurie in the Coronation year.* 1902.) *Ab. P.; Glas. Mit.*

Fergusson of Badifurrow

FORBES (Alexander): Memorials of the family of Forbes of Forbesfield. [With notes on connected . . . Fergusons.] Aberdeen, 1905. *Ab. P.; Ab. C.; St.A. U.; Glas. U.; Edin. P.; Edin. S.; Glas. Mit.*

Fergusson of Kilkerran

FERGUSSON (Sir James): The Kilkerran improvers. (In his *Lowland lairds.* 1949.) *S.C.L.; Falk. P.; Per. C.; Dund. P.; Edin. U.; Glas. Mit.; Dunb. C.*

see also **Glencairn,** Earldom of

Fergusson of Kinmundy

THE FERGUSONS of Kinmundy, and their kinsfolk. 3 v. n.p., n.d. *(MS.) Edin. P.*

Fergusson of Pitfour

PITFOUR PAPERS. Copies of Pitfour papers, transcribed by James and William Ferguson of Kinmundy, 31st Dec. 1896. n.p., 1896. *(MS.) Edin. P.*

Fernie

PATERSON (James): Scottish surnames: a contribution to genealogy. Edinburgh, 1866. *Arb. P.; Glas. Mit.; Ab. P.; Dund. Q.*

Ferrier

GENEALOGY of the Ferriers of Kirklands. [n.p., n.d.]. *St.A. U.*

Fife, Duke of, *see* **Duff,** Duke of Fife

Fife, Earldom of

WOOD (William): A short account of the Earls of Fife . . Edinburgh(?), 1896. *Ab. U.*

Findlater

FINDLATER (W.): Genealogical tree of Findlater family. Dublin, 1921. *Ab. U.; Edin. P.* (n.d.).

MAIDMENT (James): Genealogical fragments. Berwick, 1855.
Edin. P.; Edin. S.; Glas. Mit.; Glas. U.; Inv. P.; Edin. Ant.

Findlater, Earl of, *see* **Ogilvy,** Earl of Findlater

Findlay of Coltfield
MEMORANDUM of the family of the Findlays of Coltfield, in the
parish of West Alves, co. Elgin, Scotland, extracted from the
parish register prior to the year 1800. n.p., 1874. *Edin. P.*

Finlay
FINLAY (James) *& Co., Ltd.*: James Finlay and Company,
manufacturers and East India merchants, 1750-1950. Glasgow, 1951. *Ayr P.; Per. C.; Glas. Mit.*

Fitz-Simon, *see* **Fraser**

Fleming
FLEMING (John Arnold): Flemish influence in Britain. 2 v.
Glasgow, 1930. *S.C.L.; Ruth. P.; Dumb. P.; Glas. Mit.*

HUNTER (William): Biggar and the house of Fleming. Biggar,
1862. *Dumf. C.; Pee. C.; Glas. U.; Edin. U.; Edin. S.;
Edin. L.L.*

— — 2nd ed. Edinburgh, 1867. *S.C.L.; Clack. C.; Lan. C.;
Haw. P.; Inv. P.; Ham. P.; Ab. P.; Glas. U.; Pai. P.; Edin. P.;
Edin. S.; Glas. Mit.; Edin. L.L.*

Fleming, Earl of Wigtown
GRANT (Francis James), *ed.*: Charter chest of the Earldom of
Wigtown, 1214-1681. Edinburgh, 1910. (Scottish Record
Soc., 36.) *S.C.L.; Dund. P.*

Fletcher of Saltoun
RECOLLECTIONS respecting the family of the Fletchers of Salton.
Edinburgh, 1803. *Edin. P.; Edin. L.L.*

Forbes
FORBES (Hon. Mrs. A.): Who was Kenneth, first King of Scots?
[A discussion of the origin of the clan Forbes.] Aberdeen,
1911. *Ab. P.; Edin. P.; Edin. S.*

FORBES (Arthur Carroll): The Descendants of William Forbes:
a genealogical and biographical history of the branch of the
family of Forbes as descended from Wm. Forbes of Aberdeen,
Scotland. [U.S.A.], 1955. *Ab. P.*

LUMSDEN (Matthew): Genealogy of the family of Forbes . . .
1580; ed. by W. Forbes. Inverness, 1819. *Ab. P.; Inv. P.;*

Nai. C.; Glas. Mit.; Glas. U.; Edin. P.; Edin. S.; Per. P. (1883); *Edin. L.L.; Ab. C.*

TAYLER (Alistair) & TAYLER (Henrietta): The House of Forbes. Aberdeen, 1937. (Third Spalding Club.) *Fife C.; Dund. P.; Ab. P.; Elg. P.; Inv. P.; Ang. C.; Mont. P.; Edin. U.; Ork. C.; Dund. Q.; Glas. U.; Falk. P.; Edin. P.; Edin. S.; Glas. Mit.*

Forbes of Blackton

FERGUSON (James): Two Scottish soldiers of fortune . . . and a Jacobite laird and his forbears. Aberdeen, 1888. *Ab. P.; Edin. P.; Edin. S.; Glas. Mit.*

Forbes of Corse and Craigievar

FORBES (Hon. John), *Admiral of the Fleet*: Memoirs of the Earls of Granard . . . Ed. by G. A. Hastings [Forbes], Earl of Granard. London, 1868. *St.A. U.*

Forbes of Echt

BROWNE (George Forrest), *Bishop*: Echt-Forbes family charters, 1345-1727: records of the Forest of Birse . . . Edinburgh, 1923. *S.C.L.; Ab. P.; Edin. U.; St.A. U.; Edin. P.; Edin. S.; Glas. Mit.; Edin. Ant.*

Forbes of Forbesfield

FORBES (Alexander): Memorials of the family of Forbes of Forbesfield. [With notes on connected Morgans, Duncans and Fergusons.] Aberdeen, 1905. *Ab. P.; Ab. C.; St.A. U.; Glas. U.; Edin. P.; Edin. S.; Glas. Mit.; Edin. L.L.*

Forbes of Monymusk

FORBES (Louisa Lillias): Circular genealogical table of the Forbes family of Monymusk and Pitsligo, 1460-1880. n.p., 1880. *Ab. P.; St.A. U.; Edin. P.; Edin. S.; Edin. L.L.*

FORBES (Sir William): Narrative of the last sickness and death of Dame Christian Forbes. Edinburgh, 1875. *Edin. P.*

Forbes of Pitsligo

[NOTES on the collateral families of Forbes of Pitsligo.] 1938. (*Typescript.*) *Ab. P.*

Forbes of Schivas

BURR (Mrs. Helen Alexander): Forbes family of Schivas. [c. 1931.] (*Typescript.*) *Edin. L.L.*

Forbes of Skellater

NEIL (James): Ian Roy of Skellater, a Scottish soldier of fortune. Aberdeen, 1902. *Edin. L.L.*

Forbes of Tolquhoun

[DAVIDSON (J.)]: The Genealogy of the house of Tolquhon. Aberdeen, 1839. *Edin. P.; Edin. L.L.*

Forbes of Watertoun

FORBES (John): Memoranda relating to the family of Forbes of Waterton. Aberdeen, 1857. *Ab. P.; Ab. C.; St.A. U.; Edin. P.; Edin. S.*

Forbes-Leith

STIRLING (Anna Maria D. W. Pickering), *Mrs. Stirling*: Fyvie Castle: its lairds and their times. London, 1928. *S.C.L.; Elg. P.; Mid. C.; Glas. Mit.; Ren. C.; Fife C.; Ab. C.; West L.C.; Banff C.; Fras. P.; Dunb. C.; Edin. U.*

Forbes-Robertson of Hazlehead

BULLOCH (John Malcolm): The Forbes-Robertson family of Hazlehead. Aberdeen, 1927. (Extract from *The Tiger and the Sphinx; the journal of the Gordon Highlanders.*) *Ab. P.*

— The Picturesque ancestry of Sir Johnston Forbes-Robertson. Aberdeen, 1926. *Ab. P.; Edin. U.*

Fordyce

FORDYCE (Alexander Dingwall): Family record of the name of Dingwall-Fordyce, including relatives of both names and connections. 2 v. Toronto, 1885-88. *Ab. P.; Ab. C.; Edin. P.; Edin. S.; Glas. Mit.*

Fordyce of Uyeasound, Shetland

CLARK (John): Genealogy, records and intermarriages of the Fordyce, Bruce and Clark families at Uyeasound, Unst, Shetland. 2nd ed. Falkirk, 1902. *Zet. C.; Edin. P.; Ork. C.* (Falkirk, 1899).

Forrester of Torwood

FERGUSSON (Sir James): The Foresters of the Torwood. (In his *Lowland lairds*. 1949.) *S.C.L.; Falk. P.; Per. C.; Dund. P.; Edin. U.; Glas. Mit.; Dunb. C.*

Foulis

FOULIS (William Ainslie), *comp.*: Foulis family: miscellaneous papers. n.d. (*MS. & typescript papers.*) *Edin. P.*

— Genealogical chart of the families of Foulis. n.d. (*MS.*) *Edin. P.*

Franceis, *see* **French**

Francis, *see* **French**

Francus, *see* **French**

Fraser

DAVIDSON (Arthur Aitken): A Highland family. London, 1924. *Ab. U.; Glas. Mit.*

FRASER (Alexander): The Clan Fraser in Canada: souvenir of the first annual gathering of the Clan in Toronto in 1894. Toronto, 1895. *Inv. P.*

FRASER (James): Chronicles of the Frasers: the Wardlaw MS. . . . or the true genealogy of the Frasers; ed. by Wm. Mackay. Edinburgh, 1905. (Scottish History Soc., v. 47.) *S.C.L.; Inv. P.; Ab. P.; Dund. Q.; Glas. U.; Dund. P.; Edin. P.; Edin. S.; Glas. Mit.*

KELLY (Bernard W.): The Fighting Frasers of the Forty-Five and Quebec, etc. London, 1908. *Ab. U.; Edin. P.; Edin. S.; Glas. Mit.*

MACKENZIE (Alexander): History of the Frasers of Lovat, with genealogies of the principal families of the name, to which is added those of Dunballoch and Phopachy. Inverness, 1896. *S.C.L.; Sti. P.; Nai. C.; Dund. P.; Ab. P.; Inv. P.; Inv. C.; St.A. U.; Ab. U.; Dund. Q.; Glas. U.; Edin. P.; Edin. S.; Glas. Mit.; Edin. L.L.; Edin. Ant.*

[SIMSON (Archibald)]: Annals of such patriots of the distinguished family of Fraser, Frysell, Sim-son or Fitz-Simon, as have signalised themselves in the public service of Scotland. Edinburgh, 1795. *Inv. P.; Edin. P.; Edin. S.; Glas. Mit.*

—— 2nd ed., edited by A. Fraser of Lovat. Edinburgh, 1805. *Haw. P.; Inv. P.; Inv. C.; St.A. U.; Edin. L.L.*

WARRAND (Duncan): Some Fraser pedigrees. Inverness, 1934. *S.C.L.; Ab. P.; Inv. P.; Edin. U.; Edin. P.; Edin. S.; Glas. Mit.; Edin. L.L.; Edin. Ant.*

Fraser of Ardachy

CAMPBELL (Thomas Fraser): The Frasers of Ardachy. n.d. (*Typescript.*) *Inv. P.; Edin. L.L.*

Fraser of Durris

FRASER (Sir William): Memorial of the family of the Frasers [of Durris]. [Edinburgh, 1904.] *Ab. U.; Ab. C.*

Fraser of Fraserfield

SOME account of the family of Fraserfield or Balgownie. n.p., [c. 1870]. *Ab. U.*

Fraser of Guisachan

GENEALOGY of Fraser of Guisachan & Culbockie. 1867. (*MS.*) *Inv. P.*

Fraser, Lord Fraser of Lovat, *see* **Lovat,** Lord Fraser of

Fraser of Lovat

ANDERSON (John): Historical account of the family of Frisel or Fraser, particularly Fraser of Lovat. Edinburgh, 1825. *Ab. P.; Inv. P.; Ab. U.; St.A. U.; Glas. U.; Edin. P.; Edin. S.; Glas. Mit.; Camp. P.; Edin. L.L.; Edin. Ant.*

FRASER (Charles Ian): The Clan Fraser of Lovat: a Highland response to a Lowland stimulus. Edinburgh, 1952. *Sti. P.; Dund. P.; Inv. P.; Cai. C.; Lan. C.; Ayr P.; Per. C.; Cly. P.; Inv. C.; Edin. U.; Ab. P.; Pai. P.; Kirkcud. C.; Arg. C.; Edin. P.; Edin. S.; Glas. Mit.; Ber. C.; Edin. L.L.*

FRASER (Hugh): Historical account of the family of Fraser or Frizel of Lovat. 2 v. Inverness, 1850. (*MSS.*) *Inv. P.*

GENEALOGICAL tree of the family of Lovat, 1416-1823. 1867. (*MS.*) *Inv. P.*

HISTORY of the most ancient, noble and illustrious family of Fraser, particularly of the family of Lovat. 3 v. [1749.] (*MSS.*) (Intended for publication in London, 1749.) *Inv. P.*

MACDONALD (Archibald): The Old Lords of Lovat and Beaufort. Inverness, 1934. *Fife C.; Ab. P.; Inv. P.; Inv. C.; St.A. U.; Dund. Q.; Edin. P.; Edin. S.; Glas. Mit.; Edin. L.L.; Edin. Ant.*

Fraser of Philorth

SALTOUN (Alexander Fraser), *17th Baron*: The Frasers of Philorth. 3 v. Edinburgh, 1879. *S.C.L.; Ab. P.; Inv. P.; Fras. P.; Moth. P.; St.A. U.; Ab. U.; Glas. U.; Edin. P.; Edin. S.; Glas. Mit.; Ab. C.; Edin. L.L.*

SHORT genealogical account of Fraser of Philorth or Saltoun. 1867. (*MS.*) *Inv. P.*

Fraser of Powis

BURNETT (John George), *ed.*: Powis papers, 1507-1894. Aberdeen, 1951. (Third Spalding Club.) *Glas. Mit.*

Fraser of Touch

GIBSON (John C.): The Lands and lairds of Touch. Stirling, 1929. *Edin. P.; Edin. S.*

French

FRENCH (A. D. Weld): Index armorial to an emblazoned MS. of the surname of French, Franc, Francois, Frenc, and others, both British and foreign. Boston, Mass., 1892. *Edin. S.*

— Notes on the surnames of Francus, Franceis, French, etc. in Scotland, with an account of the Frenches of Thornydykes. Boston, Mass., 1893. *Ayr P.; Haw. P.; Sti. P.; St.A. U.; Ab. P.; Glas. U.; Dund. P.; Pai. P.; Edin. P.; Edin. S.; Glas. Mit.; Edin. L.L.; Edin. Ant.*

Frendraught, Lord

ABSTRACT of the evidence on the claim of David Maitland Makgill of Rankeilour to be served heir of line in general of James Crichton, First Viscount Frendraught. [1839.] *Edin. L.L.*

Frisel, *see* **Fraser** of Lovat

Frysell, *see* **Fraser**

Fyvie, Lord, *see* **Seton,** Lord Fyvie

Gair

GAYRE (George Robert) & GAIR (R. L.): Gayre's book: being a history of the family of Gayre. 3 v. Gulval, 1948-54. *Edin. P.; Edin. U.* (v. 1)*; Edin. L.L.; Edin. Ant.*

Gairdner

BAILEY (William Henry): A chronicle of the family of Gairdner of Ayrshire, Edinburgh and Glasgow, and their connections from the seventeenth century. Taunton, 1947. *St.A. U.; Ab. U.; Edin. S.; Glas. Mit.*

Galbraith

SMITH (John Guthrie): Strathendrick and its inhabitants. Glasgow, 1896. *S.C.L.; Glas. Mit.*

Garden

GARDEN (William): Notes with reference to a branch of the Garden family. Edinburgh, 1887. *Ab. P.*

Gardner

MAIDMENT (James): Genealogical fragments relating to the families of . . . Gardner . . . Berwick, 1855. *Inv. P.; Edin. P.; Edin. S.; Glas. Mit.; Glas. U.; Edin. Ant.*

Garioch, Earldom of

DAVIDSON (John): Inverurie and the earldom of the Garioch. Edinburgh, 1878. *S.C.L.*

Geddes

GEDDES (Auckland Campbell Geddes), *1st Baron*: The Forging of a family. London, 1952. *S.C.L.; Mid. C.; Lan. C.; Ren. C.; Per. C.; Banff C.; Sti. C.; Dunb. C.; Ork. C.; Edin. U.; Ab. P.; Pai. P.; Edin. P.; Edin. S.; Glas. Mit.*

Geddie

GEDDIE (Henry L.): The Families Geddie and McPhail, by Jack Geddie. Fort Worth, Texas, 1959. *S.C.L.; Edin. P.*

Gemmell, Gemmill

GEMMILL (J. A.): Note on the probable origin of the Scottish surname Gemmill or Gemmell with a genealogical account of the family of Gemmill of Templehouse, Scotland. Montreal, 1898. *S.C.L.; Edin. P.* (1901?)*; Edin. L.L.* (Ottawa, 1901).

GEMMILL (J. Leiper): Notes on the probable origin of the name Gemmill or Gemmell with a genealogical account of the family of Gemmill of Raithmuir, Fenwick from c. 1518. Glasgow, 1909. *Glas. Mit.; Edin. P.*

Gerard

HARROWER (Rachel Blanche): The Gerard family. Aberdeen, 1923. (Repr. from *The Aberdeen University Review*, Mar. 1923.) *Edin. P.*

Gibb of Carriber

GIBB (Sir George Duncan), *comp.*: Life and times of Robert Gib, lord of Carriber . . . with notices of his descendants. 2 v. London, 1874. *Glas. U.; Dund. P.; Edin. P.; Edin. S.; Glas. Mit.; Edin. L.L.*

Gibb of Falkland

GIBB (Sir George Duncan), *comp.*: Pedigree of J. R. Campbell and Sir G. D. Gibb . . . Guildford, 1872. *St.A. U.*

— Pedigree of the family of Gibb . . . of Falkland. Guildford, 1874. *St.A. U.; Ab. U.; Glas. U.; Edin. P.*

Gibson of Arbroath

CORMACK (Alexander A.): Arbroath Gibsons in Sweden: the romantic saga of a Scandinavian family with its roots in Angus. (In *Arbroath Herald*, Christmas no., 1950.) *Arb. P.*

Gibson of Glencrosh

FALLOW (T. M.): Some notes on the family of Gibson of Glencrosh. Dumfries, [1905]. *Dumf. C.*

Gifford of Busta, Shetland

BRUCE (R. Stuart): Glimpses of Shetland life, 1718-1753. (In *Old-lore misc. of the Viking club*, v. 5, 1912.) *Glas. Mit.; Zet. C.*

GREIG (P. W.): Annals of a Shetland parish: Delting. Lerwick, 1892. *Zet. C.*

Gill of Blairythan & Savock

GILL (Andrew J. Mitchell): Gill of Blairythan and Savock. n.p., 1882. *Ab. P.; Edin. S.; Edin. L.L.*

Gilmour

GILMOUR (Henry F.), *comp.*: Genealogical tables giving the descendants of John Gilmour of "Dockanyfauld", Gorbals, Glasgow, dating from 1737 to 1902. n.p., n.d. *Glas. Mit.*

Glaister

GLAISTER (John): The Glaisters of Scotland and Cumberland. Kendal, 1920. *Edin. L.L.*

Gladstone

[MILLAR (Alexander Hastie)]: The Gladstones and their connection with Dundee. (Repr. from *Dundee Advertiser*, 21 Aug. 1890.) *Dund. P.*

Glasgow, Earl of, *see* **Boyle** of Kelburne, etc.

Gledstone

OLIVER ( ), *Mrs. Oliver* of Thornwood: The Gledstones and the siege of Coklaw. Edinburgh, 1878. *S.C.L.; Ber. C.; Haw. P.; Dumf. C.; Sel. P.; Ab. U.; Edin. P.; Edin. S.; Glas. Mit.*

Glen

ROGERS (Charles): Memorials of the Scottish family of Glen. Edinburgh, 1888. *Dunf. P.; Glas. U.; Edin. P.; Edin. S.; Edin. L.L.; Edin. Ant.*

Glencairn, Earldom of

GLENCAIRN peerage. [Speech of Lord Loughborough] . . . on the claim of Sir A. Fergusson of Kilkerran to this peerage with a brief account by James Maidment of the claims. [Edinburgh], 1839. *Edin. P.*

MAIDMENT (James): Reports of claims . . . to the House of Lords . . . of the Cassillis, Sutherland, Spynie and Glencairn peerages, 1760-1797. Edinburgh, 1882. *Dund. Q.; Glas. U.; Dund. P.* (1840)*; Edin. P.; Edin. S.; Glas. Mit.; Edin. L.L.* (1840)*; Edin. Ant.*

Glendinning

CLINDENING (Gerald Talbot): The House of Glendonwyn: a record of its progenitors, members and descendants for a thousand years. 12 pts. Adelaide, 1933-43. *Dumf. C.; Glas. Mit.; Edin. L.L.; Edin. Ant.*

GLENDINNING (P.): House of Glendinning. Edinburgh, 1879. (Repr. from the *Eskdale & Liddesdale Advertiser*). *Edin. P.; Glas. Mit.*

Gordon

ACCOUNT of the Dukes of Gordon. n.p., n.d. *Edin. L.L.*

BULLOCH (John Malcolm): Bibliography of the Gordons. Section I. (A to Augusta—1924. "Chinese Gordon"— Lord George Gordon.) Aberdeen, 1924. *Glas. Mit.; Glas. U.*

— The Caterans of Inveraven. Edinburgh, 1927. (Repr. from *Proceedings Soc., Antiquaries of Scot.,* v. 1, 6th ser. 1926-27.) *Ab. P.; Edin. P.*

— "Chinese" Gordon's family origins. Aberdeen, 1933. *Ab. P.*

— The Duffs and the Gordons: a table bringing out the literary instincts of the two. n.d. (*MS.*) *Edin. P.*

— The First duke of Gordon. Huntly, 1908. *Ab. P.; Edin. P.; Edin. S.; Glas. Mit.*

— The Fourth duke of Gordon's third regiment: muster roll of the Northern Fencibles, 1793-9. n.p., n.d. *Ab. P.; Edin. P.; Edin. S.*

— The Gay adventures of Sir Alexander Gordon, Knight, of Navidale. Dingwall, 1925. *Edin. P.; Edin. S.; Glas. Mit.*

— The Gay Gordons: some strange adventures of a famous Scots family. London, 1908. *Cai. C.; Elg. P.; Kil. P.; Ab. P.; Ab. C.; Coat. P.; Clack. C.; Banff C.; Edin. U.; St.A. U.; Edin. P.; Edin. S.; Glas. Mit.*

— The Gordon book. Aberdeen, 1902. *Ab. P.; Edin. P.; Edin. Ant.*

— Gordons in Germany, the Brandenburg line. Aberdeen, 1932. *Ab. P.; Edin. U.; Edin. P.; Edin. S.; Glas. Mit.; Edin. Ant.*

— Gordons in Perthshire: as pioneers to Canada. Perth, 1930. *Ab. P.; Edin. P.; Edin. S.*

— The Gordons in Poland, "Marquises of Huntly" with a line in Saxony. Peterhead, 1932. *Ab. P.; Edin. U.; Glas. Mit.; Edin. Ant.*

— The House of Gordon. 3 v. Aberdeen, 1903-12. (Vol. 3: *Gordons under arms* by C. O. Skelton and J. M. Bulloch.) (New Spalding Club, 26, 33, 39.) *S.C.L.; Elg. P.; Inv. P.; Ab. C.; Ab. P.; Glas. U.; Dund. P.; Edin. P.; Edin. S.; Glas. Mit.; Edin. L.L.*

— The Making of the West Indies: the Gordons as colonists. Peterhead, 1913. *Pet. P.* (Buckie, n.d.); *Ab. P.* (1915); *Glas. Mit.* (c. 1914).

— The Name of Gordon. Huntly, 1906. *Ab. P.; Dumf. C.; Edin. P.; Glas. Mit.*

— The Second duke of Gordon and the part he played at the battle of Sheriffmuir. Huntly, 1911. *Edin. P.; Edin. S.*

— The Strange adventures of Lewis Gordon. Elgin, 1908. *Ab. P.*

— Thomas Gordon: the independent Whig. Aberdeen, 1918. *Glas. U.; Edin. P.; Edin. S.*

DUNLOP (Jean): The Clan Gordon; "Cock o' the North". Edinburgh, 1955. *Inv. P.; Inv. C.; Lan. C.; Suth. C.; Edin. U.; Ab. P.; Per. C.; Dund. P.; Pai. P.; Edin. P.; Glas. Mit.; Cai. C.; Ber. C.; Edin. L.L.*

GORDON (C. Andrew): Concise history of the ancient and illustrious house of Gordon. Aberdeen, 1754. *Edin. P.; Edin. S.*

— — 2nd ed. with additions by A. M. Mackintosh. Aberdeen, 1890. *Elg. P.; Ab. P.; Inv. P.; Ab. C.; St.A. U.; Glas. U.; Glas. Mit.*

GORDON (William), [*of Old Aberdeen*]: History of the ancient, noble and illustrious family of Gordon, from their first arrival in Scotland in Malcolm III's time to 1690. 2 v. Edinburgh, 1726-27. *Ab. P.; Edin. P.; Edin. S.; Glas. Mit.; Banff C.* (v. 1).

[GORDON (William), [*of Old Aberdeen*]]: The History of Scotland, from the beginning of King Robert I to the year 1690 . . . and also a particular account of the antient, noble . . . family of Gordon, from their first arrival in Scotland in the reign of King Malcolm III. 2 v. London, 1732. *Ab. P.*

GORDON MEMOIRS, 1745-1887. [By Henry William Gordon, contin. by Sir Henry William Gordon.] Edinburgh, 1895. *Ab. U.*

GORDONS who were parish ministers. n.p., n.d. (*Typescript.*) *Edin. P.*

GREEN (James): The History of Scotland: from the death of Queen Margaret . . . to the accession of James II . . . [to which is prefixed An historical and genealogical account of the noble family of Gordon]. Edinburgh, 1802. *Edin. P.*

HUNTLY (Charles Gordon), *11th Marquess of*: The Cock o' the North. London, 1935. *S.C.L.; Gra. P.; Cai. C.; Ab. C.; Mid. C.; Fife C.; Banff C.; Cly. P.; St.A. U.; Ab. P.; Edin. P.; Edin. S.; Glas. Mit.*

VON GORDON (Eduard): Gordon family—a German family of Gordon from Aberdeenshire; a letter written in 1874 to Charles, 11th Marquess of Huntly. Germany, 18—. (*MS.*) *Ab. P.*

Gordon of Aberdour

BULLOCH (John Malcolm): The Gordons of Aberdour. Peterhead, 1913. *Pet. P.; Ab. P.; Edin. P.; Edin. S.*

LAWRANCE (Robert Murdoch): The Gordons of Aberdour, Auchlunies, Cairnbulg, etc. 1912. (Repr. from *Fraserburgh Herald & Northern Counties Advertiser*, Mar. 19, 1912.) *Ab. P.; Dund. Q.; Edin. Ant.*

Gordon, Earl of Aboyne

BULLOCH (John Malcolm): The Earls of Aboyne. Huntly, 1908. *Ab. P.; Elg. P.; Pet. P.; Glas. Mit.; Edin. L.L.*

Gordon of Aikenhead

BULLOCH (John Malcolm): The Gordons of Aikenhead. Aberdeen, 1930. *Ab. P.*

LEWIS GORDON of Aikenhead. n.d. (*MS.*) *Ab. P.*

Gordon of Airds, *see* Gordon of Earlston & Afton

Gordon of Auchanachy

BULLOCH (John Malcolm): Elizabeth Gordon, the long-lost "heiress" of Auchanachie . . . Banff, 1928. (From *Transactions Banffshire Field Club*, v. 45, 1927-28.) *Edin. P.*

Gordon of Birkenburn

GEORGE (James): The Gordons of Birkenburn, near Keith— their ancestry, connections and descendants. [Chart.] Keith, 1912. *Ab. U.*

Gordon of Cairnfield

BULLOCH (John Malcolm): The Gordons of Cairnfield. Keith, 1910. *Ab. P.; Edin. P.*

— Gordons of Cairnfield and Rosieburn. 1937. *Ab. P.; Edin. P.* (1910)*; Edin. S.* (1910)*; Glas. Mit.* (1910).

Gordon of Cluny

BULLOCH (John Malcolm): The Gordons of Cluny from the early years of the 18th century down to the present time. [Buckie], 1911. *St.A. U.; Ab. P.; Edin. P.; Edin. S.*

Gordon of Coldwells

BULLOCH (John Malcolm): The Gordons of Coldwells, Ellon. Peterhead, 1914. *Pet. P.; Ab. P.; Glas. U.; Edin. P.; Glas. Mit.*

Gordon of Craichlaw

MACMATH (William): The Gordons of Craichlaw; ed. by T. Fraser. Dalbeattie, 1924. *Wig. C.; Dumf. C.; Edin. U.; Ab. U.; Ab. P.; St.A. U.; Kirkcud. C.; Dund. Q.; Glas. U.; Edin. P.; Edin. S.; Glas. Mit.*

Gordon of Craig

BULLOCH (John Malcolm): The Gordons of Craig. Edinburgh, 1930. (Repr. from *Proceedings Soc. Antiquaries of Scot.*, v. 64, 1929-30.) *Ab. P.; Edin. P.; Edin. S.*

WIMBERLEY (Douglas): Memorials of the family of Gordon of Craig. Banff, 1904. *Edin. P.*

Gordon of Croughly

GORDON (George Huntly Blair): The Croughly book. [London,] 1895. *Ab. P.*

Gordon of Culvennan

REID (Robert Corsane): The Culvennan writs. 1923. (Repr. from *Trans. Dumfriesshire & Galloway Nat. Hist. & Antiquarian Society*, Jan. 1923.) *Edin. L.L.*

Gordon of Earlston & Afton

[GORDON (Sir John), *d. 1795*]: [Earlston MSS.] A short and concise abridgement of the origin of the name and illustrious family of Kenmore with their no less renowned descendants. (*Inc.* Airds, Afton and Earlston.) [c. 179-] (*MSS.*) *Edin. L.L.*

Gordon of Ellon

BULLOCH (John Malcolm): A grim Edinburgh murder: the genealogy of a legend about the Gordons of Ellon. Inverness, 1932. *Ab. P.; Edin. U.; Glas. Mit.; Edin. Ant.*

Gordon in Forfarshire

BULLOCH (John Malcolm): The Gordons in Forfarshire. Brechin, 1909. *Ab. P.; Edin. P.; Edin. S.*

Gordon of Fyvie

STIRLING (Anna Maria D. W. Pickering), *Mrs. Stirling*: Fyvie Castle: its lairds and their times. London, 1928. *S.C.L.; Elg. P.; Mid. C.; Ren. C.; Fife C.; Ab. C.; West L.C.; Banff C.; Edin. U.; Glas. Mit.; Fras. P.; Dunb. C.*

Gordon of Gight

BULLOCH (John Malcolm): The Gordons of Gight. Peterhead, 1928. (Repr. from *Transactions of the Buchan Club*, 1927.) *Edin. P.*

Gordon of Glenbuchat

BULLOCH (John Malcolm): Gordons of Glenbuchat and their connection with Stirlinghill and Peterhead. Peterhead, 1926. (Repr. from *Transactions of the Buchan Club*, 1926.) *Edin. P.*

— A missing Glenbuchat Gordon. Aberdeen, 1924. (*Newspaper cuttings.*) *Ab. P.*

Gordon, Lord Gordon

G.B. Parliament. House of Lords. Gordon peerage: speeches delivered by counsel before the Committee for Privileges and Judgements to whom was referred the petition of Sir Bruce Gordon Seton, Bt., C.B., to His Majesty claiming the title, honour and dignity of Lord Gordon in the peerage of Scotland, 1928. London, 1929. *Edin. P.; Glas. U.*

HUNTLY (Charles), *Marquis of*: Case of Charles, Marquis of Huntly . . . *Edin. L.L.*

— Additional case of the above . . . *Edin. L.L.*

SETON (Sir Bruce Gordon): Case on behalf of Sir Bruce Gordon Seton, Bt., of Abercorn . . . his claim . . . Lord Gordon in the peerage of Scotland. *Edin. L.L.*

— Supplemental case . . . in reply to the case for . . . Charles, Marquis of Huntly in opposition to his claim to the title . . . of Lord Gordon. . . . *Edin. L.L.*

PEDIGREE of Sir Bruce Gordon Seton. *Edin. L.L.*

Gordon of Gordonstoun, *see* **Sutherland,** Earldom of

Gordon in Griamachary

BULLOCH (John Malcolm): The Family of Gordon in Griamachary, in the parish of Kildonan. [Dingwall], 1907. *Ab. P.; Edin. P.; Glas. U.; Pet. P.; Edin. S.*

BULLOCH (John Malcolm) & SKELTON (Constance Oliver): A notable military family: the Gordons in Griamachary, in the parish of Kildonan. Huntly, 1907. *Ab. P.; Glas. Mit.*

Gordon, Earl, Marquess of Huntly

HUNTLY (Charles Gordon), *11th Marquess of, ed.*: The Records of Aboyne, MCCXXX-MDCLXXXI. Aberdeen, 1894. (New Spalding Club, 13.) *S.C.L.; Glas. Mit.; Edin. L.L.*

PAPERS from the charter chest of the Duke of Richmond, at Gordon Castle. (In *Misc. Spalding Club*, v. IV, 1849.) *S.C.L.*

SINCLAIR (Alexander): Historical, genealogical and miscellaneous tracts. n.p., n.d. *Dumf. C.; Edin. Ant.*

Gordon of Invergordon

BULLOCH (John Malcolm): The Families of Gordon of Invergordon, Newhall, also Ardoch, Ross-shire and Carroll, Sutherland. [Dingwall], 1906. *Ab. P.; Suth. C.; Pet. P.; Edin. P.; Edin. S.; Edin. L.L.*

Gordon of Kirkhill

BULLOCH (John Malcolm): The Gordons of Kirkhill. Huntly, 1927. *Ab. P.; Edin. U.; Edin. P.; Edin. S.; Glas. Mit.*

Gordon of Knockespoch

BULLOCH (John Malcolm): Knockespock Gordon's connection with America. 1934. *Ab. P.*

WIMBERLEY (Douglas): A genealogical account of the family of Gordon of Knockespoch. Banff, 1903. *Ab. P.; Edin. P.*

Gordon of Laggan

BULLOCH (John Malcolm): The Gordons of Laggan. (In *Transactions Banffshire Field Club*, v. 27, 1906-7.) *Edin. S.*

Gordon of Lesmoir

BULLOCH (John Malcolm): The Gordons of Lesmoir claim to the baronetcy in 1887. 1936. *Ab. P.*

WIMBERLEY (Douglas): Memorials of the family of Gordon of Lesmoir in the county of Aberdeen. Inverness, 1893. *St.A. U.; Ab. U.; Ab. C.; Edin. L.L.*

— Memorials of four old families. 1894. *Ab. P.; Inv. P.; Dund. Q.; Edin. P.; Edin. S.; Glas. Mit.*

Gordon of Minmore

BULLOCH (John Malcolm): The Gordons and Smiths at Minmore, Auchorachan and Upper Drumin in Glenlivet. Huntly, 1910. *Ab. P.*

Gordon of Mosstown

BULLOCH (John Malcolm): A Logie-Buchan laird and his loans: the Gordons of Mosstown. Aberdeen, n.d. *Edin. P.*

Gordon of Nethermuir

BULLOCH (John Malcolm): The Gordons of Nethermuir. Peterhead, 1913. *Ab. P.; Pet. P.; Edin. P.; Edin. S.; Glas. Mit.*

Gordon of Salterhill

BULLOCH (John Malcolm): The Gordons of Salterhill, and their Irish descendants. Keith, 1910. *Ab. P.; Edin. P.; Edin. S.*

Gordon of Sheelagreen

BULLOCH (John Malcolm): The "Mutiny" of the Atholl Highlanders and an account of the Sheelagreen Gordons. Buckie, 1911. *Ab. P.*

Gordon, Earl of Sutherland, *see* **Sutherland,** Earldom of

Gordon in Sutherland

BULLOCH (John Malcolm): The Gordons in Sutherland. Dingwall, 1907. *Ab. P.; Inv. P.* (1908)*; Elg. P.; Pet. P.* (1908)*; Edin. P.; Edin. S.; Glas. Mit.*

Gordon of Techmuiry

BULLOCH (John Malcolm): The Gordons of Techmuiry. Peterhead, 1933. *Ab. C.; Edin. P.*

Gordon of Terpersie

WIMBERLEY (Douglas): Notes on the family of Gordon of Terpersie. Inverness, 1900. *Ab. P.; Glas. Mit.; Ab. C.*

Gordon of Wardhouse

BULLOCH (John Malcolm): Gay Gordons as Spaniards: the story of the Wardhouse family. 1933. *Ab. P.*

— Gordons of Wardhouse and Beldorney. Banff, 1909. *Edin. P.*

Gordon-Lennox, Duke of Richmond and Gordon

KENT (John): Records and reminiscences of Goodwood and the Dukes of Richmond, 1672-1896. London, 1896. *Elg. P.; St.A. U.; Glas. Mit.*

Gourlay

ROGERS (Charles): Memorials of the Scottish house of Gourlay. Edinburgh, 1888. *Kir. P.; Fife C.; Sti. C.; Dunf. P.; St.A. U.; Ab. U.; Glas. U.; Edin. P.; Edin. S.; Glas. Mit.; Edin. L.L.; Edin. Ant.*

Graeme

GRAEME (Patrick Sutherland): Pateas amicis: the story of the house of Graemeshall in Orkney. Kirkwall, 1936. *Cai. C.; Ork. C.*

see also **Graham**

Graham

GRAEME (Louisa Grace): Or and sable: a book of the Graemes and Grahams. Edinburgh, 1903. *Dund. P.; Sti. P.; Per. C.; Ork. C.; St.A. U.; Ab. U.; Ab. P.; Glas. U.; Edin. P.; Edin. S.; Glas. Mit.; Edin. L.L.*

GRAHAM (James): The Grahams of Wallacetown, Knockdolian, Grugar, Auchenharvie, Tamrawer, Dougalston, Kilmannan and Kilmardinny. Glasgow, 1887. *Edin. L.L.*

SMITH (John Guthrie): Strathendrick and its inhabitants. Glasgow, 1896. *S.C.L.; Glas. Mit.*

STEWART (John): The Grahams, with tartans and arms in colour, and a map. Edinburgh, 1958. *Edin. P.; Inv. P.; Cai. C.; Ber. C.*

Graham, Earl of Airth, *see* **Airth**, Earldom of

Graham of Auchencloich

GRAHAM (John St. John Noble): The Grahams of Auchencloich and Tamrawer: a record of seven centuries. Lisbon, 1952. *S.C.L.; Sti. C.; Dund. P.; Edin. P.; Glas. Mit.; Edin. L.L.; Edin. Ant.*

Graham of Breckness

[ORIGINAL family papers.] *Ork. C.*

Graham on the Borders

BAIN (Joseph): The Grahams or Graemes of the debateable land —their traditional origin considered. [1886.] (Repr. from the *Archaeological journal*, v. XLIII.) *Glas. Mit.; Edin. L.L.*

GRAHAM (John): The Condition of the Border at the Union: destruction of the Graham clan. 2nd ed. London, 1907. *S.C.L.; Ab. P.; Edin. P.; Edin. S.; Glas. Mit.*

Graham of Gartmore

[MCINTYRE (Alex. C.)]: The Grahams of Gartmore. Glasgow, 1885. *Sti. P.; Dumb. P.; Glas. Mit.; Edin. Ant.*

Graham, Earl of Menteith

BURNETT (George): The "Red book of Menteith" reviewed: in reply to charges of literary discourtesy made against the reviewer in a letter to the author of that work. Edinburgh, 1881. *Sti. C.; St.A. U.; Ab. U.; Ab. P.; Dund. P.; Edin. L.L.; Glas. Mit.; Edin. Ant.*

COWAN (Samuel): Three Celtic earldoms: Atholl, Strathearn, Menteith, with facsimile of Foundation Charter of Inchaffray. Edinburgh, 1909. *Per. C.; Sti. P.; Dund. P.; Ab. P.; Per. P.; Glas. Mit.*

FRASER (Sir William): The Red book of Menteith. 2 v. Edinburgh, 1880. *S.C.L.; Sti. P.; Sti. C.; Dumb. P.; Moth. P.; Ab. U.; Glas. U.; Dund. P.; Edin. P.; Edin. S.; St.A. U.; Edin. L.L.; Edin. Ant.*

Graham, Duke of Montrose, *see* **Montrose,** Duke of

Graham of Tamrawer

GRAHAM (James Edward), *K.C.*: The Grahams of Tamrawer: a short account of their history. Edinburgh, 1895. *St.A. U.; Glas. U.; Edin. P.; Edin. S.; Edin. L.L.*

see also **Graham** of Auchencloich

Graham-Patterson, *see* **Patterson**

Grant

ANDERSON (Peter John): Major Alpin's ancestors and descendants. Aberdeen, 1904. *Ab. P.; Inv. P.; St.A. U.; Glas. U.; Ab. U.; Edin. P.; Edin. S.; Glas. Mit.; Edin. L.L.*

A BRIEF account of the family of the Grants; with the life of Sir Francis Grant, Lord Cullen. n.p., n.d. *Ab. P.; Glas. Mit.*

[CASSILLIS (Archibald Kennedy), *Earl of*]: The Rulers of Strathspey: a history of the lairds of Grant and Earls of Seafield. Inverness, 1911. *Inv. P.; Banff C.; Elg. P.; St.A. U.; Ab. U.; Ab. P.; Kirkcud. C.; Dund. Q.; Edin. P.; Edin. S.; Glas. Mit.; Edin. Ant.*

ELLIOT (William Hume): The Story of the "Cheeryble" Grants, from the Spey to the Irwell. Manchester, 1906. *St.A. U.; Edin. S.*

FAMILY of Grants. Edinburgh, 1883. *Ab. U.*

FRASER (Sir William): The Chiefs of Grant. 3 v. Edinburgh, 1883. *S.C.L.; Elg. P.; Inv. P.; Moth. P.; St.A. U.; Ab. U.; Ab. P.; Glas. U.; Edin. P.; Edin. S.; Glas. Mit.; Edin. L.L.; Edin. Ant.*

A FULL and correct genealogy of the honourable family of Grant of Grant, brought down to the year 1826. Elgin, 1826. *Edin. Ant.*

[GRANT (Sir A.)]: Account of the root, rise and offspring of the clan Grant. 1872. (*MS.*) *Inv. P.*

— Ane account of the rise and offspring of the name of Grant. Aberdeen, 1876. *Ab. P.; Ab. U.; Edin. L.L.*

GRANT (Charles), *Vicomte de Vaux*: Memoires . . . de la maison de Grant. London, 1796. *Inv. P.; Ab. U.; Glas. U.; Edin. P.* (1806)*; Edin. L.L.; Edin. Ant.*

GRANT (Isabel Frances): The Clan Grant; the development of a clan. Edinburgh, 1955. *Inv. P.; Inv. C.; Suth. C.; Edin. U.; Lan. C.; Ab. P.; Per. C.; Dund. P.; Pai. P.; Edin. P.; Glas. Mit.; Cai. C.; Ber. C.; Edin. L.L.*

GRANT (Maria M.): Notes on clan Grant. 1903. (*Typescript.*) *Ab. U.*

MSS. notes and newspaper cuttings relating to the Grants, Leiths, MacKintoshes of Blervie. *Inv. P.*

MEMORIAL of the majority of the Rt. Hon. Viscount Reidhaven, Master of Grant. Banff, 1872. (Repr. from the *Banffshire Journal*, 8th Oct., 1872.) *Edin. P.*

Grant of Corrimony

GRANT (Sir Francis James): The Grants of Corrimony. Lerwick, 1895. *Inv. P.; St.A. U.; Ab. U.; Edin. P.; Edin. S.; Glas. Mit.; Edin. L.L.; Edin. Ant.*

Grant of Glenmoriston

SINCLAIR (Allan): Reminiscences, historical and traditional of the Grants of Glenmoriston. Edinburgh, 1887. *Cai. C.; Ab. P.; Inv. P.; Ab. U.; Mor. C.; Edin. P.; Edin. S.; Glas. Mit.*

Gray

[GRAY (Patrick)]: Kalendar showing descent of the Gray family from Fergus the Scoto-Irish King, A.D. 503-1892. n.d. *Dund. P.*

GRAY (Peter): The Descent and kinship of Patrick, Master of Gray. Dundee, 1903. *S.C.L.; Arb. P.; Dund. P.; Ab. P.; Per. P.; Edin. P.; Glas. Mit.; Edin. L.L.*

— The House of Gray. Pedigree of Patrick Gray of Southfield. [Dundee, 1908.] *Dund. P.*

THE SCOTTISH family of Gray. [Genealogical chart.] [1914.] *Glas. Mit.*

Gray, Lord Gray

GRAY (Alexander): Case of Alexander Gray (with the pedigree of Gray, Lord Gray). n.p., [1880]. *Edin. L.L.*

MINUTES of evidence . . . Mrs. Eveleen Smith . . . claiming to be Baroness Gray. 1896. *Edin. L.L.*

SMITH (Mrs. Eveleen): Case on behalf of Mrs. Eveleen Smith . . . 1896. *Edin. L.L.*

Gray of Skibo

GRAY (Peter): Skibo: its lairds and history. Edinburgh, 1906. *S.C.L.; Dunf. P.; Ab. U.; Ab. P.; Dund. P.; Suth. C.; Edin. P.; Edin. S.; Glas. Mit.; Edin. L.L.*

Gregor, *see* **MacGregor**

Gregory

GREGORY (Georgina): A short account of the family of Gregorie, from the time they gave up the name of Macgregor. n.p., 1873. *Edin. L.L.*

GREGORY (Philip Spencer): Records of the family of Gregory. Edinburgh, 1886. *Ab. U.; Edin. P.*

STEWART (Agnes Grainger): The Academic Gregories. Edinburgh, 1901. *S.C.L.; Ab. C.; Kil. P.; Clack. C.; Ruth. P.; St.A. U.; Ab. P.; Glas. U.; Dund. P.; Falk. P.; Edin. P.; Edin. S.; Glas. Mit.*

Grierson of Lag

FERGUSSON (Alexander): The Laird of Lag, a life sketch. Edinburgh, 1886. *Glas. Mit.*

HAMILTON-GRIERSON (Sir Philip James): The Lag charters, 1400-1720. Edinburgh, 1958. (Scottish Record Soc.) *Edin. P.; Edin. L.L.; Ab. P.*

Grierson of Marwhirn

CORRESPONDENCE re Grierson of Marquhirn (Glencairn) and their descendants. n.d. (*MSS. & typescript.*) *Dumf. C.*

Groat

TRAILL (H. L. Norton): The Family of Groat. (In *Viking club Old-lore miscellany*, v. 9, 1933, pp. 148-151.) *Ork. C.*

Grosett

[GROSETT (Walter)]: An account of the family of the Muir-heads of Lachop . . . n.p., n.d. *Edin. P.*

Gunn

SINCLAIR (Thomas): The Gunns. Wick, 1890. *Inv. P.; Cai. C.; Sti. P.; Ab. U.; Edin. P.; Edin. S.; Glas. Mit.; Edin. L.L.*

Guthrie

EDWARDS (David Herschell): The Auld Neuk house . . . the birthplace of the Guthries. Brechin, 1916. *Dund. P.; Edin. P.*

GUTHRIE (Charles John), *Lord Guthrie*: Genealogy of the descendants of Rev. Thomas Guthrie, D.D., and Mrs. Anne Burns, or Guthrie, connected chiefly with the families of Chalmers and Traill . . . Edinburgh, 1902. *Arb. P.; Ab. P.; St.A. U.; Glas. U.; Edin. P.; Edin. S.; Glas. Mit.*

GUTHRIE (David Charles) of Craigie, *ed.*: The Guthrie family, 1178-1900. Northampton, 1906. *Dund. P.*

GUTHRIE (Laurence Rawlin), *comp.*: American Guthrie and allied families . . . with some post-revolution emigrants and some allied families. Chambersburg, Penn., 1933. *Forf. P.; Edin. S.*

Hadden

[TOUGH (J. D.)]: A short narrative of the life of an Aberdonian; to which is added An account of the Hadden family. Aberdeen, 1848. *Ab. P.; Glas. Mit.*

Haddington, Earl of, *see* **Hamilton,** Earl of Haddington

Hadow

HADOW (Arthur Lovell): [The Pedigree of the Hadow family descended from Principal James Hadow. Text and tables. 2 v.] Kemsing, 1953. (*Typescript.*) *St.A. U.*

Haig of Bemersyde

[HAIG (Charles Edwin)]: Haig of Bemersyde, co. Berwick. [Genealogical chart.] [Edinburgh, 1907.] *St.A. U.; Edin. P.* (2nd ed. 1907); *Edin. L.L.*

RUSSELL (John): The Haigs of Bemersyde: a family history. Edinburgh, 1881. *S.C.L.; Ab. P.; Haw. P.; Inv. P.; Ber. C.; Nai. C.; Gala. P.; Clack. C.; Ang. C.; Rox. C.; Sel. P.; St.A. U.; Ab. U.; Glas. U.; Edin. P.; Edin. S.; Glas. Mit.; Edin. L.L.; Edin. Ant.*

STUART (Mrs. Alexander), *ed.*: "Tyde what may": a Haig family magazine. 5 pts. Edinburgh, 1894-1900. *Edin. P.; Edin. L.L.* (4 pts.).

Haig of Stirlingshire

HAIG (Charles Edwin): Robert Haig of St. Ninians. n.p., [1895]. *Edin. P.*

Halcro

CLOUSTON (J. Storer): The Origin of the Halcros. (In *Proceedings Orkney Antiquarian Soc.*, v. 11, 1933, pp. 59-65.) *Ork. C.; Zet. C.*

SCOTT (Ebenezer Erskine): The Erskine-Halcro genealogy. London, 1890. *S.C.L.; Dunf. P.; Inv. P.; Ork. C.; Sti. C.; Edin. S.; Glas. Mit.*

— — New ed. Edinburgh, 1895. *Forf. P.; Ab. P.; Pai. P.; Ork. C.; Glas. U.; Zet. C.; Edin. P.; Arb. P.; Glas. Mit.; Edin. L.L.; Edin. Ant.; Ber. C.; Inv. P.; St.A. U.; Dunf. P.*

Haldane of Barmony

ROGERS (Charles): Four Perthshire families: Roger, Playfair, Constable and Haldane of Barmony. Edinburgh, 1887. *Sti. P.; Glas. U.; St.A. U.; Dund. P.; Per. P.; Dunf. P.; Edin. S.; Edin. L.L.; Edin. Ant.*

— The Scottish house of Roger, with notes respecting the families of Playfair and Haldane of Barmony. 2nd ed. Edinburgh, 1875. *Dunf. P.; Edin. P.; Edin. S.; Glas. Mit.*

Haldane of Gleneagles

[HALDANE (Alexander)]: Memoranda relating to the family of Haldane of Gleneagles. London, 1880. *Edin. P.; Edin. S.; Edin. L.L.*

HALDANE (Sir James Aylmer Lowthorpe): The Haldanes of Gleneagles. Edinburgh, 1929. *S.C.L.; Per. C.; Sti. P.; Fife C.; Edin. U.; Ab. U.; Edin. P.; Edin. S.; St.A. U.; Glas. Mit.; Edin. L.L.; Edin. Ant.*

Haliburton

ROGERS (Charles): Genealogical memoirs of the family of Sir Walter Scott of Abbotsford; with a reprint of his Memorials of the Haliburtons. London, 1877. (Grampian Club, 13.) *Kil. P.; Dunf. P.; Dumf. C.; Haw. P.; Inv. P.; Sti. P.; Dund. Q.; Glas. U.; Dund. P.; Edin. P.; Edin. S.; Glas. Mit.; Edin. L.L.*

SCOTT (*Sir* Walter): Memorials of the Haliburtons. Edinburgh, 1824. *Ab. P.* (n.d.)*; Edin. P.; Edin. S.; Glas. Mit.; Glas. U.*

Halkerston of Halkerston Beath

McCALL (Hardy Bertram): Some old families: contribution to the genealogical history of Scotland. Birmingham, 1890. *S.C.L.; Edin. P.; Edin. S.; Sel. P.; Edin. L.L.; Edin. Ant.*

Halkett of Pitfirrane

ANGUS (William), *ed.*: Inventory of Pitfirrane writs, 1230-1794. Edinburgh, 1932. (Scottish Record Society, 67.) *S.C.L.*

Hall

WATSON (Charles Brodie Boog): Traditions and genealogies of some members of the families of Boog, Heron, Leishman, Ross, Watson. Perth, 1908. *St.A. U.; Edin. P.; Edin. S.*

Hamilton

AITON (William): An inquiry in to the pedigree, descent, and public transactions of the chiefs of the Hamilton family, and showing how they acquired their estates. Glasgow, 1827. *Ham. P.; Glas. U.; Edin. S.; Glas. Mit.*

ANDERSON (John): Historical and genealogical memoirs of the house of Hamilton; with genealogical memoirs of the several branches of the family. Edinburgh, 1825. *Lan. C.; Ham. P.; St.A. U.; Glas. U.; Pai. P.; Air. P.; Edin. P.; Edin. S.; Glas. Mit.* (+Suppl. 1827)*; Edin. L.L.*

"AUDI Alteram Partem." Pedigree of the Hamilton family. London, 1867. *Edin. P.; Edin. S.*

BASKERVILL (Patrick Hamilton): The Hamiltons of Burnside, North Carolina, and their ancestors and descendants. Richmond, Va., 1916. *Glas. Mit.*

BURNET (Gilbert), *Bp.*: The Memoires of the lives and actions of James and William, Dukes of Hamilton and Castleherald. (Pt. 2 of History of the Church and state of Scotland.) London, 1677. *Lan. C.; Inv. P.; Ham. P.; Glas. Mit.; Edin. L.L.*

HAMILTON (Charles William): Index tables to the families of Hamilton. Dublin, 1863. *Edin. P.; Edin. L.L.*

HAMILTON (Dr. Francis) of Bardowie: Memoirs of the house of Hamilton, corrected with an addition. Edinburgh, 1828. *Ham. P.; Lan. C.; Glas. U.; St.A. U.; Pai. P.; Air. P.; Edin. P.; Edin. S.; Glas. Mit.; Edin. L.L.; Edin. Ant.*

HAMILTON (George): A history of the house of Hamilton. Edinburgh, 1933. *Lan. C.; Edin. U.; Ab. U.; Kirkcud. C.; Glas. U.; Edin. P.; Edin. S.; Glas. Mit.; Edin. L.L.; Edin. Ant.*

HAMILTON (Sir James): The Hamilton manuscripts: containing some account of the settlement of the territories of the upper Clandeboye, Great Ardes, & Dufferin in the county of Down; ed. by T. K. Lowry. Belfast, 1867. *Edin. P.; Edin. S.*

JOHNSTON (George Harvey): The Heraldry of the Hamiltons: with notes on all the males of the family, and description of the arms, plates and pedigrees. Edinburgh, 1909. *Lan. C.; Ham. P.; Edin. P.; Edin. S.; Glas. Mit.; Edin. L.L.*

MILLER (Alfred G.): The House of Hamilton, a historical sketch; and other local papers. 1895. (Repr. from the *Hamilton Advertiser.*) *Ham. P.*

— The House of Hamilton. n.d. (*Typescript.*) *Ham. P.*

RIDDELL (John): Reply to the misstatements of Dr. Hamilton of Bardowie, in his late "Memoirs of the house of Hamilton, corrected", respecting the descent of his family; with an appendix of original matter, partly affecting the Hamiltons, and the Stewarts, and representation of the old Earls of Lennox, etc. Edinburgh, 1828. *Ham. P.; St.A. U.; Glas. U.; Lan. C.; Pai. P.; Air. P.; Edin. P.; Edin. S.; Glas. Mit.; Edin. L.L.; Edin. Ant.*

Hamilton, Marquess, Duke of Abercorn

ABERCORN (James Hamilton), *1st Duke of*: Consultation pour James Hamilton, Marquis d'Abercorn . . . contre le duc d'Hamilton . . . Paris, 1865. *Edin. P.; Edin. S.*

Hamilton of Broomhill

BIRNIE (John): Account of the families of Birnie and Hamilton of Broomhill. Edinburgh, 1838. *S.C.L.; Glas. U.; Edin. P.; Edin. S.; Edin. L.L.*

Hamilton of Bargany

DALRYMPLE (Hon. Hew Hamilton): A short account of the Hamiltons of Bargany. Edinburgh, 1897. *S.C.L.; Wig. C.; Edin. P.; Edin. L.L.; Edin. Ant.*

Hamilton of Fala

DALRYMPLE (Hon. Hew Hamilton): A short account of the Hamiltons of Fala and of Fala House. n.p., 1907. *Wig. C.; Mid. C.; Edin. P.*

Hamilton, Earl of Haddington

FRASER (Sir William): Memorials of the Earls of Haddington. 2 v. Edinburgh, 1889. *S.C.L.; Rox. C.; Ber. C.; Moth. P.; St.A. U.; Ab. U.; Glas. U.; Edin. P.; Edin. S.; Glas. Mit.; Edin. L.L.; Edin. Ant.*

Hamilton, Duke of Hamilton

NEEDHAM (Marchamont): The Manifold practises and attempts of the Hamiltons, and particularly of the present Duke of Hamilton . . . to get the crown of Scotland. 1648. *Edin. P.*

Hamilton of Innerwick

[NAPIER (Mark)]: A "memorie", historical and genealogical of my mother's paternal lineage, namely the Hamiltons of Innerwick, the Lothian Kerrs, and the Earls of Angus, Lords of Bonkyl in the 14th century, including an episodical account of the First and Last Duke of Douglas and his barbarous treatment of his only sister, the beautiful and calumniated heiress of the House of Douglas. Edinburgh, 1872. *Kirkcud. Bro.*

Hamilton of Olivestob

EATON (Arthur W. H.): The Olivestob Hamiltons. New York, 1893. *Dumf. C.; Edin. P.; Edin. S.; Edin. L.L.*

Hannay

HANNAY (William V.): The Genealogy of the Hannay family. New York, 1913. *Wig. C.*

Hardy

McCALL (Hardy Bertram): Memoirs of my ancestors: genealogical memoranda. [Hardy and McCall.] Birmingham, 1884. *Edin. P.; Edin. S.; Glas. Mit.*

— Some old families: contribution to the genealogical history of Scotland. Birmingham, 1890. *S.C.L.; Edin. P.; Edin. S.; Sel. P.; Edin. L.L.; Edin. Ant.*

Harkness

HEWISON (James King): Dalgarnoc: its saints and heroes: a history of Morton, Thornhill and the Harknesses. Dumfries, 1935. *S.C.L.; Ab. P.; Glas. Mit.*

Haws

HAWS (George W.): The Haws family and their seafaring kin. Dunfermline, 1932. *Dund. Q.; Dunf. P.; Glas. Mit.*

Hay

ALLAN (John Hay), "*J. S. S. Stuart*": Genealogical table of the Hays . . . 1170 to 1840 . . . n.p., 1840. *Edin. P.*

FORBES (Louisa Lillias): Hay of Smithfield and Haystoun, 1712-1880. 1879. (*MS.*) *Edin. P.; Edin. S.; Edin. L.L.*

Hay of Alderstoun

FRASER (Sir William): Genealogical table of the families of Brisbane of Bishoptoun & Brisbane, Makdougall of Makerstoun; and Hay of Alderstoun, etc. [Chart.] Edinburgh, 1840. (*Photocopy.*) *S.C.L.*

Hay of Delgaty

INNES (Sir Thomas) of Learney: Hays of Delgaty. 1936. (From *Trans. Banffshire Field Club*, 1936.) *Edin. L.L.*

Hay of Duns Castle

HAY (Francis Stewart): Family of Hay of Duns Castle. Edinburgh, n.d. *Ber. C.; Edin. P.* (1922).

Hay of Erroll

THE ERROLL papers, 1188-1727. (In *Misc. Spalding Club*, v. II, 1842.) *S.C.L.*

MELVILLE (Lawrence): Errol: its legends, lands and people. Perth, 1935. *Dund. P.; Glas. Mit.*

Hay of Tweeddale

HAY (Father Richard Augustine): Genealogie of the Hayes of Tweeddale; ed. by James Maidment. Edinburgh, 1835. *Haw. P.; Rox. C.; Pee. C.; St.A. U.; Gree. P.; Ab. U.; Glas. U.; Edin. P.; Edin. S.; Glas. Mit.; Edin. L.L.; Edin. Ant.*

Hay of Yester

HARVEY (Charles C. H.) & MACLEOD (John), *comps.*: Calendar of writs preserved at Yester House, 1166-1625. Edinburgh, 1930. (Scottish Record Soc., 55.) *S.C.L.; Glas. Mit.*

Henderson

HENDERSON (Ralph), *comp.*: Records of my family. Carlisle, 1926. *Edin. P.*

Henderson of Borrowstounness

GENEALOGICAL chart of the Hendersons of Borrowstounness. n.p., 1892. *Edin. P.; Edin. Ant.*

Hepburn of Monkrig

DUNCAN (James Alexander): Descent of the Hepburns of Monkrig. Edinburgh, 1911. *Dund. Q.; Edin. P.; Edin. S.; Glas. Mit.; Edin. Ant.*

Hepburn of Wauchton

HEPBURN (Edward): Genealogical notes of the Hepburn family. London, 1925. *Edin. S.; Edin. L.L.*

80

Heriot

REID (R. C.): The Heriots of Ramornie, from the 15th to 18th centuries. Dumfries, 1931. *Kir. P.; Dumf. C.; St.A. U.; Edin. P.; Edin. S.; Edin. L.L.*

Heriot of Trabroun

BALLINGALL (G. W.): Selections from old records regarding the Heriots of Trabroun. Haddington, 1894. *S.C.L.; Ayr P.; Glas. Mit.*

Heron

WATSON (Charles Brodie Boog): Traditions and genealogies of some members of the families of Boog, Heron, Leishman, Ross and Watson. Perth, 1908. *Edin. P.; Edin. S.; St.A. U.; Edin. L.L.; Edin. Ant.*

Herries

HERRIES-CROSBIE (Charles Howard): The Story and pedigree of the Lords Herries of Herries in the male line. Wexford, [19—]. *Dumf. C.; Wig. C.; Edin. L.L.*

Herries, Lord Herries of Terregles

CONSTABLE-MAXWELL (William): Case on behalf of William Constable Maxwell of Nithsdale . . . claiming to be Lord Herries of Terregles . . . London, 1849-1858. *Edin. P.*

MAXWELL (William) of Carruchan: Case for William Maxwell of Carruchan, Esq., claiming to be Earl of Nithsdale, Lord Maxwell, Eskdale & Carlyle & Lord Herries. 1848. *Edin. L.L.*

— Supplemental case for William Maxwell of Carruchan . . . in opposition to the case of William Constable Maxwell, Esq., claiming the title, honour and dignity of Lord Herries of Terregles . . . 1853. *Glas. Mit.; Edin. Ant.*

Hill

DEUCHAR (A.): General collections relating to the Hill family. n.d. (*MS.*) *Glas. Mit.*

HILL (William Henry): Early records of an old Glasgow family, 1520-1791. Glasgow, 1902. *Glas. Mit.; Edin. P.*

Holland

BULLOCH (John Malcolm): Broadford Works and the Hollands. Aberdeen, 1930. (Cuttings taken from the *Bon-Accord and Northern Pictorial.*) *Ab. P.*

Home

BARTY (Alex. Boyd): Argaty, its lairds and its barony book. Stirling, 1929. *Edin. P.*

CLARK (Mrs. Jacobina): Mrs. Jacobina Clark, appellant, and the Rt. Hon. William, Earl of Home, respondent . . . Edinburgh, 1753. *Edin. P.; Edin. S.*

see also **Hume; Milne-Home**

Home of Broomhouse
 LOGAN-HOME (George John Ninian): Historical notes on Broomhouse and the Home family. Edinburgh, n.d. (Repr. from *Hist. of Berwick. Nat. Club*, v. xxv.) *Edin. L.L.*

Home of Renton, *see* **Dunbar,** Earldom of

Honeyman
 HONEYMAN (Abraham van Doren): The Honeyman family in Scotland and America from 1584-1908. Plainfield, N.J., 1909. *Edin. S.*

Hope
 SETON (George): Memoir of Alexander Seton . . . with an appendix containing . . . genealogical tables of the legal families of Erskine, Hope, Dalrymple and Dundas. Edinburgh, 1882. *Dunf. P.; Glas. Mit.*

Hope of Hopetoun
 HOPES of Hopetoun. (From *Edinburgh Courant,* Sept. 1881.) *Edin. P.*

Houldsworth
 MACLEOD (William Houldsworth) & HOULDSWORTH (Sir Henry Hamilton): Beginnings of the Houldsworths of Coltness. Glasgow, 1937. *Ayr P.; Falk. P.; Air. P.; Edin. P.; Edin. S.; Glas. Mit.*

Hume
 DRUMMOND (Henry): Histories of noble British families. Vol. 2: Dunbar, Hume, Dundas. London, 1846. *Edin. P.; Glas. U.; Glas. Mit.; Edin. S.*
 MILNE-HOME (David): Biographical memoranda of the persons whose portraits hang in the dining-room at Milne-Graden (Berwickshire). Edinburgh, 1862. *Edin. P.; Glas. Mit.; Ber. C.*

Hume, Earl of Marchmont
 A SELECTION from the papers of the Earls of Marchmont, in the possession of the Rt. Hon. Sir George Henry Rose, 1685-1750. 3 v. London, 1831. *Ber. C.; Glas. U.; Edin. P.*

see also **Marchmont,** Earldom of

82

Hume of Polwarth

[WARRENDER (Margaret)]: Marchmont and the Humes of Polwarth. Edinburgh, 1894. *Haw. P.; Mid. C.; Gala. P.; Ber. C.; Rox. C.; Sel. P.; St.A. U.; Ab. U.; Glas. U.; Edin. P.; Edin. S.; Glas. Mit.; Edin. L.L.; Edin. Ant.*

Hume of Wedderburn

HUME (David): Davidis Humii de familia Humia Wedderburnensi liber. Edinburgh, 1839. (Abbotsford Club.) *Glas. U.; Edin. P.; Edin. S.; Glas. Mit.*

HUME (Edgar Erskine): A colonial Scottish Jacobite family: the establishment in Virginia of a branch of the Humes of Wedderburn. Richmond, Va., 1931. *Edin. P.; Edin. S.*

Hunter

HUNTER (Andrew Alexander): The Pedigree of Hunter of Abbotshill and Barjarg and cadet families: Hunter of Bonnytoun and Doonholm, Hunter-Blair of Blairquhan, Hunter of Auchterarder, Hunter of Thurston. London, 1905. *St.A. U.; Ab. U.; Edin. S.; Glas. Mit.; Edin. L.L.*

Hunter of Forfarshire

GUTHRIE (G. G. Hunter): Hunters of Forfarshire, 1528-1928. n.p., n.d. *Forf. P.*

Hunter of Hunterston

SHAW (Mackenzie S.), *ed.*: Some family papers of the Hunters of Hunterston. Edinburgh, 1925. (Scottish Record Soc., 58.) *S.C.L.; Glas. U.; Dund. P.; Edin. U.; Edin. S.; Edin. P.; Glas. Mit.; Edin. L.L.; Edin. Ant.*

Huntly, Earl of, Marquess of, *see* **Gordon,** Earl of, Marquess of Huntly

Hutcheson of Lambhill

HILL (William Henry): History of the hospital and school in Glasgow founded by George and Thomas Hutcheson of Lambhill, A.D. 1639-41; with notices of the founders and of their family, properties and affairs . . . Glasgow, 1881. *Glas. Mit.; Edin. L.L.*

Hutchison

DEUCHAR (A.): Genealogical collections relative to the family of Hutchison. n.d. (*MS.*) *Glas. Mit.*

Imbrie in U.S.A.

> IMBRIE (Addison Murray): Genealogy of the Imbrie family of Western Pennsylvania, descendants of James Imbrie, pioneer settler, and his wife, Euphemia Smart. Comp. by Boyd Vincent Imbrie and M. E. Philbrook. Pittsburgh, Penn., 1953. *Edin. Ant.*

Imrie of Lunan

> BLAIR-IMRIE (William): A record of Lunan: its descent and transmission, 1189-1849. Edinburgh, 1902. *Arb. P.*

Inglis of Auchindinny & Redhall

> INGLIS (John Alexander): The Family of Inglis of Auchindinny and Redhall. Edinburgh, 1914. *S.C.L.; Mid. C.; St.A. U.; Ab. U.; Glas. U.; Ab. P.; Kirkcud. C.; Edin. P.; Edin. S.; Glas. Mit.; Edin. L.L.; Edin. Ant.*

> — Inglis of Auchindinny and Redhall: the family tree. [Edinburgh, 1903.] *Edin. P.; Edin. S.; Edin. L.L.*

Inglis of Cramond

> [WOOD (John Philip)]: Inglis of Cramond. (In his *Memorials of various families.* c. 1830. (MS.).) *Edin. P.*

Innes

> FORBES (Duncan): Ane account of the familie of Innes, comp. . . . 1698. With an appendix of charters and notes. Ed. by C. Innes. Aberdeen, 1864. (Spalding Club, 34.) *S.C.L.; Elg. P.; Inv. P.; Ab. C.; Ab. P.; Glas. U.; Dund. P.; Edin. P.; Edin. S.; Glas. Mit.; Edin. L.L.*

> INNES (Sir Thomas) of Learney: The Inneses of Benwall and Blairton and collateral branches. Edinburgh, 1955. *Ab. U.; Edin. P.*

> HISTORICALL account of the origine and succession of the family of Innes . . . Edinburgh, 1820. *Ab. U.; Edin. P.; Edin. S.; Edin. L.L.*

Innes of Balnacraig

> STIRTON (John): A day that is dead. 2nd ed. Forfar, 1929. *Inv. P.; Ab. P.; Edin. P.; Glas. Mit.; Dund. P.; Per. C.*

Innes in Caithness

> SINCLAIR (Thomas): The Innesses of Caithness. n.d. (*Press cuttings* collected and bound by John Mowat, of Caithness.) *Cai. C.*

Innes of Coxton

> THE GENEALOGY of the family of Innes of Coxtown . . . n.p., [1819.] *Ab. U.*

Innes of Cromey

INNES (Sir Thomas) of Learney: Innes of Cromey. (From *Trans. Banffshire Field Club*, 1934.) *Edin. L.L.*

Innes of Edingight & Balveny

INNES (Thomas) of Learney: The Chronicles of the family of Innes of Edingight and Balveny. Aberdeen, 1898. *Elg. P.; Ab. P.; Inv. P.; Edin. U.; St.A. U.; Kirkcud. C.; Glas. U., Edin. P.; Edin. S.; Edin. L.L.*

Innes of Mathiemill

INNES (Colin W.): Innes of Mathiemill. New York, 1958. *Edin. L.L.*

Innes of Newseat of Scurdargue

INNES (A. N.): Notes on the family of Innes of Newseat of Scurdargue from records both public and private, and family letters. London, 1931. *Elg. P.; Ab. P.; St.A. U.; Ab. U.; Edin. P.; Edin. S.; Glas. Mit.; Edin. L.L.*

Innes of Pethnick

INNES (Sir Thomas) of Learney: Innes of Pethnick. (From *Trans. Banffshire Field Club*, 1935.) *Edin. L.L.*

Irvine

THOM (Robert W.): Wyseby: a legend of the first Irvings. Edinburgh, 1844. *Glas. Mit.*

see also **Irving**

Irvine of Cults

BULLOCH (Joseph Gaston Baillie): History and genealogy of the families of Bulloch & Stobo, and Irvine of Cults. Washington, 1911. *Ab. P.* (+1892)*; Edin. S.*

Irvine of Drum

ANDERSON (Robert): The Irvines of Drum. Peterhead, 1920. *Ab. P.*

LESLIE (Jonathan Forbes): The Irvines of Drum and collateral branches. Aberdeen, 1909. *Ab. P.; Ab. C.; St.A. U.; Ab. U.; Edin. P.; Edin. S.; Glas. Mit.; Edin. L.L.*

WIMBERLEY (Douglas): A short account of the family of Irvine of Drum in the county of Aberdeen. Inverness, 1893. *St.A. U.; Ab. U.; Ab. C.; Edin. L.L.*

— Memorials of four old families. 1894. *Ab. P.; Inv. P.; Edin. P.; Edin. S.; Glas. Mit.; Dund. Q.*

Irving

Irving (John Beaufin) of Bonshaw: [The Book of the Irvings]. The Irvings, Irwins, Irvines or Erinveines or any other spelling of the name: an old Scots Border clan. Aberdeen, 1907. *Dumf. C.; Ab. P.; Edin. P.; Edin. S.; Glas. Mit.; Ab. U.; Edin. L.L.*

Hosmer (Ralph Sheldon) & Fielder (M. T. I.), *comps.*: Genealogy of that branch of the Irwin family in New York founded in the Hudson River Valley by William Irwin, 1700-1787. Ithaca, N.Y., 1938. *Dumf. C.; Ab. P.*

Irving of Bonshaw

Fitzmaurice (Frances Rhoda) *Hon. Mrs. James Fitzmaurice*: Bonshaw Tower: the Irvings and some of their kinsfolk. Bonshaw Tower, Dumfries, [1898]. *Dumf. C.*

Irving of Hoddom

Irving (George): The Irvings of Hoddom. 1902. (From *Trans. Dumfriesshire & Galloway Natural Hist. & Antiq. Soc.* 1900-02.) *Dumf. C.*

Irving of Newton

Irving (Miles): The Irvings of Newton: an appendix to the *Book of the Irvings*. [Aberdeen,] n.d. *Dumf. C.; Ab. U.* (1909)*; Edin. L.L.*

Irwin, *see* **Irving**

Iver, *see* **Maciver**

Jaffray

Jaffray (Alexander): Diary; ed. by John Barclay. London, 1833. *Ab. P.; Glas. Mit.* (2nd ed. 1834 + 3rd ed. Aberdeen, 1856).

Jaffray (Robert): Jaffray genealogy, being an account of a branch of this family which was particularly associated with Stirlingshire. New York, 1926. *Sti. C.*

Jarvie

Spencer (C. L.): Some notes on the Spencers, Jarvies, and Rintouls in Glasgow, comp. from family tradition and public records. 1935. (*Typescript.*) *Glas. Mit.*

Johnston

Cuthbert (Alexander A.), *comp.*: Genealogical chart of the Johnston family, Bathgate. n.p., [1908]. *Glas. Mit.; Edin. L.L.*

GENEALOGICAL chart of the Johnston family. [1730-1887.] n.p., n.d. *Edin. L.L.*

JOHNSTON (George Harvey): Heraldry of the Johnstons . . . Edinburgh, 1905. *Dumf. C.; Edin. P.; Edin. S.; Glas. Mit.*

JOHNSTONE (Catherine Laura): The Johnstons in Edinburgh. n.d. (Repr. mainly from her *History of the Johnstones*.) *Edin. P.; Glas. Mit.*

Johnston of Caskieben

JOHNSTON (Alexander): Genealogical account of the family of Johnston of that ilk, formerly of Caskieben in the shire of Aberdeen. Edinburgh, 1832. *Ab. P.; Edin. L.L.*

— Short memoir of James Young, merchant burgess of Aberdeen, and Rachel Cruickshank his spouse, and of their descendants. Aberdeen, 1861. *Ab. P.; Ab. C.; Edin. P.; Edin. S.; Edin. L.L.*

— — [New ed.] ed. by W. Johnston. Aberdeen, 1894. *Ab. P.; Edin. P.; Edin. S.; Edin. L.L.*

Johnstone

JOHNSTONE (Catherine Laura): History of the Johnstones, 1191-1909 with descriptions of Border life. (And Supplement.) 2 v. Edinburgh, Glasgow, 1909-1925. *Ab. P.; Dumf. C.; Ab. U.; Edin. P.; Edin. S.; Glas. Mit.; Edin. Ant.* (v. 1).

— — [Supplement only.] Glasgow, 1925. *Dumf. C.; Arb. P.; Ayr P.; Dund. P.; Dunf. P.; Kil. P.; Gree. P.; Per. P.; Sel. P.*

Johnstone, Earl of Annandale

FRASER (Sir William): The Annandale family book of the Johnstones. 2 v. Edinburgh, 1894. *Dumf. C.; Rox. C.; St.A. U.; Ab. U.; Glas. U.; Edin. P.; Edin. S.; Glas. Mit.; Edin. L.L.; Edin. Ant.*

— A century of romance of the Annandale peerages, with letters of Henry, Lord Brougham. n.p., 1894. (Repr. from *The Annandale family book*.) *Dumf. C.; St.A. U.; Ab. U.*

Johnstone of Elphinstone

BULLOCH (James): The Johnstones of Elphinstone. [Haddington, 1948.] (Extr. from *Trans. East Lothian Antiquarian & Field Naturalist's Soc.*, v. IV.) *Edin. Ant.*

Johnstone of Lochwood

REID (Robert Corsane): Lochwood tower. 1926. (Repr. from *Trans. Dumfriesshire & Galloway Nat. Hist. & Antiquarian Soc.*) *Edin. L.L.*

Keddie

[KEDDIE (Henrietta)], *"Sarah Tytler"*: Three generations: the story of a middle-class Scottish family. London, 1911. *Lan. C.; Kir. P.; Edin. P.; Edin. S.*

Keir

CAMPBELL (Julia Beatrice): A few words about an old Highland family. (Auchindarroch misc. I.) Glasgow, n.d. *Edin. S.; Glas. Mit.* (Glasgow, [1894]).

MOILLIET (Mrs. Amelia): Sketch of the life of James Keir, Esq., F.R.S., . . . [with a genealogy of the family of James Keir]. London, [1859]. *Edin. P.*

Keith

MS. notes and press cuttings on the family of Keith. n.d. *Edin. P.*

Keith, Earl Marischal

ANDERSON (Robert): Field Marshal Keith. Peterhead, 1910. *Ab. P.*

BUCHAN (P[eter]): Account of the ancient and noble family of Keith, Earls Marischal of Scotland. Peterhead, 1820. *Ab. P.; Inv. P.; Pet. P.; Ab. C.; Glas. U.; Forf. P.; Dund. P.; Edin. P.; Edin. S.; Glas. Mit.; Edin. L.L.; Edin. Ant.*

MCLEAN (Neil N.): Memoir of Marshal Keith, with a sketch of the Keith family by a Peterheadian. Peterhead, 1869. *Ab. P.; Pet. P.; Edin. P.; Glas. Mit.*

Keith of Whiteriggs

MAIDMENT (James): Genealogical fragments relating to the families of . . . Keith . . . Berwick, 1855. *Inv. P.; Glas. U.; Edin. P.; Edin. S.; Glas. Mit.; Edin. Ant.*

Kellie, Earldom of

MAR (John Francis Miller Erskine), *9th Earl of*: Case of John Francis Miller Erskine, Earl of Mar, Lord Erskine, Garioch & Alloa claiming . . . Earl of Kellie, Viscount Fenton and Lord Dirltoun . . . *Edin. L.L.*

MINUTES of evidence . . . 1832-35. *Edin. L.L.*

see also **Mar,** Earldom of

Kemp

HITCHIN-KEMP (Fred) & *others*: A general history of the Kemp and Kempe families of Great Britain and the colonies. London, [1902]. *S.C.L.; Edin. S.*

88

Kennedy

FERGUSSON (Sir James): The Kennedys: "twixt Wigton and the town of Ayr"; with tartan and chief's arms in colour, and a map. Edinburgh, 1958. *Edin. P.; Inv. P.; Cai. C.; Ber. C.*

GENEALOGICAL chart of the family of Kennedy, 1100-1903. n.d. (*MS.*) *St.A. U.*

MS. notes and press cuttings on the family of Kennedy. n.d. *Edin. P.*

MAXWELL (Sir Herbert Eustace): A Scottish vendetta (Kennedy family). 1894. (Excerpt from the *Nineteenth Century*, 1894.) *Edin. P.*

MOONEY (John): Kennedys in Orkney and Shetland. (In *Proceedings Orkney Antiquarian Soc.*, v. 10, 1932, pp. 17-20, and v. 11, 1933, pp. 19-26.) *Ork. C.; Zet. C.; Edin. L.L.* (Repr. as pamphlet).

PITCAIRN (Robert): Historical and genealogical account of the principal families of the name of Kennedy. Edinburgh, 1830. *Inv. P.; St.A. U.; Ab. U.; Glas. U.; Edin. P.; Edin. S.; Glas. Mit.; Edin. L.L.; Edin. Ant.; Ayr P.*

Kennedy, Marquess of Ailsa

PEDIGREE of . . . Archibald Kennedy, Marquess of Ailsa . . . born 25th August, 1816. Edinburgh, 1849. *Edin. P.*

Kennedy of Auchtyfardle

GOURLAY (James): The Kennedys of Auchtyfardle, and other papers. n.p., 1936. *Dumf. C.; Edin. P.*

Kennedy, Earl of Cassillis

[COWAN (David)]: Historical account of the noble family of Kennedy, Marquess of Ailsa and Earl of Cassillis, with notices of some of the principal cadets thereof. Edinburgh, 1849. *Ayr P.; Glas. U.; Edin. P.; Edin. S.; Glas. Mit.; Edin. L.L.*

Kennedy, Earl of Cassillis, *see also* Cassillis, Earldom of

Kennedy of Dunure

TAYLER (Henrietta): The Seven sons of the provost. London, 1949. *S.C.L.; Banff C.; Ayr C.; Cai. C.; Per. C.; Fife C.; West L. C.; Inv. P.; Ayr P.; Dunb. C.; Ork. C.; Edin. U.; Mid. C.; Ab. P.; Glas. U.; Pai. P.; Edin. P.; Edin. S.; Glas. Mit.*

Ker

KERR (Robert), *comp.*: "Cunningham" Kers; Triorne, Crummock, Kersland, and Auchengree, Ayrshire. n.p., 1896. *Edin. P.*

REID (Christian Leopold): Pedigree of the family of Ker of
Cessford, Greenhead, and Prymsideloch, and later of Hose-
law, Roxburghshire, etc. Newcastle, 1914. *Haw. P.; Edin. P.;
Edin. L.L.*

Ker, Earl of Ancram
LAING (David), *ed.*: Correspondence of Sir Robert Kerr, 1st
Earl of Ancram, and his son, William, 3rd Earl of Lothian.
2 v. Edinburgh, 1875. (Bannatyne Club.) *S.C.L.; Haw. P.;
Glas. U.; Dund. P.; Edin. P.; Edin. S.; Glas. Mit.; Edin. L.L.*

Ker of Cessford, *see* **Ker**

Ker of Corbethouse
[STODART (Robert Riddle): Kerr of Gateshaw, Kerr of Corbet-
house and Moir of Otterburn]. n.p., n.d. (Repr. from
The Genealogist, 1st ser., vol. III.) *Glas. U.; Edin. L.L.*

Ker of Gateshaw, *see* **Ker** of Corbethouse

Ker of Kersland
[KERR (Robert Malcolm)]: Notices of the family of Kerr of
Kerrisland . . . London, 1880. *Glas. Mit.*

Ker, Lord, Duke, etc. of Roxburghe, *see* **Roxburghe,** Lord, Earl of,
Duke of

Ker of Yair
THE GENEALOGY of the families of Karr of Yair and of Kippie-
law. n.d. (*MSS.*) *Mid. C.*

Ker-Reid of Hoselaw
REID (Christian Leopold): Pedigree of the family of Ker of
Cessford . . . Ker-Reid of Hoselaw, Roxburghshire . . . of
Newcastle upon Tyne and London . . . Australia and U.S.A.
Newcastle, 1914. *Haw. P.; Edin. P.; Edin. L.L.*

Kerr in Dunipace
KERR (Wilfred Brenton): From Scotland to Huron: a history
of the Kerr family. Seaforth, Canada, 1949. *Glas. Mit.*

Kilmarnock, Earl of, *see* **Boyd,** Earl of Kilmarnock

Kilwinning, Lord
BALFOUR (Francis Walter): Case on behalf of Francis Walter
Balfour of Fernie . . . 1862. *Edin. L.L.*

— Supplemental case on behalf of the above . . . 1864. *Edin.
L.L.*

BRUCE (Alexander Hugh): Case on behalf of Alexander Hugh Bruce of Kennet, only son of the late Robert Bruce . . . *Edin. L.L.*

BRUCE (Robert): Case on behalf of Robert Bruce of Kennet, claiming to be Lord Balfour of Burley and Lord Kilwinning in the peerage of Scotland. [1860.] *Edin. L.L.*

— Supplemental case on behalf of the above . . . 1864. *Edin. L.L.*

FRASER (William): Case for the Earl of Eglinton. *Edin. L.L.*

— Remarks for the Earl of Eglinton. *Edin. L.L.*

MINUTES of evidence . . . 1861-64. *Edin. L.L.*

PROCEEDINGS . . . 1864. *Edin. L.L.*

King of Newmill

YOUNG (Robert): Memoir of the family of Kings of Newmill; ed. by W. Cramond. Banff, 1904. *Ab. P.; Edin. S.; Edin. Ant.*

Kinloch

[KINLOCH (W.)]: Papers relating to the families of Kinloch of that ilk and of Aberbothrie. n.p., n.d. *Edin. P.*

WAYNE (Eve T.): Kinloch of that ilk: a short account of the family. n.p., n.d. *Dund. P.; Dund. Q.; Edin. P.; Per. P.* (1922).

Kinloch of Gilmerton

[WOOD (John Philip)]: Pedigree of Kinloch of Gilmerton. (In his *Memorials of various families* . . . c. 1830.) (*MS.*) *Edin. P.*

Kinloss, Lord

AILESBURY (George Wm. Frederick Brudenell), *Marquis of*: Case of George William Frederick Brudenell, Marquis of Ailesbury in opposition to [claim of Richard Plantagenet . . .]. *Edin. L.L.*

BUCKINGHAM & CHANDOS (Richard Plantagenet), *3rd Duke of*: Case on behalf of Richard Plantagenet, Duke of Buckingham and Chandos, on his claim to Lord Kinloss in the peerage of Scotland. *Edin. L.L.*

— Supplemental case . . . *Edin. L.L.*

MINUTES of evidence . . . 1867. *Edin. L.L.*

see also **Bruce,** Baron Bruce of Kinloss

Kinnaird

[MACLAUCHLAN (John)]: The Silver wedding of Lord and Lady Kinnaird, and the coming of age of the Master of Kinnaird, August, 1900, with a sketch of the history of the Barons of Kinnaird. Dundee, 1900. *S.C.L.; Dund. P.; Per. C.; Edin. P.*

Kinnaird of Culbin

> MURRAY (Rev. James G.): The Kinnairds of Culbin. Inverness, [1938]. *S.C.L.; Dund. P.; Mor. C.*

Kirkaldy of Grange

> [GRANT (James)]: Memoirs and adventures of Sir William Kirkaldy of Grange. Edinburgh, 1849. *Glas. Mit.*

Kirkness

> SMITH (William): The Knights of Stove in Kirkness, Sandwick, Orkney. (In *Viking Society, Old-lore misc. of Orkney and Shetland*, v. 5, 1912, pp. 120-1.) *Ork. C.*

Kirko

> GRIERSON (Sir Philip J. Hamilton): The Kirkos of Glenesland, Bogric, Chapel and Sundaywell [Dunscore parish]. (From *Trans. Dumfries & Galloway Nat. Hist. & Antiquarian Soc.*, Jan. 1915). *Kirkcud. Bro.*

Kirkpatrick

> KIRKPATRICK (Alexander de Lapère): Chronicles of the Kirkpatrick family. London, 1897. *Dumf. C.; Ab. U.; Edin. L.L.*

Kirkpatrick of Capenoch

> GLADSTONE (John): The Kirkpatricks at Capenoch, 1727-1846. Dumfries, 1929. (From *Trans. Dumfriesshire & Galloway Natural History & Antiquarian Society*, 3rd ser. v. XV, 1928-29.) *Dumf. C.*

Kirkpatrick of Closeburn

> ANSWERS for Sir Thomas Kirkpatrick of Closeburn, to the petition of Hugh Blair of Dunrod, and Andrew Houston of Calderhall, his cedent, January 24, 1737. 1737. *Glas. Mit.*

> KIRKPATRICK (Charles): Records of the Closeburn Kirkpatricks. 1953. (*Typescript.*) *Dumf. C.; Edin. L.L.*

Knox

> CRAWFORD (William): Knox genealogy: descendants of William Knox and John Knox, the Reformer. Edinburgh, 1896. *Ab. P.; Dumf. C.; Sti. C.; St.A. U.; Edin. P.; Edin. S.; Glas. Mit.; Edin. L.L.; Edin. Ant.*

> ROGERS (Charles): Genealogical memoirs of John Knox and of the family of Knox. London, 1879. (Grampian Club, 16.) *Kil. P.; Dunf. P.; Inv. P.; Dumf. C.; Sti. P.; Ab. U.; Ab. P.; Dund. Q.; Glas. U.; Dund. P.; Edin. P.; Edin. S.; Glas. Mit.; Edin. L.L.; Edin. Ant.*

Knox of Ranfurly

BLAKE (Alice Elizabeth Blake), *Mrs. Warenne*: Memoirs of a vanished generation, 1813-1855. London, 1909. *Ren. C.*

Lamb

LAMB (Mabel), *ed.*: Some annals of the Lambs: a Border family. London, 1926. *Edin. P.*

Lamont

CLAN LAMONT JOURNAL, v. 1, 1912- . Hereford, 1912- . *Edin. P.* (v. 1-3, 1912-1925); *Edin. L.L.* (v. 1, 2).

CLAN LAMONT SOCIETY. Report of the first general meeting . . . 22nd February, 1897. Glasgow, 1897. *Glas. Mit.; Edin. L.L.* (+3rd Feb. 1899).

LAMONT (Augusta): Records and recollections of Sir James Lamont of Knockdow. [n.p., 1950.] *Arg. C.*

LAMONT (Sir Norman), *ed.*: An inventory of Lamont papers, 1231-1897. Edinburgh, 1914. (Scottish Record Soc., 54.) *S.C.L.; Dun. P.; Ab. P.; Glas. U.; Dund. P.; Arg. C.; Edin. P.; Edin. S.; Glas. Mit.*

LAMONT (Norman), *aft. Sir Norman*: Sketches of the history of the clan. [Glasgow,] 1899. *Edin. S.; Edin. L.L.*

LAMONT (William): The Lamont tartan: an address delivered to the Clan Lamont Society. Glasgow, 1910. *Glas. Mit.*

— The Lamont tartan, two papers addressed to the Clan Lamont Society. Glasgow, 1924. *Glas. Mit.*

McKECHNIE (Hector): The Lamont clan, 1235-1935: seven centuries of clan history from record evidence. Edinburgh, 1938. *S.C.L.; Arg. C.; Kil. P.; Edin. U.; St.A. U.; Ab. U.; Dun. P.; Kirkcud. C.; Edin. P.; Edin. S.; Glas. Mit.; Edin. L.L.; Edin. Ant.*

Lang

LANG (Patrick Sellar), *comp.*: The Langs of Selkirk. Melbourne, 1910. *Edin. P.; Edin. S.*

Lauder

YOUNG (James), *ed.*: Notes on historical references to the Scottish family of Lauder. Glasgow, 1884. *Dunf. P.; St.A. U.; Glas. U.; Edin. P.; Edin. S.; Glas. Mit.*

see also **Dick-Lauder**

Lauder of the Bass

LAWDER (C. A. B.): The Lawders of the Bass and their descendants. Belfast, 1914. *Edin. P.; Edin. S.*

Lauder of Hatton

FINDLAY (John Ritchie): Hatton House. Edinburgh, n.d. *Edin. S.*

Lauderdale, Earldom of

MAITLAND (Frederick Henry): Case of Major Frederick Henry Maitland . . . 1885. *Edin. L.L.*

MAITLAND (Sir James Ramsay Gibson): Case of Sir James Ramsay Gibson Maitland, Bt., [claiming titles] Earl of Lauderdale, Viscount of Lauderdale, Viscount Maitland, Lord Maitland of Thirlestane and Lord Thirlestane and Boltoun in the peerage of Scotland. 1885. *Edin. L.L.*

MINUTES of evidence, etc. 1885. *Edin. L.L.*

see also **Maitland,** Earl of Lauderdale

Laurie

LAURIE (Peter G.): Sir Peter Laurie. A family memoir. Brentwood, 1901. *St.A. U.; Edin. P.*

Laurin

[MACLAURIN (Daniel)]: History in memoriam of the Clan Laurin . . . to 1558. London, n.d. *Edin. S.*

Law of Lauriston

FAIRLEY (John A.): Lauriston Castle: the estate and its owners. Edinburgh, 1925. *Ab. P.; Glas. U.; Edin. U.; Edin. P.; Edin. S.; Glas. Mit.; Edin. L.L.*

WOOD (John Philip): Memoirs of the life of John Law of Lauriston . . . Edinburgh, 1824. *Glas. Mit.*

Lawrance

LAWRANCE (Robert Murdoch): A branch of the Aberdeenshire Lawrances. Aberdeen, 1925. *Ab. P.; Ab. U.; Edin. P.; Edin. S.; Glas. Mit.; Edin. L.L.*

— The Pedigree of the Aberdeenshire Lawrances. Aberdeen, 1912. *Ab. P.; Edin. S.; Edin. L.L.; Edin. Ant.*

Lay

LAY (Arthur Croall Hyde): Four generations in China, Japan and Korea. Edinburgh, 1952. *Lan. C.; Glas. Mit.*

Leatham, *see* **Letham**

94

Leckie

COOK (William B.): Lairds of Leckie. Stirling, 1906. (Repr. from *Stirling Sentinel*.) *Edin. P.*

LECKIE (R. G. E.): Leckie of that ilk. Vancouver, 1913. *Edin. L.L.*

Ledingham

[LEDINGHAM (Alex.)]: A historic Aberdeen family and its branches. Peterhead, 1924. *Ab. P.*

Leighton of Usan

LEIGHTON (Clarence F.): Memorials of the Leightons of Ulishaven (Usan), Angus, and other Scottish families of the name. A.D. 1260-1931. London, 1931. *Glas. Mit.* (Pt. 1, 1260-1518); *Edin. Ant.*

Leishman

LEISHMAN (James Fleming): Matthew Leishman of Govan . . . Paisley, 1921. *Glas. Mit.*

LEISHMAN (Matthew): [Letter books containing copies of his letters written between 1855 and 1874 with digest of letters and index.] 3 v. n.d. (*MSS.*) *Glas. Mit.*

WATSON (Charles Brodie Boog): Traditions and genealogies of some members of the families of Boog, Heron, Leishman, Ross, Watson. Perth, 1908. *Edin. P.; Edin. S.; St.A. U.; Edin. L.L.; Edin. Ant.*

Leith

MSS. notes and newspaper cuttings relating to the Grants, Leiths, MacKintoshes of Blervie. n.d. *Inv. P.*

Leith of Fyvie

STIRLING (Anna Maria D. W. Pickering), *Mrs. Stirling*: Fyvie Castle: its lairds and their times. London, 1928. *S.C.L.; Elg. P.; Mid. C.; Glas. Mit.; Ren. C.; Fife C.; Ab. C.; Banff C.; West L. C.; Fras. P.; Dunb. C.; Edin. U.*

Leith of Harthill

BICKLEY (Francis Lawrance): The Leiths of Harthill. London, 1937. *S.C.L.; Glas. U.; Ab. P.; Ab. C.; St.A. U.; Edin. P.; Glas. Mit.; Edin. Ant.*

Leith of Leith-Hall

LEITH-HAY (Henrietta) & LOCHHEAD (Marion): Trustie to the end: the story of the Leith Hall family. Edinburgh, 1957. *S.C.L.; Per. C.; Cai. C.; Edin. P.; Glas. Mit.*

Lendrum

WILKEN (J.): Extracts from "Ellon in bygone days": a lecture. n.d. (*Typescript.*) *Ab. P.*

Lennox, *see* **Gordon-Lennox**

Lennox, Duke of

DARNLEY (John Bligh), *Earl of*: Case of John, Earl of Darnley, . . . claiming the titles, honours, and dignities of Duke of Lennox, Earl of Darnley, Lord Aubigny, Torbolton and Dalkeith. [n.p., 18—.] *St.A. U.; Edin. L.L.*

Lennox, Earldom of

DENNISTOUN (James): Cartularium comitatus de Levenax. Edinburgh, 1833. (Maitland Club, 24.) *Glas. U.; Dund. P.; Cly. P.; Edin. P.; Edin. S.; Glas. Mit.; Edin. L.L.*

FRASER (Sir William): The Lennox. 2 v. Edinburgh, 1874. *S.C.L.; Dumb. P.; Cly. P.; Ayr P.; Edin. U.; Ab. U.; Glas. U.; Edin. P.; Edin. S.; Glas. Mit.; St.A. U.; Edin. L.L.; Edin. Ant.*

[HAMILTON (Robert)]: Case of Margaret Lennox of Woodhead, in relation to the title, honours and dignity of the ancient Earls of Lennox, with genealogical tree. Edinburgh, 1813. *Dumb. P.; Glas. U.; Glas. Mit.; Edin. L.L.*

NAPIER (Mark): History of the partition of the Lennox. Edinburgh, 1835. *Ab. P.; Cly. P.; Edin. U.; Gree. P.; Dund. Q.; Glas. U.; Pai. P.; Edin. P.; Edin. S.; Glas. Mit.; Edin. L.L.; Edin. Ant.*

— The Lannox of auld: an epistolary review of "The Lennox" by William Fraser. Edinburgh, 1880. *Cly. P.; Ayr P.; St.A. U.; Glas. U.; Edin. P.; Glas. Mit.; Edin. L.L.*

RIDDELL (John): Additional remarks upon the question of the Lennox or Rusky representation, and other topics, in answer to the author [i.e. M. Napier] of "History of the partition of the Lennox", etc. Edinburgh, 1835. *S.C.L.; St.A. U.; Glas. U.; Edin. P.; Edin. S.; Glas. Mit.; Edin. L.L.; Edin. Ant.*

RIDDELL (John): Tracts, legal and historical, etc. Edinburgh, 1835. *S.C.L.; Edin. P.; Edin. S.*

RIDDELL (John), & *others*: The Pedigree of Her Royal and Most Serene Highness the Duchess of Mantua . . . her descent from . . . the houses of . . . Lennox, Napier, etc. New ed. London, 1885. *Edin. P.; Edin. L.L.* (1879).

Lennox of Woodhead, *see* **Lennox,** Earldom of

Leslie

LAURUS Leslaeana explicata, sive clarior enumeratio personarum utriusque sexus cognominis Leslie, unacum affinibus, titulis, officiis, dominiis, gestisque celebrioribus breviter indicatis... Graecii, 1692. *St.A. U.*

LESLIE (Col. [Charles]) of Balquhain: Historical records of the family of Leslie, 1067-1869. 3 v. Edinburgh, 1869. *S.C.L.; Ab. C.; Ab. U.; Elg. P.; Ab. P.; Inv. P.; St.A. U.; Dund. Q.; Glas. U.; Edin. P.; Edin. S.; Glas. Mit.; Edin. L.L.; Edin. Ant.; Fife C.*

LESLIE (Percy C.): The Family of Leslie. (From the records compiled by Charles Leslie.) n.p., 1953. *Ab. U.*

Leslie of Balquhain

LESLIE (Col. Charles) of Balquhain: Pedigree of the family of Leslie of Balquhain . . . from 1067 to 1861. Bakewell, 1861. *Edin. P.; Glas. Mit.; Edin. L.L.*

Leslie, Earl of Leven

FRASER (Sir William): The Leven and Melville peerages. 1857. (*MSS.*) *Edin. L.L.*

— The Melvilles, Earls of Melville, and the Leslies, Earls of Leven. 3 v. Edinburgh, 1890. *S.C.L.; Kir. P.; Fife C.; Moth. P.; St.A. U.; Dund. P.; Edin. P.; Edin. S.; Glas. Mit.; Edin. L.L.*

Leslie of Pitcaple

DOCUMENTS relating to the family of Leslie of Pitcaple, 1692-1741. *Ab. P.*

Leslie of Powis

BURNETT (John George), *ed.*: Powis papers, 1507-1894. Aberdeen, 1951. (Third Spalding Club.) *Glas. Mit.*

Leslie of Tarbert

PIELOU (P. Leslie): The Leslies of Tarbert, co. Kerry, and their forebears. Dublin, 1935. *Glas. Mit.*

Leslie of Warthill, Wartle

PEDIGREE of William Leslie of Warthill, tracing direct descent from at least twelve distinct nationalities before the Norman Conquest, 1066. Aberdeen, n.d. *Edin. P.*

Letham

LEATHAM (Louis Salisbury): The Letham or Leatham family book of remembrance; the story of Robert Letham and his wife Janet Urquhart, with . . . data on their ancestry and descendants. Ann Arbor, Mich., 1955. *Inv. C.; Glas. Mit.*

Leven, Earl of, *see* **Leslie,** Earl of Leven

Leveson-Gower, Duke of Sutherland
> FRASER (Sir William): The Sutherland book. 3 v. Edinburgh, 1892. *Glas. U.; Edin. P.; Edin. S.; Glas. Mit.*

Light
> STEUART (M.): History of the family. n.d. (*MS.*) *Edin. S.*

Lightbody
> LIGHTBODY (William): Lightbody records, 1550-1930, Scotland and abroad. Farnham, 1932. *Glas. Mit.; Edin. L.L.*

Lindsay
> CLAN LINDSAY SOCIETY publications, Edinburgh. No. 1, 1901— *Dumf. C.* (nos. 1-18, 19)*; Glas. U.* (v. I-IV, nos. 17, 18 of v. V)*; Dund. P.* (v. I, nos. 1-4)*; Edin. P.; Glas. Mit.; Edin. L.L.* (1901-07).

> CRAWFORD (Alexander William Crawford Lindsay), *25th Earl of*: Lives of the Lindsays, or A memoir of the houses of Crawford and Balcarres. 3 v. 2nd ed. London, 1849. *S.C.L.; Arb. P.; Lan. C.; St.A. U.; Forf. P.; Dund. P.; Edin. Ant.*

> — 3 v. 3rd ed. London, 1958. *Fife C.; Ab. P.* (+1st ed. Wigan, 1840)*; Inv. P.; Ang. C.; Kir. P.; Gree. P.* (v. 1)*; Mont. P.; Bre. P.; Glas. U.; Dund. P.; Edin. P.; Edin. S.; Glas. Mit.; Edin. L.L.*

> FOLKARD (Henry T.): A Lindsay record: a handlist of books written by or relating to the Clan Lindsay . . . in the Wigan Free Public Library. Wigan, [1899]. *Ab. P.*

> JERVISE (Andrew): History and traditions of the land of the Lindsays in Angus and Mearns. Edinburgh, 1853. *Per. C.; Arb. P.; Ab. P.; Dund. Q.; Dund. P.; Edin. L.L.*

> — — 2nd ed. rev. by James Gammack. Edinburgh, 1882. *S.C.L.; Ang. C.; Gree. P.; Per. C.; Arb. P.; Ab. P.; Glas. U.; Pet. P.; Dund. P.; Edin. P.; Edin. S.; Glas. Mit.*

> LINZEE (John William): The Lindesie and Limesi families of Great Britain . . . 2 v. Boston, Mass., 1917. *Glas. Mit.; Edin. P.*

Lindsay, Earl of, *see* **Lindsay,** Lord Lindsay of the Byres

Lindsay of Almerieclose, Arbroath
> TURNBULL (G. O.): Our Lindsay forbears. n.d. (*Typescript.*) *Arb. P.*

Lindsay, Lord Lindsay of the Byres

BETHUNE (Sir John Trotter): Case on behalf of Sir John Trotter Bethune on his claim to the honours and dignities of Lord Lindsay of the Byres. Edinburgh, 1877. *Ab. P.; Gree. P.; Edin. L.L.*

— Minutes of evidence . . . the petition of Sir J. T. Bethune of Kilconquair . . . to declare him entitled to . . . Lord Lindsay of the Byres, and of Earl Lindsay and Lord Parbroath, and of Viscount of Garnock and Lord Kilbirny, Kingsburn & Drumry. Edinburgh, 1877. *Glas. Mit.; Gree. P.; Edin. L.L.*

EXTRACTS from the Minutes of Evidence given upon the Crawford Peerage claim, 1845-48. Edinburgh, 1877. *Edin. L.L.*

Lindsay, Earl of Crawford, *see* **Crawford,** Earldom of

Lindsay of Edzell, *see* **Lindsay** of Glenesk

Lindsay of Evelick

SINTON (Rev. Thomas): Lindsay of Evelick. (In his *Family and genealogical sketches.* 1911.) *Inv. P.; Edin. S.*

Lindsay of Glenesk

[MORTON (Peter Douglas)]: The Lindsay family of Glenesk and Edzell: an old Forfarshire family. (From *Arbroath Guide,* 2/12/1922-21/4/1923.) *Arb. P.*

Lindsay, Duke of Montrose, *see* **Montrose,** Duke of

Lindsay, Lord Spynie, *see* **Spynie,** Lord

Liston

McCALL (Hardy Bertram): Some old families: a contribution to the genealogical history of Scotland. Birmingham, 1890. *S.C.L.; Edin. P.; Edin. S.; Sel. P.; Edin. L.L.; Edin. Ant.*

Livingston

MS. notes and press cuttings on the family of Livingston. n.d. *Edin. P.*

Livingston of Callendar

LIVINGSTON (Edwin Brockholst): The Livingstons of Callendar, and their principal cadets. Edinburgh, 1920. *Falk. P.; Edin. U.; Ab. U.; Edin. P.; Edin. S.; Glas. Mit.; Edin. L.L.; Edin. Ant.*

LIVINGSTONE (Sir Thomas): Abstract of the written evidence . . . for proving Sir Thomas Livingstone of Ogilface and Bedlormie, nearest and lawful heir of James, 1st Earl of Calander. n.p, 1821. *Edin. P.; Edin. L.L.*

Livingston of Dunipace

> GIBSON (John C.): Lands and lairds of Dunipace. Stirling, 1903. *Edin. P.; Edin. S.; Glas. Mit.*

Livingston of Lismore

> THE BACHUL or pastoral staff of St. Malouaig . . . n.p., n.d. (*MS.*) *Edin. P.*

Livingston of Livingston Manor

> LIVINGSTON (Edwin Brockholst): The Livingstons of Livingston Manor. New York, 1910. *Edin. P.*

Loch

> LOCH (Gordon), *aft. Percy Gordon Dalyell*: The Family of Loch. Edinburgh, 1934. *Pee. P.; Edin. U.; St.A. U.; Edin. P.; Edin. S.; Glas. Mit.; Edin. L.L.; Edin. Ant.*

Lochhead

> LOCHHEAD (John): A reach of the river: a family chronicle, 1880-1954. Gillingham, Dorset, 1955. *Pai. P.; Edin. P.*

Lockhart

> LOCKHART (Ninian) & *Sons, Ltd.*: Textile manufacturers, Linktown works, Kirkcaldy, Scotland, 1797-1947. [Kirkcaldy, 1947.] *Kir. P.*

Lockhart of Carnwath

> DICKSON (David): David Dickson, son of William Dickson of Kilbucho . . . appellant . . . George Lockhart, respondent. Edinburgh, 1748. *Edin. P.; Edin. S.*

Logan

> LOGAN-HOME (George John Ninian): History of the Logan family. Edinburgh, 1934. *Dund. P.; Ber. C.; St.A. U.; Edin. P.; Edin. S.; Glas. Mit.; Edin. L.L.*

> LOGAN (William): History of the Logans, and clan songs. 1922. *Glas. Mit.*

Logan of Knockshinnoch

> H. (J. M.): Logans of Knockshinnoch. Edinburgh, 1885. *Glas. U.; Edin. P.; Edin. S.; Glas. Mit.*

Logie

> FORRESTER (David Marshall): Logiealmond. Edinburgh, 1944. *S.C.L.*

Lorimer

STODART (Robert Riddle): Genealogy of the Lorimers of Scotland. n.p., n.d. *Ab. U.; Edin. L.L.*

Lovat, Lord Fraser of Lovat

FRASER (Rev. A. G.): Case of Rev. A. G. Fraser . . . 1845. *Edin. L.L.*

FRASER (John): Case of John Fraser of Carnarvon . . . 1885. *Edin. L.L.*

FRASER (Simon), *11th Lord Fraser of Lovat*: Memorials for Simon, Lord Fraser of Lovat, and other documents bearing on his claim to the title. [Edinburgh,] 1729. *Inv. P.; Edin. P.; Edin. S.; Edin. Ant.*

FRASER (Thomas Alexander): Case of Thomas Alexander Fraser of Lovat . . . *Edin. L.L.*

— Additional case . . . 1854. *Edin. L.L.*

THE LOVAT peerage and estates: a short history of the case, with evidence in the support of the claim of John Fraser. Edinburgh, 1885. *Inv. P.*

LOVAT (Simon Fraser), *Lord*: Case of Simon, Lord Lovat, in opposition thereto. 1885. *Edin. L.L.*

MINUTES of evidence . . . 1826 and 1855. *Edin. L.L.*

MINUTES of evidence . . . 1856-57. *Edin. L.L.*

MINUTES of evidence and other papers. 1885. *Edin. L.L.*

REPORT of evidence. 1826. *Edin. L.L.*

Lumsden

LUMSDEN (H. W.): Memorials of the families of Lumsdaine, Lumisden, or Lumsden. Edinburgh, 1889. *Ab. P.; St.A. U.; Glas. U.; Edin. P.; Edin. S.*

Lyle of Renfrewshire

LYLE (William): "De insula": or, the Lyles of Renfrewshire. Glasgow, 1936. *Edin. U.; Glas. Mit.; Edin. Ant.*

Lyon

ROSS (Andrew): The Lyons of Cossins and Wester Ogil, cadets of Glamis. Edinburgh, 1901. *Ab. P.; St.A. U.; Forf. P.; Edin. P.; Edin. S.; Glas. Mit.; Edin. L.L.*

Lyon of Glamis

STIRTON (John): Glamis: a parish history. Forfar, 1913. *S.C.L.*

Lyon of Ogil

LYON (William): Lyon of Ogil. London, c. 1869. *Edin. P.*

Lyon, Earl of Strathmore

[ROSS (Andrew), *Ross Herald*]: Lyon, Earl of Strathmore & Kinghorne. [1911.] (From the MS. from the *Scots Peerage*, vol. VIII, 1911.) *Forf. P.*

see also **Bowes(-Lyon),** Earl of Strathmore

Macalister, *see* **Macdonald**

Macaulay

MACAULAY (   ): Memoirs of the clan "Aulay" . . . Carmarthen, 1881. *Edin. S.*

WELLES (Edward Randolph): Ardincaple Castle and its lairds. Glasgow, 1930. *Dumb. P.; Edin. P.; Edin. S.; Glas. Mit.*

Macaulay of Lewis

THOMAS (Frederick W. L.): Traditions of the Macaulays of Lewis. Edinburgh, 1880. (From *Proceedings Soc. Antiquaries,* n.s. v. II, 1880.) *Edin. P.; Glas. Mit.*

Macbean

EXTRACTS from Birth, Marriage and Death records [for Dores, Inverness, Petty, Rothimurcus] . . . relating to the name Macbean. (Entries for Rothimurcus parish relate to Mackintosh, Macbean and Shaw.) [c. 1604-1800.] (*MSS.*) *Inv. P.*

Macbeth

MACBETH (John): Macbeth: King, Queen and clan. Edinburgh, 1921. *Arb. P.; Ab. P.; Inv. P.; Kil. P.; Edin. U.; Edin. P.; Glas. Mit.*

MACBETH (Malcolm): An abstract of a genealogical collection. Vol. 1. St. Louis, Mo., 1907. *Edin. P.*

see also **Beaton** of Islay

McCall

MCCALL (Hardy Bertram): Memoirs of my ancestors. Birmingham, 1884. *Ab. U.; Mid. C.; Edin. P.; Edin. S.; Glas. Mit.; Edin. L.L.*

— Some old families: a contribution to the genealogical history of Scotland. Birmingham, 1890. *S.C.L.; Edin. P.; Edin. S.; Sel. P.; Edin. L.L.; Edin. Ant.*

MacClellan, *see* **MacLellan**

MacColl

MacColl Society, Glasgow. Cuairtear chloinn cholla: journal of the MacColl Society, v. 1- 1932- . *Edin. P.; Glas. Mit.*

McCombie

Fenn (Mrs. E. Mc.): The McCombies of Dalkilry. 1953. *Banff C.; Edin. L.L.*

Smith (William McCombie): Memoir of the family of McCombie. Edinburgh, 1887. *Ab. P.; Inv. P.; Ab. U.; St.A. U.; Edin. P.; Edin. S.; Glas. Mit.*

— Memoir of the families of McCombie and Thoms. New ed. Edinburgh, 1890. *Dunf. P.; Ab. P.; Ab. U.; Nai. C.; Zet. C.; Dunb. P.; Ab. C.; St.A. U.; Dund. Q.; Glas. U.; Dund. P.; Pai. P.; Edin. P.;Edin. S.; Glas. Mit.; Edin. L.L.; Edin. Ant.*

MacConnel

Macconnel (David Connor): Facts and traditions collected for a family record [of the MacConnels]. Edinburgh, 1861. *Edin. P.*

McConnel (Ernest Whigham Jardine): James McConnel (of Carsriggan), his forbears and descendants. 1931. *Dumf. C.*

McCormick

Thomson (David Couper), *comp.*: [Genealogical chart of] McCulloch, Turner, McCormick and Russell. Dundee, 1943. *Edin. L.L.; Edin. Ant.*

McCorquodale

Macintyre (Peter): The Barons of Phantilands, or the Mac-Corquodales and their story. n.p., n.d. *Edin. S.*

Rose (David Murray): The McCorquodales of Phantilans. (Repr. from *Oban Times*, 17 Feb. 1900.) *Ab. U.; Edin. Ant.*

MacCrimmon

Macleod (Fred. T.): The MacCrimmons of Skye: hereditary pipers to the Macleods of Dunvegan. Edinburgh, 1933. *S.C.L.; Mid. C.; Ross C.; Inv. P.; Lan. C.; Ab. U.; St.A. U.; Ab. P.; Falk. P.; Edin. P.; Edin. S.; Glas. Mit.; Edin. L.L.; Edin. Ant.*

Poulter (George Collingwood Brownlow): A history of the Clan Mac Crimmon. 2 pts. n.p., 1938-39. *Edin. Ant.*

Poulter (George Collingwood Brownlow) & Fisher (Charles P.): The MacCrimmon family ... from 1500-1936. Camberley, 1936. *Ab. U.; Edin. P.; Edin. S.; Glas. Mit.; Edin. Ant.*

McCuiston

McQuiston (Leona Bean), *comp.*: The McQuiston, McCuiston and McQuesten families, 1620-1937. Louisville, Ky., 1937. *Glas. Mit.; Edin. L.L.*

McCulloch

Thomson (David Couper), *comp.*: [Genealogical chart of] McCulloch, Turner, McCormick and Russell. Dundee, 1943. *Edin. L.L.; Edin. Ant.*

McCulloch of Glastullich

[Rose (David Murray)]: The MacCullochs of Glastullich. (Repr. from the *North Star*, Dec. 16, 1897.) *Edin. S.*

Macdonald

Barron (Evan Macleod): Inverness and the Macdonalds. Inverness, 1930. *Inv. P.; Ab. U.; Ab. P.; Edin. P.; Edin. S.; Glas. Mit.*

Bradley (Edward): Argyll's Highlands; or, MacCailein Mor and the Lords of Lorne; with traditionary tales and legends of . . . the Campbells and Macdonalds . . . Ed. by John Mackay. Glasgow, 1902. *Glas. Mit.*

Buchanan (Hector Macdonald): Historical and genealogical account . . . *see* Historical and genealogical account . . .

Bulloch (John Malcolm): The Macdonald ancestors of Rudyard Kipling and Stanley Baldwin. (From the *Glasgow Herald*, 5th July, 1923.) Glasgow, 1923. *St.A. U.*

Clan Donald Journal, Glasgow. Vol. 1-3[4], 1896-1898. *Glas. Mit.*

Clan Donald Roll of Honour, 1914-1918, with a short history of the clan. Glasgow, 1931. *Ayr P.; Glas. U.; Edin. P.; Glas. Mit.; Edin. S.*

Fear Raonuillich, *pseud.*: Letters to the editor of the Inverness Journal; by "Fear Raonuillich" and "Also a Fear Raonuillich", chiefly relating to the title of Macranald. 1817, 1818. Edinburgh, 1818. *St.A. U.; Ab. U.; Edin. U.* (+2nd ser. 1819)*; Edin. L.L.*

Grant (Isabel Frances): The Clan Donald: a Gaelic principality as a focus of Gaelic culture. [Macdonalds, Macdonells, Macalisters and their septs.] Edinburgh, 1952. *Sti. P.; Dund. P.; Inv. P.; Cai. C.; Lan. C.; Ayr P.; Per. C.; Fife C.; Cly P.; Inv. C.; Edin. U.; Ab. P.; Kirkcud. C.; Pai. P.; Arg. C.; Edin. P.; Edin. S.; Glas. Mit.; Ber. C.; Edin. L.L.; Edin. Ant.*

HISTORICAL and genealogical account of the clan or family of Macdonald, from Somerled . . . to the present period; more particularly as relating to . . . the Clan Ranald. Edinburgh, 1819. *S.C.L.; Inv. P.; Edin. L.L.*

[MACDONALD (A. S.)]: The Clan Donald: its battles and its chiefs. Glasgow, n.d. *Edin. P.*

MACDONALD (Angus J.) & MACDONALD (Archibald M.): The Clan Donald. 3 v. Inverness, 1896-1904. *S.C.L.; Inv. P.; Cly. P.; St.A. U.; Ab. U.; Camp. P.; Glas. U.; Edin. P.; Edin. L.L.; Edin. Ant.; Edin. S.; Glas. Mit.*

MACDONALD (Sir Archibald): [Estate account book, 1813-1818]. 1818. *(MS.) Edin. P.*

MACDONALD (Edith): Annals of the Macdonald family. London, 1928. *S.C.L.*

[MACDONALD (Hugh)]: History of the Macdonalds. [c. 1630.] (In *Highland papers*, ed. by J. R. N. Macphail, v. I. Scottish History Society, 2nd ser. v. V.) *S.C.L.; Arg. C.*

MACDONALD (Keith Norman): Macdonald bards from mediaeval times. Edinburgh, 1900. *Ab. U.*

MACDONALD (W. H.), *ed.*: Yearbook of the Macdonald Society. Glasgow, 1899. *Glas. Mit.*

MACINTYRE (James): Castles of Skye: stronghold and house of clan Donald. Inverness, 1938. *Inv. P.; Edin. P.; Edin. S.; Glas. Mit.*

Macdonald of Clanranald

MACDONALD (Angus R.): The Chief of Clan Donald—who is he? Note, in protest, against the finding in Clan Donald; ed. by A. Macdonald, minister of Killearnan, and A. Macdonald, minister of Kiltarlity. London, 1905. *Ab. U.; Glas. Mit.*

MACDONALD (Charles): Moidart, or Among the Clanranalds. Oban, 1889. *Inv. P.; Inv. C.; Ab. U.; Edin. P.; Edin. S.; Glas. Mit.; Edin. L.L.*

MACKENZIE (Alexander): History of the MacDonalds of Clanranald. Inverness, 1881. *Inv. P.; Nai. C.; Inv. C.; Ab. U.; Glas. U.; Edin. P.; Edin. S.; Camp. P.; Edin. L.L.*

Macdonald of Glengarry

MACKENZIE (Alexander): History and genealogy of the Macdonalds of Glengarry. Inverness, 1881. *Inv. P.; St.A. U.; Ab. U.; Glas. U.; Edin. P.; Edin. S.*

[RIDDELL (John)]: Vindication of the "Clanronald of Glengarry" against the attacks made upon them in the Inverness Journal and some recent printed performances. With remarks as to the descent of the family who style themselves "of Clanronald". Edinburgh, 1821. *Inv. P.; Inv. C.; St.A. U.; Edin. P.; Glas. Mit.; Edin. L.L.; Edin. Ant.*

Macdonald of Isla

FRASER-MACKINTOSH (Charles): The Last Macdonalds of Isla. Glasgow, 1895. *Inv. P.; Nai. C.; Edin. U.; Ab. U.; Arg. C.; Edin. P.; Glas. Mit.; Camp. P.*

Macdonald of the Isles

INVERNESS COURIER: Extracts from the Inverness Courier relative to the ancient Kingdom of the Isles. London, 1822. *St.A. U.; Glas. Mit.; Edin. L.L.*

MACDONALD (Alice Bosville): A romantic chapter in family history. London, 1911. *Ab. U.; Edin. P.; Edin. S.*

MACDONALD (Alice E. M.), *Lady Macdonald of the Isles*: The House of the Isles. [Edinburgh, 1925.] *Cai. C.; St.A. U.; Edin. S.; Edin. P.; Edin. L.L.; Edin. Ant.*

MACKENZIE (Alexander): History of the Macdonalds and Lords of the Isles. Inverness, 1881. *Inv. P.; Ab. U.; Dund. Q.; Glas. U.; Edin. P.; Edin. S.; Glas. Mit.; Edin. L.L.*

STIRLING (Anna Maria D. W. Pickering), *Mrs. Stirling*: Macdonald of the Isles. London, 1913. *Kil. P.; Clack. C.; Cai. C.; Inv. P.; Per. C.; Ab. U.; Glas. U.; Edin. P.; Edin. S.; Glas. Mit.; Camp. P.*

Macdonald of Keppoch

MACDONALD (Angus), *M.D., of Taunton*: A family memoir of the Macdonalds of Keppoch . . . written from 1800 to 1820 . . . Ed. by C. R. Markham . . . with some notes by C. E. Stuart, Comte d'Albanie. London, 1885. *St.A. U.; Ab. U.; Edin. P.; Edin. S.; Glas. Mit.*

MACDONALD (John Paul): A Keppoch song . . . the origin and history of the family . . . etc. [Montrose], 1815. *Ab. P.; Glas. U.; Edin. P.; Edin. S.; Glas. Mit.*

Macdonald of Sanda

GENEALOGICAL and historical account of the family of Macdonald of Sanda. London, 1825. *S.C.L.; Camp. P.; Edin. P.* (n.d.)*; Edin. S.; Glas. Mit.* (n.d.)*; Inv. P.*

Macdonell

HILL (George): Historical account of the Macdonells of Antrim, including notices of some other septs, Irish and Scottish. Belfast, 1873. *Inv. P.; Edin. P.; Edin. S.; Glas. Mit.; Camp. P.; Edin. L.L.*

see also **Macdonald**

Macdonell of Glengarry

KELLY (Bernard W.): Fate of Glengarry, or the Expatriation of the Macdonells: an historico-biographical study. Dublin, 1905. *Glas. Mit.*

MACDONELL (Alexander Ranaldson) *v.* MACDONALD (Ranald George): Information for A. R. M. of Glengarry . . . pursuer against R. G. Macdonald of Casteltirrim . . . defender. (*And* Defences for R. G. M.; Information for R. G. M.) 3 pts. (in 1). [Edinburgh, 1824.] *Edin. U.*

Macdonell of Keppoch

MACDONELL (Josephine M.): An historical record of the branch of "Clann Domhnuill" called the MacDonells of Keppoch and Gargavach. Glasgow, 1931. *Edin. U.; Edin. P.; Glas. Mit.*

MacDougall

MACDOUGALL (D.): MacDougall genealogy. Known descendants in the U.S. of America of Robert McDougall of Western Scotland; 1748-1832. n.d. (*Typescript.*) *Inv. P.*

MacDougall of Lorn

THE GALLEY of Lorn. Historical, traditional, and other records of the Chlann Dughaill. 7 pts. (in 1). Sheffield, 1909. *S.C.L.; Edin. L.L.*

MacDougall of Makerston

FRASER (Sir William): Genealogical table of the families of Brisbane of Bishoptoun & Brisbane; Makdougall of Makerstoun; and Hay of Alderstoun, etc. [Chart.] Edinburgh, 1840. (*Photocopy.*) *S.C.L.*

Macduff

[RAVENSCROFT ( )]. Memorials of the antient and illustrious family of Macduff . . . Aberdeen, 1848. *Glas. Mit.*

McEachran of Killelan

MCKERRAL (Andrew): Two old Kintyre lawsuits, with some notes on . . . McShennags of Lephenstrath; Omeys of Kilcolmkill; and McEachrans of Killelan. n.p., 1941. *Glas. Mit.*

Macewan

MACEWEN (R. S. T.): The Clan Ewan: some records of its history. Glasgow, 1904. *Ab. P.; Inv. P.; St.A. U.; Ab. U.; Edin. P.; Glas. Mit.*

Macfarlane

LITTLE (C. M.), *Mrs. Little*: History of the Clan MacFarlane, (Macfarlane), Macfarlan, Macfarland, Macfarlin. Tottenville, N.Y., 1893. *St.A. U.; Ab. U.; Edin. S.; Edin. Ant.*

MACFARLANE (James): History of Clan MacFarlane. Glasgow, 1922. *S.C.L.; Dumb. P.; Inv. P.; Ayr P.; Ab. U.; Edin. S.; Edin. P.; Glas. Mit.; Edin. L.L.*

MACFARLANE (W. B.): The Church of Clan Macfarlane. (From *Trans. Scottish Eccles. Soc.*, v. V, pt. 2, 1917-18.) *S.C.L.; Edin. P.*

WINCHESTER (H. S.): Traditions of Arrochar and Tarbet and the Macfarlanes. n.p., n.d. *Edin. P.; Glas. Mit.* ([1920]).

Macgillivray of Dunmaglas

[LETTERS and documents relating to the Macgillivrays of Dunmaglass. 1857.] *Inv. P.*

MacGregor

CLAN GREGOR. Edinburgh, 1825. *Edin. L.L.*

CLAN GREGOR SOCIETY: Prospectus of a plan for the formation of the Clan Gregor Society. Edinburgh, 1823. *Inv. P.; Edin. P.*

GREGORY (Donald), *ed.*: Historical notices of the Clan Gregor. Pt. 1: Earlier history of the Clan Gregor. Edinburgh, 1831. (*No more published.*) *Ab. P.; Inv. P.; Ab. U.; Glas. Mit.*

HOWLETT (Hamilton): Highland constable: life and times of Rob Roy MacGregor. [With genealogical chart.] Edinburgh, 1950. *S.C.L.; Inv. P.*

KERMACK (William Ramsay): The Clan MacGregor (Clan Gregor): the nameless clan. Edinburgh, 1953. *Cai. C.; Ber. C.; Inv. P.; Clack. C.; Inv. C.; Rox. C.; Dunb. C.; Edin. U.; Lan. C.; Dunf. P.; Ab. P.; Pai. P.; Arg. C.; Edin. S.; Glas. Mit.; Edin. P.; Ren. C.; Per. C.; Dund. P.; Edin. L.L.; Edin. Ant.*

MACGREGOR (Amelia Georgina Murray): History of the Clan Gregor, from public records and private collections. 2 v. Edinburgh, 1898-1901. *S.C.L.; Ab. P.; Inv. P.; Dun. P.; Sti. P.; Ab. U.; St.A. U.* (v. 1)*; Edin. P.; Edin. S.; Glas. Mit.; Edin. Ant.*

MacGregor (John): The Macgregors of Dundurn and Balnacoull, and Innergeldie. n.p., n.d. *Edin. P.; Edin. L.L.*

MacGregor, Grierson and Grier: chart of pedigrees. London, [c. 1882]. *Edin. S.*

Macleay (Kenneth), *the elder*: Historical memoirs of Rob Roy and the Clan Macgregor. Glasgow, 1819. *S.C.L.* (Edin., 1881)*; Ab. P.; Ab. U.* (1881)*; Glas. U.* (1818, 1840)*; Pai. P.; Edin. P.* (1818, 1881)*; Edin. S.* (1818, 1881)*; Glas. Mit.* (+1881).

Millar (Alex. Hastie): Gregarach: the strange adventures of Rob Roy's sons. London, n.d. *Clack. C.; Edin. S.; Glas. Mit.; Edin. P.*

Scott (Sir Walter): The Highland clans, with a particular account of Rob Roy and the Macgregors. Edinburgh, 1856. *Ab. P.; Edin. P.; Glas. Mit.*

— . . . History of the Clan MacGregor, with details of Rob Roy. Glasgow, 1893. *Camp. P.; Per. C.; Arg. C.; Glas. Mit.; Gala. P.*

Stewart (D.), *M.A.*: The Life . . . of Rob Roy Macgregor, with an historical sketch of the celebrated Clan Macgregor. Newcastle upon Tyne, n.d. *Dund. P.*

MacGregor of Rannoch

Cameron (R. W. D.): MacGregors of Rannoch. Inverness, 1888. (Repr. from *Celtic Magazine*, v. 13, 1888.) *Edin. S.*

McGrigor

McGrigor (G. D.): The Family of McGrigor. 1941. (*Typescript.*) *Edin. L.L.*

MacGrouther

MacGregor (John): The McGrouthers of Meigor in Glenartney. Exeter, [1919]. (Repr. from *Genealogist*, n.s. v. XXXV.) *Ab. U.; Edin. P.; Edin. S.; Edin. Ant.*

MacHardy

Arms, crest and tartan, with a short account of the origin of the name MacHardy. London, [1894]. *Edin. L.L.*

Macintyre

Macintyre (Duncan): The MacIntyres of Glencoe and Camusna-h-erie. Edinburgh, 1901. *Ross C.; Edin. P.; Edin. S.*

MacIver

[CAMPBELL (Peter Colin)]: Account of the Clan Iver. Aberdeen, 1873. *Ab. P.; St.A. U.* (c. 1878)*; Ham. P.* (Dingwall, [1910])*; Ross C.* (Dingwall, 1925)*; Edin. P.* ([1878])*; Edin. S.* (+[1878])*; Glas. Mit.; Edin. L.L.; Ab. U.*

Mack

McCRIE (James): History of the Macks of Ninewar, near Duns, 1752-1800. Lennoxtown, 1886. *Edin. P.*

Mackay

CLAN MACKAY SOCIETY: War Memorial volume: containing a list of those bearing the name MacKay who were killed or died in the Great War, 1914-18, and a list of those upon whom honours were conferred. Glasgow, 1924. *Inv. P.; Glas. Mit.*

GENEALOGY of the Arichliney Mackays for five centuries. n.p., n.d. *Inv. P.*

MacDOUGALL (Margaret Oliphant): Clan Mackay: a Celtic resistance to feudal superiority. Edinburgh, 1953. *Inv. P.; Inv. C.; Dunb. C.; Ayr P.; Edin. U.; Cly. P.; Lan. C.; Dund. P.; Dunf. P.; Ab. P.; Ren. C.; Per. C.; Pai. P.; Arg. C.; Edin. P.; Edin. S.; Glas. Mit.; Cai. C.; Ber. C.; Edin. L.L.; Edin. Ant.*

MACKAY (Alexander), *comp.*: Black Castle MS.: Historical and genealogical sketch of the noble family of Reay with an account of the different branches. 1832. (*Typescript.*) *Edin. S.*

MACKAY (Angus): The Book of Mackay. Edinburgh, 1906. *Ab. P.; Inv. P.; Cai. C.; Suth. C.; Ab. U.; St.A. U.; Glas. U.; Edin. P.; Edin. S.; Glas. Mit.; Edin. L.L.; Edin. Ant.*

[MACKAY (David N.), *comp.*]: [History of the Clan Mackay Society . . .]. Constitution, list of office-bearers and members and Council's and Treasurer's annual reports for session, 1910-11. Glasgow, [1912]. *Glas. Mit.; Edin. P.*

MACKAY (George): Mackay regiments. 1940. *Per. C.*

— A Scots Brigade flag for Amsterdam in 1930, being a narrative of some happenings, old and new, concerning the Clan Mackay. Stirling, 1931. *Per. C.; Edin. U.; St.A. U.; Edin. P.* (n.d.)*; Glas. Mit.; Edin. Ant.*

— Two unpublished letters from James Graham to Sir Donald Mackay of Far. Edinburgh, 1941. (Repr. from the *Juridical Review.*) *Per. C.*

110

MACKAY (Robert): History of the house and clan of Mackay. Edinburgh, 1829. *S.C.L.; Ab. P.; Inv. P.; Inv. C.; St.A. U.; Ab. U.; Glas. U.; Edin. P.; Edin. S.; Glas. Mit.; Edin. L.L.; Edin. Ant.*

MACKAY (William): Origin of the Clan Mackay: a paper read before the Clan Mackay Society. Inverness, 1890. *Inv. P.; Ab. U.*

Mackay of Achmonie

MACKAY (William): The Men from whom we have come: a short history of the Mackays of Achmonie. Inverness, 1925. *Inv. P.; Edin. P.*

Mackay of Bighouse

WIMBERLEY (Douglas), *ed.*: Selections from some family papers of the Mackays of Bighouse. Inverness, [1896-99]. *Ab. P.; Ab. U.; Edin. P.; Glas. U.*

MacKean

BUCHANAN (Roberdeau): Genealogy of the family of MacKean of Pennsylvania. Lancaster, Pa. 1890. *Edin. L.L.*

McKEAN (Frederick George): McKean historical notes, being quotations from historical & other records relating chiefly to the MacIain-Macdonalds, many calling themselves McCain, McCane, McEan, MacIan etc. Washington, 1906. *Glas. U.; Edin. U.*

McKee

McKEE (Raymond Walter): The Book of McKee. Dublin, 1959. *Edin. L.L.*

Mackenzie

DUNLOP (Jean): The Clan MacKenzie: independence in the North. Edinburgh, 1953. *Inv. P.; Inv. C.; Rox. C.; Dunb. C.; Edin. U.; Lan. C.; St.A. U.; Ab. P.; Ren. C.; Per. C.; Dund. P.; Arg. C.; Edin. S.; Glas. Mit.; Edin. P.; Cai. C.; Ber. C.; Edin. L.L.; Edin. Ant.*

[M'KENZIE (John) of Applecross]: Genealogie of the Mackenzie family, preseeding ye year 1661. Wreatin in 1669 by a Persone of Qualitie. Ed. . . . by J. W. Mackenzie. Edinburgh, 1829. *Ayr P.; Cai. C.; Ab. U.; Glas. Mit.; Edin. L.L.; Edin. Ant.*

— — Dingwall, 1843. *Stor. P.; Ab. U.; Edin. S.; Edin. P.; Glas. Mit.; Edin. L.L.*

— — Also in *Highland Papers*, ed. by J. R. N. Macphail, v. II. (Scottish Hist. Soc., 2nd ser. v. XII.) *S.C.L.*

MACKENZIE (A. Donald): Some notes. n.p., 1915. *Ab. U.*

MACKENZIE (Alexander): The Family of Lochend; abdg. from *History and genealogies of the Clan Mackenzie.* [Inverness, 1879.] *Edin. P.*

MACKENZIE (Alexander): History of the Clan Mackenzie, with genealogies of the principal families of that name. Inverness, 1879. *Cai. C.; Inv. P.; Nai. C.; Ab. U.; Glas. U.; Edin. P.; Edin. S.; Glas. Mit.; Edin. L.L.; Edin. Ant.*

—— 1894. *Sti. P.; Edin. U.; Ab. U.; St.A. U.; Ab. P.; Edin. P.; Dund. Q.; Glas. U.; Glas. Mit.; Edin. L.L.; Edin. Ant.*

MACKENZIE (Alexander): The Reputed Fitzgerald origin of the Mackenzies. Inverness, 1892. *Inv. P.; Ab. U.*

MACKENZIE (Sir Alex. Muir): Memoirs of Delvine; with notes on the clan Mackenzie. n.p., 1901. *(Typescript.) Edin. P.; Edin. S.*

MACKENZIE (Alex. W.), *ed.*: Heraldry of the Clan Mackenzie. Columbus, Ohio, 1907. *Edin. P.*

MACKENZIE (G.): History of the Mackenzies. n.d. *(MS.) Glas. Mit.*

MACKENZIE (George): Letter written by Colonel George Mackenzie with a short account of his descendants by Alex. W. Mackenzie. Columbus, Ohio, 1905. *Edin. P.*

MACKENZIE (Hector): History of the Mackenzies, written in 1710. *(MS.) Glas. Mit.*

MACKENZIE (James D.): Genealogies of the Clan Mackenzie. Edinburgh, 1879. *Inv. P.* (+2/1894)*; Ab. U.; Edin. P.; Edin. L.L.*

MACKENZIE genealogy. n.d. *(MS.) Edin. P.*

MACKENZIE MSS. [History of Clan Mackenzie from 1260 A.D. to c. 1633 A.D.] n.d. *(MS.) Glas. Mit.*

[MACRAE (John)]: The Brief genealogical historical account of the origin, rise and growth of the family sirname of Mackenzie . . . to 1678. n.p., n.d. *(MS.) Edin. P.*

Mackenzie of Applecross

[HOLLOWAY (Edward)]: Clan Mackenzie—Mackenzies of Applecross—descendants of Roderick Roy. [New York, n.d.] *(Not pub.) Edin. L.L.*

Mackenzie of Ballone

MACKENZIE (Hector Hugh): The Mackenzies of Ballone (incl. an account of the Tolmies of Uiginish, Skye). Inverness, 1941. *S.C.L.; Inv. P.; Ross C.; Inv. C.; Ab. U.; St.A. U.; Ab. P.; Edin. P.; Edin. S.; Glas. Mit.; Edin. L.L.*

Mackenzie, Earl of Cromartie

FRASER (Sir William): The Earls of Cromartie: their kindred, country and correspondence. 2 v. Edinburgh, 1876. *S.C.L.; Inv. P.; Ab. U.; St.A. U.; Glas. U.; Edin. P.; Edin. S.; Glas. Mit.; Edin. L.L.; Edin. Ant.*

MEMOIRS of the lives and families of the Lords Kilmarnock, Cromartie and Balmerino. London, 1746. *Ayr P.*

Mackenzie of Dailuaine

MACKENZIE (Alexander): Ancestry of Thomas Mackenzie of Dailuaine. Inverness, 1896. *Nai. C.; Edin. P.*

Mackenzie of Dolphinton

MACKENZIE (Alice Ann), *comp.*: Dolphinton. n.p., 1888. *Edin. L.L.*

Mackenzie of Gairloch

BOSWELL (James): Answers for Hector Mackenzie, younger, of Gairloch and Roderick Mackenzie of Redcastle, his tutor . . . to the petition of Sir Alexander Mackenzie of Gairloch, Bt. Jan. 8, 1768. *Edin. P.*

Mackenzie of Kilcoy, *see* **Buchan,** Earldom of

Mackenzie of Redcastle

KETTLE (Rosa Mackenzie), [*i.e. Mary Rosa Stuart Kettle*]: The Last Mackenzie of Redcastle. London, 1888. *Edin. P.*

Mackenzie of Rosehaugh

BARTY (James Webster), *ed.*: Ancient deeds and other writs in the Mackenzie-Wharncliffe charter-chest. With short notices of Sir George Mackenzie of Rosehaugh; the first Earls of Cromartie, etc. Edinburgh, 1906. *St.A. U.; Dund. P.; Edin. U.; Edin. P.; Edin. S.; Glas. Mit.; Edin. L.L.*

Mackenzie, Earl of Seaforth

A DEDUCTION of the family of Seaforth down to . . . 1755. (*MS.*) *Glas. Mit.*

MACKENZIE (Edward Mackenzie), *formerly Edward Mackenzie Thompson*: Genealogy of the stem of the family of Mackenzie, Marquesses and Earls of Seaforth. [Melbourne, 1904.] *Ross C.; Ab. U.; Edin. P.*

MS. letters relating to the Mackenzies of Seaforth, 1814-1816. *Glas. Mit.*

MS. letters relating to the management of the estate of Seaforth, 1712-1740. *Glas. Mit.*

see also **Stewart-Mackenzie** of Seaforth

MacKerlie

McKERLIE (Emmeline Marianne H.): Two sons of Galloway: Robert McKerlie (1778-1855) and Peter (1817-1900). Dumfries, n.d. *Edin. S.; Dumf. C.* [1928]; *Kirkcud. C.*

Mackie

SKETCH pedigree chart, the ancestry of Mr. Maitland Mackie of Tarves. c. 1957. (*MS.*) *Ab. P.*

Mackinnon

CLAN MACKINNON SOCIETY, Glasgow. Annual reports, 1910-1911 and 1925-1926. *Glas. Mit.; Edin. Ant.* (1925-26).

CLAN MACKINNON SOCIETY. The Clan—and what it stands for. n.p., [1931]. *S.C.L.; Glas. Mit.; Edin. Ant.*

CLAN MACKINNON SOCIETY. Constitution and rules as revised 1st November, 1898 and 17th April, 1907. n.p., n.d. *Edin. Ant.*

CLAN MACKINNON SOCIETY. The Record of a clan. Helensburgh, n.d. (Repr. from *Helensburgh & Gareloch Times.*) *Edin. Ant.*

DOWNIE (Sir A. Mackenzie) & MACKINNON (A. D.): Genealogical account of the family of Mackinnon; repub. by L. Mackinnon of Duisdale. [2nd ed.] London, 1883. *Inv. P.; Edin. P.; Edin. S.; Glas. Mit.; Edin. L.L.* (+ Plymouth, 1882); *Edin. Ant.* (+ Plymouth, 1882).

MACKINNON (C. R.): The Clan MacKinnon: a short history. Coupar Angus, 1958. *S.C.L.; Edin. P.; Edin. Ant.*

MACKINNON (Donald D.): Memoirs of the Clan Fingon. Tunbridge Wells, [1884]. *Inv. P.; Ab. U.* (1899); *Edin. P.; Edin. S.; Glas. Mit.* (1899); *Edin. L.L.*

— Reply from the author of "Memoirs of the Clan Fingon" to a pamphlet entitled "The Family of Mackinnon" by Lauchlan Mackinnon. Tunbridge Wells, n.d. *Edin. P.; Edin. S.*

Mackintosh

BROOKER (J. G.): Family tree of the MacKintosh family from Wm. McIntosh of Botriphnie who died in 1856. Calcutta, 1939. *Ab. P.*

BULLOCH (Joseph Gaston Baillie): The Family of Baillie of Dunain, etc. Green Bay, Wis., 1898. *Inv. P.; Ab. U.; Edin. S.*

CLAN CHATTAN: journal of the Clan Chattan Association. Ascot. Vol. 1, 1934- . *Edin. P.; Edin. L.L.*

CLAN CHATTAN ASSOCIATION. [Pamphlet, containing lectures on the chiefship, etc.] Oban, 1895. *Inv. P.*

EXTRACTS from Register of Deeds and Register of Acts & Decreets relating to the name of Mackintosh. (17th & 18th centuries.) (*MSS.*) *Inv. P.*

FRASER-MACKINTOSH (Charles): Confederation of Clan Chattan: its kith and kin. Glasgow, 1898. *S.C.L.; Inv. P.; Inv. C.; Ab. U.; Edin. S.; Edin. P.; Glas. U.; Glas. Mit.; St.A. U.; Ab. P.*

— Dunachton, past and present: episodes in the history of the Mackintoshes. Inverness, 1866. *Inv. P.; Glas. U.; Edin. P.; Glas. Mit.*

GENEALOGY of the family of Mackintosh, from their origin until 1680. Inverness, 1865. (*MS. transcribed for C. Fraser-Mackintosh.*) *Inv. P.*

MACKINTOSH (Alexander Mackintosh), *formerly A. M. Shaw*: Historical memoirs of the house and clan of Mackintosh, and of the Clan Chattan. London, 1880. *Ab. P.; Inv. P.; Nai. C.; Inv. C.; Ab. U.; Glas. U.; Edin. P.; Edin. S.; Glas. Mit.; Edin. L.L.; Edin. Ant.*

— The Mackintoshes and Clan Chattan. Edinburgh, 1903. *S.C.L.; Inv. P.; Nai. C.; Ab. U.; Glas. U.; Edin. P.; Edin. S.; Glas. Mit.; Edin. L.L.; Edin. Ant.*

— Mackintosh families in Glenshee and Glenisla. Nairn, 1916. *Ab. P.; Inv. P.; Dund. P.; Edin. U.; Ab. U.; St.A. U.; Edin. P.; Edin. S.; Glas. Mit.* (+1907); *Edin. L.L.*

MACKINTOSH (Margaret) of Mackintosh: The Clan Mackintosh and the Clan Chattan. Edinburgh, 1948. *S.C.L.; Ab. C.; Dund. P.; Lan. C.; Gree. P.; Ren. C.; Ross C.; Ham. P.; Nai. C.; Inv. C.; Inv. P.; St.A. U; Ab. P.; Kirkcud. C.; Falk.P.; Edin. P.; Edin. S.; Glas. Mit.; Edin. L.L.*

MACPHERSON (Sir Aeneas): The Loyall dissuasive . . . and other papers . . . Clan Chattan; ed. by A. D. Murdoch. Edinburgh, 1902. (Scottish Hist. Soc., v. 41.) *S.C.L.; Inv. P.; Ab. P.; Dund. Q.; Glas. U.; Dund. P.; Edin. P.; Glas. Mit.; Edin. L.L.*

MACPHERSON (Alex. Cluny): Hail, Clan Chattan!: a clan ode . . . 28th Oct. 1896. Kingussie, 1897. *Ab. U.; Edin. P.*

MACPHERSON (John): Notes on the names of Clan Chattan and what they indicate. Edinburgh, 1874. *Inv. P.*

MSS. notes and newspaper cuttings relating to the Grants, Leiths, MacKintoshes of Blervie. *Inv. P.*

PATON (Henry), *ed.*: The Mackintosh muniments, 1442-1820, preserved in the Charter room at Moy Hall. Edinburgh, 1903. *Inv. P.; Ab. U.; St.A. U.; Edin. P.; Edin. S.; Glas. Mit.; Edin. L.L.; Edin. Ant.*

SMITH (William M'Combie): Memoir of the families of M'Combie and Thoms, originally M'Intosh and M'Thomas. New ed. Edinburgh, 1890. *Inv. P.; Dund. Q.; Glas. U.; Dund. P.; Edin. P.; Edin. S.; Glas. Mit.*

— Memoir of the family of M'Combie, a branch of the clan M'Intosh. Edinburgh, 1887. *Inv. P.; Edin. P.; Edin. S.; Glas. Mit.*

Mackintosh of Borlum

MACKINTOSH (Alex. M.): Brigadier MacKintosh of Borlum. Nairn, 1918. *Inv. P.*

MACLEAN (John): The Mackintoshes of Borlum, etc. (In *Historical & traditional sketches of Highland families & of the Highlands.* New ed. 1895.) *Glas. Mit.*

Maclagan

MACLAGAN (Sir Edward Douglas): Maclagan families. Edinburgh, 1936. *Per. P.; Edin. S.; Edin. L.L.*

MACLAGAN (R. C.): The Clan of the bell of St. Fillan. Edinburgh, [1879]. *Dund. Q.; Edin. S.; Edin. P.; Glas. Mit.; Edin. Ant.*

McLandsborough

McLANDSBOROUGH (John): Our Galloway ancestors: their descendants and connections. Bradford, 1898. *Wig. C.; Dumf. C.*

Maclaurin, *see* Laurin

McLea

McLEA (Duncan): An account of the name of McLea. 1743. (In *Highland Papers*; ed. by J. R. N. Macphail, v. IV. Scottish Hist. Soc., 3rd ser. v. XXII.) *S.C.L.; Arg. C.*

Maclean

CLAN MACLEAN ASSOCIATION. List of members and office-bearers ... 1908-1909. Glasgow, [1908]. *Glas. Mit.*

MACKECHNIE (John): The Clan Maclean: a Gaelic seapower. Edinburgh, 1954. *Inv. P.; Inv. C.; Dunb. C.; Edin. U.; Lan. C.; Ab. P.; Dunf. P.; Per. C.; Cai. C.; Dund. P.; Pai. P.; Ber. C.; Edin. P.; Glas. Mit.; Edin. L.L.; Edin. Ant.*

[MACLEAN (Alexander)]: A breif [sic] genealogical account of the ffamily [sic] of McLean . . . Edinburgh, 1872. *Edin. P.*

MCLEAN (Charles M.): History of Clan Tarlach o'Bui. Aberdeen, 1865. *Edin. P.; Glas. Mit.*

MACLEAN (James Noel Mackenzie), *ed.*: Clan Gillean (The Macleans). London, 1954. *Ab. P.; Edin. P.; Glas. Mit.; Edin. L.L.; Edin. Ant.*

MACLEAN (John Patterson), *ed.*: An account of the surname of Maclean, or Macghillean, from the MS. of 1751, and A sketch of the life and writings of Lachlan MacLean, with other information pertaining to the Clan Maclean. Xenia, Ohio, 1914. *Ab. U.; Edin. P.; Edin. S.; Glas. Mit.*

— The Family of Maclean, ed. from the MS. entitled "A brief general account of the family of Maclean, from its first settling in the island of Mull . . . in the year 1716", now in the Advocates Library, Edinburgh. Toronto, 1915. *Ab. U.; Edin. P.; Edin. S.; Glas. Mit.*

— History of the Clan Maclean, from its first settlement at Duard Castle to the present time. Cincinnati, Ohio, 1889. *S.C.L.; Inv. P.; Sti. P.; Dund. P.; Inv. C.; Ab. U.; St.A. U.; Glas. U.; Glas. Mit.; Edin. P.; Edin. S.*

— A Maclean souvenir. Franklin, 1918. *Edin. P.; Glas. Mit.*

— [Pamphlet on the chiefship of the Clan Maclean]. *Glasgow, 1895. Inv. P.; Glas. Mit.*

— Renaissance of the Clan Maclean; gathering at Duart Castle in 1912. Columbus, Ohio, 1913. *Inv. P.; Ab. U.; Arg. C.; Edin. P.; Edin. S.; Glas. Mit.*

MACLEAN (Lachlan): Historical . . . account . . ., *see* [SINCLAIR (John Campbell)]: Historical . . . account . . .

SINCLAIR (Alex. Maclean): The Clan Gillean. Charlottetown, Canada, 1899. *Inv. P.; Ab. U.; Glas. U.; Edin. P.; Edin. S.; Glas. Mit.; Edin. L.L.*

— Na bàird Leathanach: the Maclean bards. 2 v. Charlottetown, Canada, 1898-1900. *Glas. Mit.*

[SINCLAIR (John Campbell)]: Historical and genealogical account of the Clan of Maclean, from its first settlement at Castle Duart. By a Seneachie. London, 1838. *Inv. P.; Ab. U.; St.A. U.; Glas. U.; Glas. Mit.; Edin. P.; Edin. L.L.*

Maclean of Boreray

MACKENZIE (Hector Hugh): The Macleans of Boreray (with cadet families and branches). Inverness, 1946. *S.C.L.; Inv. P.; Inv. C.; Ab. U.; Ab. P.; Edin. P.; Edin. S.; Edin. L.L.*

Maclean of Drimnin

   [MACLEAN (John), *comp.*]: Pedigree of the Macleans of Drimnin. [Glasgow? 1909.] *Glas. Mit.*

Maclean of Duart

   MACLEAN (John), *comp.*: Genealogy of the Macleans of Dowart, 1910. Chiefs of the clan. [Glasgow? 1910.] *Glas. Mit.*

   PAPERS relating to the Macleans of Duart, 1670-1680. (In *Highland Papers*, ed. by J. R. N. Macphail, v. I. Scottish Hist. Soc., 2nd ser. v. V.) *S.C.L.; Arg. C.*

Maclellan of Kirkcudbright

   MACCLELLAN (John): Record of the House of Kirkcudbright; rev. & enl. by G. P. MacClellan. Dalbeattie, 1906. *Wig. C.; Edin. P.; Edin. L.L.* (with addit. notes).

   RECORDS of the McClellands of Bombie and Kirkcudbright. Castle Douglas, 1874.] *Edin. L.L.*

Macleod

   CLAN MACLEOD MAGAZINE. 1935—date. *Edin. P.; Glas. Mit.; Edin. L.L.* (1935-41).

   THE CLAN Macleod parliament held at Dunvegan castle, Aug. 15th, 1956. 1956. (*Typescript.*) *Ab. U.*

   GRANT (Isabel Frances): Clan Macleod: with their rock-built fortress they have endured. Edinburgh, 1953. *Per. C.; Dund. P.; Pai. P.; Arg. C.; Edin. P.; Inv. P.; Inv. C.; Sti. C.; Dunb. C.; Ayr P.; Edin. U.; Cly. P.; Lan. C.; Dunf. P.; Ab. P.; Ren. C.; Glas. Mit.; Ber. C.; Cai. C.; Edin. S.; Edin. L.L.; Edin. Ant.*

   GRANT (Isabel Frances): The Macleods: the history of a clan, 1200-1956. London, 1959. *S.C.L.; Edin. L.L.; Inv. P.*

   MACKENZIE (Alexander): History of the Macleods, with genealogies of the principal families of the name. Inverness, 1889. *S.C.L.; Inv. P.; Cai. C.; St.A. U.; Ab. U.; Glas. U.; Edin. P.; Edin. S.; Glas. Mit.; Edin. L.L.*

   MACKINNON (Donald): The Macleods . . . their chiefs and cadets. Cupar, Fife, 1950. *Edin. P.; Glas. Mit.*

   MACLEOD (Roderick Charles): The Macleods: a short sketch of their clan history, folk-lore, tales and biographical notices of some eminent clansmen. Edinburgh, 1906. *Ab. P.; Edin. U.; St.A. U.; Dunf. P.; Kirkcud. C.; Arg. C.; Edin. P.; Edin. S.; Glas. Mit.; Edin. L.L.; Ab. U.*

— The Macleods: their history and traditions. [Edinburgh], 1929. *S.C.L.; Ab. P.; Inv. C.; Ab. U.; Dund. Q.; Edin. P.; Edin. S.; Glas. Mit.; Edin. Ant.*

— Norman Magnus Macleod of Macleod . . . a memorial of a noble life. Inverness, 1930. *Edin. P.*

Macleod of Arnisdale

MACKINNON (Donald): The Macleods of Arnisdale, compiled from family and other documents. Dingwall, 1929. *St.A. U.; Ab. U.; Edin. P.; Edin. S.; Glas. Mit.; Edin. L.L.; Edin. Ant.*

Macleod of Dunvegan

MACLEOD (Roderick Charles): The Book of Dunvegan. 2 v. Aberdeen, 1938-39. (Third Spalding Club.) *S.C.L.; Elg. P.; Inv. P.; Edin. U.; Ab. P.; Dund. Q.; Glas. U.; Dund. P.; Edin. P.; Edin. S.; Glas. Mit.*

— The Macleods of Dunvegan from the time of Leod to the end of the 17th century. [Edinburgh], 1927. *S.C.L.; Inv. P.; Ross C.; Edin. U.; St.A. U.; Ab. U.; Ab. P.; Edin. P.; Edin. S.; Glas. Mit.; Edin. L.L.; Edin. Ant.*

Macleod of Lewis

THE EWILL trowbles of the Lewes, and how the Macleoid of the Lewes was with his whol trybe destroyed and put from the possession of the Lewes. (In *Highland papers*, ed. by J. R. N. Macphail, v. II. Scottish Hist. Soc., 2nd ser. v. XII.) *S.C.L.*

McMath

McMATH (Frank Mortimer): Collections for a history of the ancient family of McMath. Memphis, Tennessee, 1937. *Dumf. C.*

Macmillan

MACMILLAN (George A.): Records of the clan: an address at their annual gathering . . . Glasgow, 1902. *Ab. U.*

MACMILLAN (Hugh): The Clan Macmillan: addresses given at the annual gatherings of the Clan Society. London, 1901. *St.A. U.; Ab. U.; Glas. U.; Edin. P.; Glas. Mit.*

MACMILLAN (Rev. Somerled): The Emigration of Lochaber Macmillans to Canada in 1802. [Ipswich, Mass.] 1958. *Pai. P.*

— The Macmillans and their septs. Glasgow, 1952. *S.C.L.; Edin. Ant.; Kir. P.; Inv. P.; Ab. P.; St.A. U.; Kirkcud. C.; Edin. P.; Edin. S.; Glas. U.; Glas. Mit.*

MORGAN (Charles): The House of Macmillan, 1843-1943. London, 1943. *Per. C.*

Macnab

    CLAN MACNAB ASSOCIATION. Historic notes on the Clan Macnab, Edinburgh, 1911. *Edin. P.*

    MCNAB (John): The Clan McNab: a short sketch. Edinburgh, 1907. *Ab. P.; St.A. U.; Ab. U.; Glas. U.; Edin. P.; Glas. Mit.; Edin. S.*

    MACNABB (Archibald Corrie), *comp.*: A brief outline of the story of the Clan Macnab. [Glasgow], 1951. *Edin. P.*

    WILD (Roland): Macnab, the last laird. London, 1938. *Inv. P.*

MacNachtan, *see* **MacNauchtan**

MacNair

    GOURLAY (James): Robin Macnair and Jean Holmes in company. (In his *The Kennedys at Auchtyfardle, & other papers.* n.p., 1936.) *Edin. P.; Dumf. C.*

    MCNAIR (James Birtley): McNair, McNear, and McNeir genealogies. (*And Supplement.*) 2 v. Chicago, Illinois, 1923-1928. *S.C.L.; Ayr P.; Dund. P.; Sti. P.; Gree. P.; Edin. U.; St.A. U.; Ab. U.; Glas. U.; Dund. Q.; Edin. P.; Glas. Mit.; Edin. L.L.; Edin. Ant.*

    — — Supplement, 1955. Los Angeles, California, 1955. *S.C.L.; Edin. U.; Ab. U.; St.A. U.; Edin. P.; Edin. L.L.; Edin. Ant.*

MacNauchtan

    MACNAGHTEN (Angus I.): The Chiefs of Clan Macnachtan and their descendants. Windsor, 1951. *Dund. P.; Inv. P.; St.A. U.; Ab. U.; Dund. Q.; Glas. U.; Pai. P.; Arg. C.; Edin. P.; Edin. S.; Glas. Mit.; Edin. L.L.*

    MCNAUGHTON (Duncan): The Clan Macnachtan. Bearsden, 1956. *Inv. P.; Per. C.; Edin. P.*

    MACNAUGHTAN of that ilk. (From *Crawford MSS.* in *Highland Papers*, ed. by J. R. N. Macphail, v. I. Scottish Hist. Soc., 2nd ser. v. V.) *S.C.L.; Arg. C.*

    MCNITT (Virgil V.): The MacNauchtan saga. 2 v. Palmer, Mass., 1951. *Dumf. C.; Kirkcud. C.; Edin. L.L.*

McNaught of Kilquhanity

    MCNITT (Virgil V.): The Macnaughts of Kilquhanitie: a historical sketch of the Scottish progenitors of an American family. New York, 1917. *Kirkcud. Bro.*

MacNeil

MACKAY (Frank Forbes): MacNeill of Carskey: his estate journal, 1703-1743. Edinburgh, 1955. *S.C.L.; Inv. P.; Edin. U.; Arg. C.*

MACNEIL (Robert Lister): The Clan Macneil: Clan Niall of Scotland. New York, 1923. *S.C.L.; Edin. U.; Ab. U.; Ab. P.; Glas. U.; Edin. P.; Glas. Mit.; Edin. L.L.; Edin. Ant.*

McNish, *see* **Neish**

MacPhail

GEDDIE (Henry L.): The Families Geddie and McPhail, by Jack Geddie. Fort Worth, Texas, 1959. *S.C.L.; Edin. P.*

SINTON (Rev. Thomas): The MacPhails or Campbells. (In his *Family & genealogical sketches*, 1911.) *Inv. P.; Edin. S.; Ab. U.; Ab. P.; Dund. Q.; Edin. P.*

Macpherson

CHEYNE-MACPHERSON (W.): The Chiefs of Clan Macpherson. Edinburgh, 1947. *S.C.L.; Edin. S.; Edin. L.L.; Inv. P.; Clack. C.; Edin. Ant.; Lan. C.; Ren. C.; Fife C.; St.A. U.; Glas. U.; Glas. Mit.; Edin. P.; Ab. P.; Inv. C.; Dunb. C.; Ab. U.*

CLAN MACPHERSON ASSOCIATION. Clan Macpherson: a short note on a long history. Newtonmore, n.d. *Per. C.; Inv. P.; Glas. Mit.; Edin. P.* (1953).

CREAG DHUBH: annual of Clan MacPherson association, 1949- . *Inv. P.; Glas. Mit.; Edin. P.* ([1949]).

MACPHERSON (Sir Aeneas): The Loyall dissuasive and other papers relating to the affairs of Clan Chattan. Edinburgh, 1902. (Scottish Hist. Soc., v. 41.) *S.C.L.; Inv. P.; Ab. P.; Dund. Q.; Glas. U.; Dund. P.; Edin. P.; Glas. Mit.; Edin. S.;*

Macpherson of Cluny Macpherson

MACPHERSON (Ewen) of Cluny Macpherson: The Golden wedding of Cluny Macpherson, C. B. and Mrs. Macpherson . . . 1882. Edinburgh, 1883. *St.A. U.; Edin. Ant.*

MacPike

MACPIKE (E. F.): Pyke and MacPike families. 1927. (Repr. from *Scottish Notes & Queries*.) *Dund. Q.*

MacQuarrie

MUNRO (Robert William): Lachlan MacQuarrie, XVI of Ulva, with notes on some clansmen in India. Karachi, 1944. *Edin. P.; Edin. L.L.*

Macqueen

NYDEGGER (James Archibald): The MacQueens: a brief history of the origin of the MacQueen family, with special reference to the MacQueens of Corrybrough. Baltimore, Maryland, 1928. *Inv. P.; Edin. P.*

McQuesten, *see* **McCuiston**

McQuiston, *see* **McCuiston**

MacRae

MACRA (Rev. John): Genealogical account of the MacRas as written originally by Mr. John MacRa . . . 1704; transcr. 1786 by Farquhar MacRa. [Camden, Virginia, 1870.] *Edin. S.*

— Genealogy of the Macras. [c. 16—]. (In *Highland Papers*, ed. by J. R. N. Macphail, v. I. Scottish Hist. Soc., 2nd ser. v. V.) *S.C.L.; Arg. C.*

MACRAE (Alexander): The History of the Clan MacRae, with genealogies. Dingwall, 1899. *Ross C.; Dunf. P.; Ab. P.; Inv. P.; St.A. U.; Ab. U.; Dund. Q.; Glas. U.; Pai. P.; Edin. P.; Glas. Mit.* (+1910)*; Edin. S.* (1910)*; Edin. L.L.*

MACRAE-GILSTRAP (Ella): The Clan MacRae, with its roll of honour and service in the Great War. Aberdeen, 1923. *S.C.L.; Ab. P.; Inv. C.; Edin. P.; Glas. Mit.; Edin. L.L.*

McRobbie

BULLOCH (John Malcolm): The McRobbie family, Lumphanan, with special reference to John McRobbie Gordon, Savoy Opera director. 1937. (Cuttings taken from *Aberdeen Press & Journal*.) *Ab. P.*

McShennag

MCKERRAL (Andrew): Two old Kintyre lawsuits, with some notes on . . . McShennags of Lephenstrath, etc. n.p., 1941. *Glas. Mit.*

MacThomas

SMITH (William M'Combie): Memoir of the families of M'Combie and Thoms originally M'Intosh and M'Thomas. Edinburgh, 1890. *Dund. Q.; Glas. U.; Dund. P.; Edin. P.; Edin. S.*

McWilliam

LANG (Patrick Sellar), *comp.*: The Langs of Selkirk with some notes on [other families]. Melbourne, 1910. *Edin. P.; Edin. S.*

MCWILLIAM (Rev. John Morell), *Minister of Tynron*: McWilliam MSS. 1955. *Dumf. C.*

SCOTLAND'S lost royal line: the descendants of Duncan II. (Repr. for private circ. from *Dumfries & Galloway Standard,* Feb. 20 and Mar. 23, 1957.) *Edin. Ant.*

Main

MAIN (Robert Hall): The House of Maine. n.p., [1939]. *Edin. P.*

Maitland

ROGERS-HARRISON (George Harrison): Genealogical and historical account of the Maitland family. London, 1869. *Edin. S.; Edin. L.L.*

Maitland of Dundrennan

ROGERS-HARRISON (George Harrison): The Pedigree of the Maitland family of Dundrennan, N.B. and Otago, N.Z. London, 1905. *Kirkcud. Bro.*

Maitland, Earl of Lauderdale

[DALZEL (Andrew)]: A short genealogy of the family of Maitland, Earl of Lauderdale. Edinburgh, 1875. *Edin. P.; Edin. S.; Edin. L.L.*

Maitland in Montrose

BONAR (Horatius): Notes to genealogical chart or pedigree of the descendants of James Pyott, merchant, Montrose. n.p., 1914. *Ab. U.; Edin. P.; Edin. S.*

Makgill of Rankeilour, *see* Frendraught, Lord

Mar, Earldom of

ACT for the restoration of John Francis Erskine of Mar to the dignity and title of Earl of Mar, 17 June, 1824. *Edin. L.L.*

ARE there two Earls of Mar? [2nd ed.] London, [1876]. *Glas. Mit.; Edin. L.L.*

BARONY of Cardross and Summary of the case for the most ancient Earldom of Mar. (Repr. from *Gentleman's Mag.,* 4 s., Apr. 1, 1866.) *Edin. S.*

CRAWFORD (Alex. William Crawford Lindsay), *25th Earl of*: The Earldom of Mar in sunshine and shade. 2 v. Edinburgh, 1882. *S.C.L.; Clack. C.; Dund. P.; Ab. P.; Inv. P.; Fife C.; Glas. U.; Edin. P.; Edin. S.; Glas. Mit.; Edin. Ant.; Edin. L.L.*

DOUBLEDAY (H. Arthur): The Mar case, 1866-85, and after. London, 1936. (Repr. from v. 9 of *The Complete Peerage.*) *Clack. C.; Ab. P.*

THE EARLDOM of Mar. Exeter, 1886. *Inv. P.*

FRASER (William): Memorial of Walter Coningsby Erskine, Earl of Kellie claiming . . . Earl of Mar. 1867. *Edin. L.L.*

HALLEN (Arthur W. Cornelius): A paper on the Mar Peerage read before the Alloa Society of Natural Science & Archaeology on May 4th, 1875, tog. with the Judgment of the Committee of Privileges, pedigrees, etc. [Alloa], 1875. *Clack. C.; Ab. P.; Glas. U.; Edin. P.; Edin. S.; Glas. Mit.; Edin. Ant.*

KELLIE (Walter Coningsby Erskine), *12th Earl of*: Case on behalf of Walter Coningsby, Earl of Kellie, on his claim to the dignity of Earl of Mar, in the peerage of Scotland. n.d. *Clack. C.; Edin. L.L.*

KELLIE (Walter Henry Erskine), *13th Earl of*: Case and Additional case on behalf of Walter Henry, Earl of Kellie, claiming also to be Earl of Mar, on his claim to the honour and dignity of Earl of Mar, in the peerage of Scotland. n.d. *Glas. Mit.; Edin. L.L.*

LINDSAY (William Alex.): A short account of the Earldom of Mar and of the recent peerage case. Edinburgh, 1875. *Edin. L.L.*

M'KERLIE (Peter Handyside): Earldom of Marr with sketch of the times. Edinburgh, [1883]. *Edin. P.; Edin. S.; Edin. Ant.*

[MAR (John Francis Erskine Goodeve-Erskine), *33rd Earl of*]: Ancient and modern. n.p., 1875. *S.C.L.; Clack. C.; St.A. U.; Ab. P.; Glas. U.; Edin. P.; Glas. Mit.; Inv. P.; Edin. Ant.*

— Case for John Francis . . . Erskine, Earl of Mar, in opposition to Walter Coningsby, Earl of Kellie, claiming the dignity of the Earl of Mar. n.d. *Edin. P.; Edin. L.L.*

— Letter to the Peers of Scotland from the Earl of Mar, in reply to a letter from the Earl of Kellie. Edinburgh, [1879]. (As printed in the *Edinburgh Courant*, May 2, 1879.) *Edin. L.L.*

— Supplementary case on behalf of John Francis . . . Erskine, claiming to be Earl of Mar, Baron Garioch, in opposition to the claim of the Rt. Hon. Walter Henry, Earl of Kellie . . . 1873. *Glas. Mit.; Edin. L.L.*

MAR peerage claim, 1875. Judgment. *Glas. Mit.*

MINUTES of evidence . . . 1868-75. *Edin. L.L.*

MINUTES of the Mar Peerage case: The Case in the House of Lords; the report from the Select Committee on the Restitution Bill; Minutes of Evidence. *Clack. C.; Edin. L.L.*

NUDA veritas: shall wrong prevail? With appendix of illustrative documents. London, 1888. *Edin. P.*

PROCEEDINGS and speeches, 1873-74. *Edin. L.L.*

THE SCOTCH peerage endangered in its rights and integrity through the attack upon the old Earldom of Mar. n.p., n.d. *Edin. L.L.*

SIMPSON (William Douglas): The Earldom of Mar. Aberdeen, 1949. *S.C.L.*

— The Province of Mar. Aberdeen, 1943. (Rhind lectures.) *Edin. L.L.*

SINCLAIR (Alexander): Abstract of the case for the Earl of Mar. n.p., n.d. *Edin. L.L.*

— Observations on the inheritance and position of the most ancient Earldom of Mar. n.p., n.d. *Glas. Mit.; Edin. L.L.*

— Sketch of the succession of the most ancient Earldom of Mar. n.p., n.d. *Edin. L.L.*

[SINCLAIR (Alexander)]: Some of the particulars of the first restoration of the Earldom of Mar in 1565, and its confirmation in 1567 and 1787. n.p., n.d. *Edin. L.L.*

SOME observations on the two Earldoms of Mar. n.d. (Repr. from *The Complete Peerage.*) *Ab. P.*

SWINTON (Robert Blair): The Proceedings in the case of the Earldom of Mar, 1867-85: a résumé. London, 1889. *Edin. L.L.*

THE TERRITORIAL "Earldom of Mar". n.p., n.d. *Edin. L.L.*

March, Earldom of

SINCLAIR (Alexander): Sketch of the succession of the ancient historical Earldom of March till it was confiscated in 1413. [Edinburgh, 1870.] *Edin. L.L.*

Marchmont, Earldom of

CAMPBELL (Sir Hugh Hume) of Marchmont: Case on the part of Sir Hugh Hume Campbell of Marchmont, Bt., in relation to the claim of Francis Douglas Home, Esq., to the titles, honours and dignities of Earl of Marchmont, Viscount of Blasonberrie, Lord Polwarth of Polwarth, Redbraes & Greinlaw. 1843. *Glas. Mit.; Edin. L.L.*

HOME (Alexander): Case of Alexander Home . . . claiming the titles, honours and dignities of Earl of Marchmont, Viscount of Blazonberrie, Lord Polwarth of Polwarth, Redbraes & Greinlaw. Westminster, 1822. *Glas. Mit.; Edin. L.L.*

HOME (Francis Douglas): Additional case for Francis Douglas Home . . . son of Alexander Home, Esq., former claimant, claiming the titles, honours and dignities of Earl of Marchmont, etc. Westminster, 1842. *Glas. Mit.; Edin. L.L.*

MINUTES of evidence . . . petition of Alexander Home . . . claiming . . . Earl of Marchmont, etc. 1822. *Edin. L.L.*

MINUTES of evidence . . . petition of Francis Home . . . claiming . . . Earl of Marchmont, etc. 1838. *Edin. L.L.*

see also **Hume,** Earl of Marchmont

Marjoribanks

BURNETT (George): Mr. Joseph Foster and the Lyon Office. n.d. (Repr. from the *Genealogist*, no. 44.) *Edin. P.; Edin. S.; Glas. Mit.*

FOSTER (Joseph): The Lyon office and the Marjoribanks family. A reply to the remarks of the Lyon Clerk Depute [R. R. Stodart] entitled "Mr. Joseph Foster on the return of Members of Parliament" . . . London, [1882]. *S.C.L.; St.A. U.; Glas. U.; Dund. P.; Edin. P.; Glas. Mit.; Inv. P.; Edin. S.*

— The Lyon office in retreat. London, n.d. (Repr. from *Collectanea genealogica*, pt. XI.) *Glas. Mit.*

HISTORY of the family. 1831. (*MS.*) *Edin. S.*

Martin

[BOASE (Edward R.)]: The Family of Martin, in Angus and Fife. [1938]. (*Typescript.*) *Dund. P.; Edin. P.; Edin. S.; Edin. L.L.*

Martin of Skye

THE MARTINS of Skye: a short history of a Highland family. Glasgow, n.d. *Ab. P.; Ab. U.; Edin. P.* ([1924])*; Glas. Mit.* ([1924]).

Masterton

PATON (Victor A. Noel), *ed.*: Masterton papers, 1660-1719 . . . with pedigree, introduction and notes. Edinburgh, 1893. (Scottish Hist. Soc. Misc., v. I.) *S.C.L.; Clack. C.; Dunf. P.*

[STODART (Robert Riddle)]: A critical examination of the genealogy of Masterton of that ilk, Parkmill, etc. published in Douglas' Baronage and Crawfurd's Memorials of Alloa. London, 1878. *Edin. L.L.*

Masterton of West Fife

STODART (Robert Riddle): A critical examination of the genealogy of Masterton of that ilk. London, 1878. *Dunf. P.; Edin. P.; Edin. S.*

Matheson

MACKENZIE (Alexander): History of the Mathesons. Inverness, 1882. *Inv. P.; Ab. U.; Glas. U.; Edin. P.; Glas. Mit.; Edin. S.; Edin. L.L.*

—— 2nd ed. ed. by A. Bain. Stirling, 1900. *Ab. P.; Inv. P.; Sti. P.; Ross C.; St.A. U.; Ab. U.; Glas. U.; Edin. P.; Glas. Mit.; Edin. L.L.; Edin. Ant.*

Matheson of Lochalsh

FOSTER (William Edward): Royal descents of the [Fosters of Moreton and the] Mathesons of Shinness & Lochalsh. London, 1912. *Ab. U.; Edin. S.; Glas. Mit.*

MACKENZIE (Alexander): Sir James Matheson of the Lewis and his descent from the Mathesons of Shinness. Inverness, 1882. *Edin. P.*

Mathie

MATHIE (John), *ed.*: The Mathie family. [Glasgow, 1915.] *Glas. Mit.*

Maule of Panmure

MAULE (Hon. Harry): Registrum de Panmure: records of the families of Maule, de Valoniis, Brechin, and Brechin-Barclay, united in the line of the Barons of Panmure; ed. by John Stuart. 2 v. Edinburgh, 1874. *Arb. P.; Per. P.; St.A. U.; Ab. U.; Forf. P.; Glas. U.; Dund. P.; Edin. P.; Glas. Mit.; Edin. S.; Edin. L.L.; Edin. Ant.*

Maxtone

GRAHAM (E. Maxtone): The Maxtones of Cultoquhey. Edinburgh, 1935. *S.C.L.; Cai. C.; Per. C.; Banff C.; Per. P.; Edin. U.; St.A. U.; Edin. P.; Glas. Mit.; Edin. S.*

Maxwell of Carruchan, *see* **Herries**, Lord, of Terregles

Maxwell, Lord Herries, *see* **Maxwell**, Earl of Nithsdale

Maxwell, Earl of Nithsdale

FRASER (Sir William): The Book of Carlaverock: memoirs of the Maxwells, Earls of Nithsdale, Lords Maxwell & Herries. 2 v. Edinburgh, 1873. *Dumf. C.; St.A. U.; Ab. U.; Glas. U.; Edin. P.; Glas. Mit.; Edin. S.; Edin. L.L.; Edin. Ant.*

— Inventory of the muniments of the families of Maxwell, Herries and Nithsdale, at Terregles. 1865. *Edin. L.L.*

Maxwell of Pollok

FRASER (Sir William), *ed.*: The Cartulary of Pollok Maxwell. Edinburgh, 1875. *Rox. C.; Glas. U.; Edin. P.; Edin. S.; Glas. Mit.; Edin. L.L.; Edin. Ant.*

— Memoirs of the Maxwells of Pollok. 2 v. Edinburgh, 1863. *S.C.L.; Moth. P.; Ab. U.; Glas. U.; Edin. P.; Glas. Mit.; Edin. S.; Edin. L.L.; Edin. Ant.*

— The Pollok-Maxwell baronetcy. Statement of the right of William Stirling of Keir, and now of Pollok, to the baronetcy held by his maternal uncle the late Sir John Maxwell of Pollok; with illus. documents and the opinions of counsel on the case. Edinburgh, 1866. *Edin. P.; Glas. Mit.; Edin. L.L.*

[INVENTORIES of Pollok charters and other papers.] Glasgow, c. 1830. (Vol. commenced for the Maitland Club and then abandoned.) *Glas. Mit.*

M'CALLUM (Andrew): Some account of the Maxwells of Pollok. (In his *Pollokshaws village and burgh,* 1600-1912. 1925.) *S.C.L.*

Maxwell of Stroquhan

GOURLAY (James): Notes on the family of Maxwell of Stroquhan. (In his *The Kennedys of Auchtyfardle and other papers.* n.p., 1936.) *Dumf. C.; Edin. P.*

Meldrum of Fyvie

STIRLING (Anna Maria D. W. Pickering), *Mrs. Stirling*: Fyvie Castle: its lairds and their times. London, 1928. *S.C.L.; Elg. P.; Mid. C.; Ren. C.; Fife C.; Ab. C.; West L. C.; Banff C.; Fras. P.; Dunb. C.; Edin. U.; Glas. Mit.*

Melville

FRASER (Sir William): The Leven and Melville peerages. 1857. (*MSS.*) *Edin. L.L.*

— The Melvilles, Earls of Melville, and the Leslies, Earls of Leven. 3 v. Edinburgh, 1890. *S.C.L.; Kir. P.; Fife C.; Moth. P.; St.A. U.; Ab. U.; Glas. U.; Dund. P.; Edin. P.; Glas. Mit.; Edin. S.; Edin. L.L.; Edin. Ant.*

MELVILL *aft.* JOUBERT DE LA FERTE (Eliza Jane): The Melvill family: a roll of honour of the descendants of Capt. Philip Melvill . . . and their immediate connections by marriage, in the years of the world war, 1914-1918. London, 1920. *S.C.L.; St.A. U.*

Menteith, Earldom of

COWAN (Samuel): Three Celtic earldoms: Atholl, Strathearn, Menteith. Edinburgh, 1909. *Sti. P.; Per. C.; Ab. P.; Per. P.; Dund. P.; Glas. Mit.*

HUTCHISON (Andrew F.): The Lake of Menteith . . . with historical accounts of . . . the Earldom of Menteith. Stirling, 1899. *Ab. P.; Edin. L.L.*

NICOLAS (Sir Nicholas Harris): History of the Earldoms of Strathern, Monteith and Airth. London, 1842. *Dund. P.; Per. C.; Per. P.; St.A. U.; Ab. U.; Glas. U.; Edin. P.; Edin. S.; Glas. Mit.; Edin. L.L.*

see also **Graham,** Earl of Menteith

Menzies

DUFF (Edward Gordon): Brief notes on the Mary, Queen of Scots cabinet from Castle Menzies, Perthshire. n.p., 1913. *Glas. Mit.*

HISTORICAL MSS. COMMISSION. 6th Report. Appendix. [Report on the MSS. of Sir Robert Menzies, Bt., of that ilk . . .] London, 1877. *Glas. Mit.*

MENZIES (David Prentice): History of the Menzies Clan society. Glasgow, [1901]. *Inv. P.; Ab. U.; Ab. P.; Glas. U.; Edin. P.; Edin. S.; Glas. Mit.* (+1897); *Edin. Ant.* (+[1896]).

— The Red and white book of Menzies: the history of Clan Menzies and its chiefs. Glasgow, 1894. *Dund. P.; Ab. P.; Inv. P.; Per. C.; Dumf. C.; Per. P.; Rox. C.; Moth. P.; Ayr P.; St.A. U.; Ab. U.; Glas. U.; Pai. P.; Edin. P.* (+2nd ed. 1908); *Glas. Mit.; Edin. S.; Edin. L.L.; Edin. Ant.*

THE MENZIES CLAN SOCIETY. [Constitution, office-bearers, etc.] [Glasgow, 1894.] *Glas. Mit.*

STEWART (C. Poyntz): The Red and white book of Menzies: a review. Exeter, 1906. *Ab. U.; Ab. P.; Edin. Ant.*

Menzies in Lanark

MENZIES (Elizabeth Bailie): The Lanark manse family: narrative found in the repositories of the late Miss E. B. Menzies, of . . . Edinburgh; ed. by T. Reid. Lanark, 1901. *Per. C.; Lan. C.; Edin. P.; Edin. S.; St.A. U.*

Mercer

ROBERT MERCER and Helen Chisholm and their descendants, 1480-1554. n.p., n.d. *Edin. L.L.*

Mercer of Aldie

MERCER (G. R.): Our seven centuries: an account of the Mercers of Aldie and Meikleour. Perth, 1868. *Dunf. P.; Per. P.; Edin. P.; Glas. Mit.; Edin. L.L.*

[MERCER (Edward Smyth)]: The Mercer Chronicle, by an Irish seanachy. London, 1866. *Edin. L.L.*

SINTON (Rev. Thomas): The Mercers of Aldie. (In his *Family and genealogical sketches.* 1911.) *Inv. P.; Edin. S.; Ab. U.; Ab. P.; Dund. Q.; Edin. P.*

Michie

MICHIES abroad. n.p., 19— *Ab. P.*

PEDIGREE of Michies. n.d. (Extracts from various sources, incl. *Scottish Notes & Queries,* 2nd ser., in which fuller account is given of family.) *Edin. S.*

Middleton, Earl of Middleton

BISCOE (Anna Catharina): The Earls of Middleton, Lords of Clermont and Fettercairn, and the Middleton family. London, 1876. *Inv. P.; Mont. P.; Ab. U.; St.A. U.; Glas. U.; Edin. P.; Edin. S.; Glas. Mit.; Edin. L.L.*

Miller

COUPAR (William James): The Millers of Haddington, Dunbar and Dunfermline: a record of Scottish bookselling. London, 1914. *S.C.L.; Kir. P.; Fife C.; Dunf. P.; Ab. P.; Glas. U.; Pai. P.; Edin. P.; Edin. S.; Glas. Mit.*

Miller in Edinburgh

[MILLER (William F.)]: Memorials of Hope Park, comprising . . . particulars of . . . William Miller and . . . ancestors. n.p., 1886. *Edin. P.; Edin. S.*

Milne

CRAMOND (William): The Milnes of Banff and neighbourhood. Banff, 1894. (Repr. from *Banffshire Journal.*) *Ab. P.; Glas. Mit.; Edin. Ant.*

Milne-Home

MILNE-HOME (David): Biographical memoranda of the persons whose portraits hang in the dining-room at Milne-Graden. Edinburgh, 1862. *Ber. C.; Glas. Mit.*

Mitchell

MITCHELL (Silas Weir): A brief history of two families. The Mitchells of Ayrshire and the Symons of Cornwall. Philadelphia, Penn., 1912. *Dumf. C.; S.C.L.* (microfilm).

Mitchell in Bandeath

SOME descendants of John Mitchell in Bandeath, co. Stirling, and Janet Johnstone his wife, from 1579. [1888.] (*MS.*) *Edin. L.L.*

Moffat of Moffat

MOFFAT (Robert Maxwell): A short history of the family of Moffat of that ilk, with the genealogies of various branches in Scotland, Ireland and England, as existing at the present day; also passing notices of Moffats in France, Germany and Holland. Jersey, 1908. *Kirkcud. Bro.*

Moir

GILL (Andrew J. Mitchell): The Families of Moir and Byres. Edinburgh, 1885. *S.C.L.; Ab. P.; St.A. U.; Glas. U.; Dund. P.; Edin. P.; Edin. S.; Glas. Mit.; Edin. Ant.; Edin. L.L.*

MOIR (Alexander L.): Moir genealogy, and collateral lines. Lowell, Mass. 1913. *S.C.L.; Ab. P.; Ab. U.; Edin. P.; Edin. S.; Glas. Mit.*

Moir of Leckie

COOK (William B.): The Lairds of Leckie. Stirling, 1906. (Repr. from the *Stirling Sentinel.*) *Edin. P.*

MONTGOMERY-MOIR (George): George Montgomery-Moir of Leckie, appellant, Anne, his wife and others, respondents. 1751. *Edin. P.*

Moir of Otterburn

[STODART (Robert Riddle): Kerr of Gateshaw, Kerr of Corbethouse and Moir of Otterburn. n.p., n.d.] (Repr. from *The Genealogist*, 1st ser. III.) *Glas. U.; Edin. L.L.*

Moir of Stoneywood

BROWN (John), M.D., LL.D.,: The Moirs of Stoneywood: a Jacobite family. n.p., n.d. *Edin. P.; Edin. Ant.*

— — Also in his *John Leech and other papers.* 2nd ed. 1882. *Glas. Mit.*

Moncreiff

MONCREIFF (Frederick) & MONCREIFFE (William): The Moncreiffs and the Moncreiffes. 2 v. Edinburgh, 1929. *Glas. U.; Glas. Mit.; Per. C.; Ork. C.; Per. P.; Edin. U.; St.A. U.; Ab. U.; Edin. P.; Edin. L.L.; Edin. Ant.*

MONCREIFFE (Sir Iain): The House and family of Moncreiffe. 1957. (Repr. from *Perthshire Advertiser*, 30 Nov. 1957.) *S.C.L.*

SETON (George): The House of Moncrieff. Edinburgh, 1890. *S.C.L.; Per. P.; Edin. P.; Glas. Mit.; Edin. L.L.; Edin. Ant.*

Monfode

[KERR (Robert Malcolm)]: Notices of the families of Ker of Kerrisland and Monfode of that ilk. London, 1880. *Glas. Mit.; Edin. L.L.; Edin. Ant.*

[KERR (Robert Malcolm)]: Nugae antiquae. Glasgow, 1847-49. *Glas. U.; Glas. Mit.*

[WEIR (H. F.)]: Monfode and the lairds of Monfode . . . (From the *Ardrossan & Saltcoats Herald*, 1882.) *Glas. Mit.*

Monro of Auchinbowie

INGLIS (John Alexander): The Monros of Auchinbowie and cognate families. Edinburgh, 1911. *Mid. C.; Sti. C.; St.A. U.; Ab. U.; Glas. U.; Dund. P.; Edin. P.; Edin. S.; Glas. Mit.; Edin. L.L.; Edin. Ant.*

Monteith, *see* Menteith

Montgomerie, *see* Montgomery

Montgomery

CHALMERS (George): Letter from George Chalmers to John Anderson about the Montgomery family, April, 1809. (In [*Wood (J. P.)*]: *Memorials of various families* . . . c. 1830. (*MS.*).) *Edin. P.*

MS. notes and press cuttings on the family of Montgomerie. n.d. *Edin. P.*

MEMORABLES of the Montgomeries, a narrative in rhyme . . . [Edinburgh, 1822.] *Edin. P.; Edin. S.; Glas. Mit.* (1770).

MONTGOMERY (Bo Gabriel de): Origin and history of the Montgomerys. Edinburgh, 1948. *S.C.L.; Fife C.; Glas. U.; Edin. S.; Edin. L.L.*

MONTGOMERY (Thomas Harrison), *comp.*: Genealogical history of the family of Montgomery. Philadelphia, Penn., 1863. *Edin. P.; Edin. L.L.*

MONTGOMERY-MOIR (George): George Montgomery-Moir of Leckie, appellant, Anne [Montgomery] his wife and others, respondents. London, 1751. *Edin. P.*

Montgomery of the Ards

MONTGOMERY (William), *comp.*: The Montgomery MSS., 1603-1706. Ed. by Rev. G. Hill. Belfast, 1869. *Edin. L.L.*

Montgomery of Bridgend

ANDERSON (William): Genealogical account of the Montgomeries of Brigend of Doon, lineal representatives of the families of Eglintoun and Lyle. Edinburgh, 1859. *Edin. L.L.*

Montgomery, Earl of Eglinton

AIKMAN (James): Account of the tournament at Eglinton . . . biographical notice of the Eglinton family . . . Edinburgh, 1839. *Glas. Mit.; Edin. L.L.*

FRASER (Sir William): Memorials of the Montgomeries, Earls of Eglinton. 2 v. Edinburgh, 1859. *S.C.L.; Ayr P.; Ab. U.; St.A. U.; Glas. U.; Edin. P.; Edin. S.; Glas. Mit.; Edin. L.L.; Edin. Ant.*

FULLARTON (John): Historical memoir of the family of Eglinton and Winton. Ardrossan, 1864. *Ayr P.; Pai. P.; Glas. Mit.; Edin. L.L.; Edin. Ant.*

Montrose, Dukedom of

CRAWFORD & BALCARRES (Alexander Wm. Crawford Lindsay), *25th/8th Earl of*: Report of the speeches of Counsel . . . and of the Lord Chancellor . . . in moving the resolution, upon the claims of James, Earl of Crawford . . . to the original Dukedom of Montrose . . . preceded by an address to Her Majesty, in . . . remonstrance against the claimant . . . London, 1855. *St.A. U.; Ab. P.; Edin. P.; Edin. Ant.; Edin. L.L.*

CRAWFORD & BALCARRES (James Lindsay), *24th/7th Earl of*: Case for James, Earl of Crawford & Balcarres, etc., claiming the honour and dignity of Duke of Montrose . . . with reference to the petition and alleged right of James, Duke of Montrose to be admitted as a party in opposition to the said claim. [n.p., 18—.] *St.A. U.; Edin. L.L.* (1851).

— Case of James, Earl of Crawford and Balcarres, etc., claiming the title, honour and dignity of the original Dukedom of Montrose, created in 1488. [n.p., 18—.] *St.A. U.; Ab. P.* ([1850]); *Edin. P.* ([1850]); *Edin. S.* ([1850]); *Edin. L.L.* ([1850]).

— Examination of the supplemental case of James, Earl of Crawford and Balcarres, claiming the Dukedom of Montrose, created in 1488, with a statement of the additional evidence in support of the original case in opposition for James, Duke of Montrose. 1852. (*MS.*) *Edin. L.L.*

— Supplemental case of James, Earl of Crawford and Balcarres, claiming the Dukedom of Montrose created in 1488: including an analysis or abstract of the claimant's original case; together with the objections started to the claimant's arguments and evidence by James, Duke of Montrose (though not as a party, or as having interest in the claim); and the claimant's replies thereto. [With vol. containing addenda to the supplemental case.] [n.p., 18—.] *St.A. U.; Edin. P.* ([1852]); *Ab. P.; Edin. S.* ([1852]); *Edin. L.L.*

MONTROSE (James Graham); *4th Duke of*: Abstract of the case for James, Duke of Montrose on his petition against James, Earl of Crawford & Balcarres claiming the ancient Dukedom of Montrose. Edinburgh, 1851. *St.A. U.*

— Abstract of the supplemental case of James, Duke of Montrose, in answer to the supplemental case of James, Earl of Crawford & Balcarres, claiming the title of Duke of Montrose. Edinburgh, 1853. *St.A. U.*

— Case for James, Duke of Montrose, petitioner upon his right to appear and be heard against claim of the Earl of Crawford & Balcarres to be Duke of Montrose. 1851. *Edin. L.L.*

— Case of James, Duke of Montrose in opposition to the case of James, Earl of Crawford & Balcarres, claiming the title, honour and dignity of the Duke of Montrose. Edinburgh, 1853. *Ab. P.; Glas. Mit.; Edin. L.L.*

— Supplemental case of James, Duke of Montrose in answer to supplemental case of James, Earl of Crawford & Balcarres claiming . . . Duke of Montrose. Edinburgh, 1853. *Edin. L.L.*

MINUTES of evidence . . . 1853. *Edin. L.L.*

RIDDELL (John): Abstract of the case of James, Earl of Crawford & Balcarres, etc., claiming the original Dukedom of Montrose, created in 1488; as drawn up by J. Riddell . . . London, 1850. *St.A. U.; Edin. P.*

— Abstract of the supplemental case of James, Earl of Crawford & Balcarres, etc., claiming the original Dukedom of Montrose, created in 1488. As drawn up by J. Riddell. London, 1852. *St.A. U.*

STATEMENT of evidence for . . . Duke of Montrose in opposition to claim of the Earl of Crawford and Balcarres. 1850. *Edin. L.L.*

Moodie, Mudie

RUVIGNY & RAINEVAL (M. A. H. D. H. de la C. Massue de Ruvigny), *9th Marquis de*: The Moodie book. n.p., 1906. *S.C.L.; Ab. U.; Ork. C.; Edin. P.; Edin. S.; Edin. L.L.*

Moodie, Mudie in Angus

MUDIE (Sir Robert Francis) & MUDIE (Ian M. N.): The Mudies of Angus. Broughty Ferry, 1959. *Ang. C.*

Moodie, Mudie of Melsetter

BURROWS (Edmund H.): The Moodies of Melsetter. Cape Town, 1954. *Ork. C.*

Moray, Earl of Strathearn, *see* **Strathearn,** Earldom of

More

MORE (David Fellow): History of the More family. Binghamton, N.Y., 1893. *Edin. S.*

SIMPSON (Sir Robert Russell): The Monkrigg Will case. Edinburgh, 1923. *Edin. S.*

Morgan

FORBES (Alexander): Memorials of the family of Forbes of Forbesfield. [With notes on connected Morgans, etc.] Aberdeen, 1905. *Ab. P.; Ab. C.; St.A. U.; Glas. U.; Glas. Mit.; Edin. P.; Edin. S.*

Morgan in Dundee

THOMS (P.): An account of the Morgan Hospital, with a sketch of the Morgans of Dundee. Dundee, 1870. *Dund. P.*

Morice, Morrice

MORICE (William C.): Aberdeen parish register extracts as suppl. with index to *Morice and Morrice biographies.* Aberdeen, 1937. (*Typescript.*) *Ab. P.*

— Collection of Morice and Morrice biographies. 1923. *Ab. P.*

MORRICE (Wm. Charles): A Morrice genealogical tree dated 1946 for study in conjunction with *The Descendants of James Young and Rachel Cruickshank* by Col. Johnston. 1946. *Ab. P.*

Morrison

CLAN MORRISON SOCIETY. Report, 1912-13. n.p., [1914]. *Edin. P.*

MORISON (Alexander): The Heraldry of the Clan MacGhillemhuire, or Morrison. Edinburgh, [1910]. *Edin. P.*

MORRISON (Alick): The Clan Morrison: heritage of the Isles. Edinburgh, 1956. *Inv. P.; Edin. U.; Per. C.; Dund. P.; Edin. P.; Glas. Mit.; Cai. C.; Ber. C.; Edin. L.L.; Edin. Ant.*

MORRISON (Hew), *comp.*: Excerpts from published Scottish records and other sources relative to the family of Morrison. n.p., c. 1921. *Edin. P.*

— *ed.*: Roll of honour of the Clan Morrison (Morison, Morrison, and Gilmour). Edinburgh, [1922]. *Edin. P.*

Morrison (Leonard A.): History of the Morison or Morrison family. Boston, Mass., 1880. *Edin. P.*

Morrison (Nancy Brysson): The Clan Morrison. Glasgow, 1951. *Inv. P.; Edin. P.; Glas. Mit.*

Morton

Deuchar (A.): Genealogical collections relative to the family of Myreton or Morton. n.d. (*MS.*) *Glas. Mit.*

Moultray

Ruvigny & Raineval (M. A. H. D. H. de la C. Massue de Ruvigny), *9th Marquis de*: Moultray of Seafield and Roscobie. London, 1902. *Dunf. P.; Edin. L.L.*

Mowat

[Original family papers.] *Ork. C.*

Mudie, *see* Moodie

Muir

Marshall (G. F. L.), *comp.*: The Muir book; comp. . . . for the descendants of Sir William Muir . . ., and of Elizabeth Huntly Wemyss, his wife. Fleet, Hants, 1930. *Edin. P.*

Muirhead

[Grosett (Walter)]: An account of the family of the Muirheads of Lachop now represented by Muirhead of Breadisholm. n.p., n.d. *Edin. P.*

Munro

Clan Munro Annual. 1939— Perth, 1939-   *Edin. P.; Edin. L.L.; Edin. Ant.* (no. 1).

Fraser (Charles Ian) of Reelig: The Clan Munro (Clann an Rothaich): a beacon ablaze. Edinburgh, 1954. *Inv. P.; Inv. C.; Dunb. C.; Edin. U.; Lan. C.; Ab. P.; Per. C.; Dund. P.; Pai. P.; Edin. P.; Glas. Mit.; Cai. C.; Ber. C.; Edin. L.L.; Edin. Ant.*

Munro (Mary Seymour): Appellant in the case in the House of Lords relating to the Munro family. George Munro, of Culrain and Charles, his eldest son, being Respondents in the case. n.p., 1831. *Inv. P.*

The Munros in France: a history of a branch of the family in France, descended from the chiefs of the clan, seated at Foulis, Ross-shire. [French and English.] Stirling, 1908. *St.A. U.; Ab. U.; Ab. P.; Edin. P.; Glas. Mit.*

136

Munro of Achany

[MILL (H. G.)]: Genealogical chart of the family of Munro of Achany. n.p., 1881. *Edin. P.; Edin. L.L.*

Munro of Foulis

DODDRIDGE (Philip): Life of Colonel James Gardiner, slain at Prestonpans, also . . . the ancient family of Munroes of Fowlis. Ayr, 1813. *Inv. P.; Edin. S.* (1894); *Glas. Mit.* (1764 + 1802).

MCINNES (C. T.), *ed.*: Calendar of writs of Munro of Foulis, 1299-1823. Edinburgh, 1940. (Scottish Record Soc., 71.) *S.C.L.; Dund. P.; Edin. P.; Glas. Mit.*

MACKENZIE (Alexander): History of the Munros of Fowlis, with genealogies of the principal families of the name, to which are added those of Lexington and New England. Inverness, 1898. *Dund. P.; Ab. P.; Inv. P.; Sti. P.; Ross C.; Ab. U.; Edin. U.; St.A. U.; Glas. U.; Edin. P.; Edin. S.; Glas. Mit.; Edin. L.L.; Edin. Ant.*

MONROE (Horace): Foulis castle and the Monroes of Lower Iveagh. London, 1929. *S.C.L.; St.A. U.; Ab. U.; Ab. P.; Kirkcud. C.; Edin. P.; Edin. S.; Glas. Mit.*

Munro, U.S.A.

NORTHRUP (Guilford Smith): Genealogy of Josiah Munroe . . . St. Johns, Mich., 1912. *S.C.L.* (microfilm).

Murdoch of Cumloden

FALLOW (T. M.): A short history of the family of Murdoch of Cumloden. [1905.] (Repr. from *The Gallovidian*, 1904.) *Dumf. C.; Edin. S.*

Mure of Caldwell

[MURE (William) of Caldwell, *ed.*]: Selections from the family papers preserved at Caldwell. 2 v. in 3. Glasgow, 1854. (Maitland Club, 71.) *Glas. U.; Dund. P.; Edin. P.; Edin. S.*
— Paisley, 1883-85. (New Club.) *S.C.L.; Glas. Mit.*

Mure of Rowallan

MURE (Sir William): The Historie and descent of the house of Rowallan; written in or prior to 1657. With a preface by William Muir. Glasgow, 1825. *Kil. P.; Inv. P.; Ayr P.; St.A. U.; Glas. U.; Edin. P.; Edin. S.; Glas. Mit.; Edin. L.L.; Edin. Ant.*

Murray

JOHNSTON (George Harvey): The Heraldry of the Murrays. Edinburgh, 1910. *Dumf. C.; Glas. U.; Edin. P.; Edin. S.; Glas. Mit.*

N (M.): Unto children's children: lives and letters of the parents of the home at Graaf Reinet . . . n.p., 1909. *Edin. P.*

PAUL (Sir James Balfour): Murrays of Romanno, Broughton and Stanhope. [Edinburgh, 1899.] *Edin. S.*

Murray, Earl of, Marquess of, Duke of Atholl

CHRONICLES of the Atholl and Tullibardine families; coll. and arranged by John, 7th Duke of Atholl. 5 v. Edinburgh, 1908. *Per. P.; Ab. U.; Edin. P.; Glas. Mit.; Edin. S.*

ROBERTSON (James Alexander): Comitatus de Atholis. The Earldom of Atholl . . . [Edinburgh], 1860. *Per. P.; Glas. U.; Edin. P.; Edin. S.; Edin. L.L.; Edin. Ant.*

Murray of Blackbarony

MURRAY (Sir Digby), *11th Bt.*: Murray of Blackbarony. 1891. *Zet. C.*

Murray of Elibank

ELIBANK (Arthur Cecil Murray), *3rd Viscount*: The Five sons of "Bare Betty". London, 1936. *Mid. C.; Dumb. P.* (1938); *Inv. P.; Glas. U.; Edin. P.; Edin. S.; Glas. Mit.*

— The Murrays of Elibank. Edinburgh, 1917. *Ab. P.; Edin. P.; Edin. S.; Edin. L.L.*

Murray of Ochtertyre

KIPPEN (Albert D.): The Murrays of Ochtertyre. Crieff, 1893. *Glas. Mit.*

Murray of Polmaise

[COOK (William B.)]: Genealogical chart, 1358-1907, of the Murrays of Touchadam and Polmaise. London, 1907. *Sti. C.; Edin. L.L.*

Murray of Stanhope

LINEAGE and pedigree of the house of Murray of Stanhope, co. of Peebles-shire. n.p., n.d. *Edin. L.L.*

Murray of Touchadam, *see* **Murray of Polmaise**

Murray, Earl of, Marquess of Tullibardine, *see* **Murray, Earl of, Marquess of, Duke of Atholl**

Mushet of Dalkeith

OSBORN (Fred M.): The Story of the Mushets. London, 1952. *Mid. C.; Glas. U.; Edin. P.*

Mylne

MYLNE (Robert Scott): The Master masons to the crown of Scotland and their works. Edinburgh, 1893. *S.C.L.; Ab. P.; Glas. Mit.*

Myreton, *see* **Morton**

Nairn

MUIR (Augustus): Nairns of Kirkcaldy: a short history of the company (1847-1956). Cambridge, 1956. *Per. C.; Kir. P.*

Nairn of Dunsinane

ROUGHEAD (William), *ed.*: Trial of Katherine Nairn. Edinburgh, 1926. *S.C.L.; Glas. Mit.*

Nairne

NAIRNE (Charles Sylvester): John Nairne, 1711-1795, minister of Anstruther Easter, and his descendants. [Glasgow], 1931. *St.A. U.; Edin. U.; Edin. P.; Edin. S.; Edin. L.L.*

Nairne, Lord

ELPHINSTONE (Margaret Mercer): Case of Margaret Mercer Elphinstone of Aldie, Baroness Keith . . . claiming the title . . . Baroness Nairne . . . 18—. *Edin. L.L.*

MINUTES of evidence . . . Emily Jane Mercer Elphinstone de Flahaut, Dowager Marchioness of Lansdowne . . . entitled to the title . . . of Baroness Nairne in the peerage of Scotland. 1873. *Edin. L.L.*

Naismith

GENEALOGICAL tables to 1911. *Ham. P.; Glas. Mit.*

N (W. W.): Mrs. John Naismith of Drumloch . . . and other Naismith memoirs. Glasgow, 1911. *Edin. P.*

Napier

RIDDELL (John): Tracts, legal and historical, etc. Edinburgh, 1835. *S.C.L.; Edin. P.; Edin. S.*

SMITH (John Guthrie): Strathendrick and its inhabitants. Glasgow, 1896. *S.C.L.; Glas. Mit.*

see also **Lennox,** Earldom of

Napier of Kilmahew

[KERR (Robert Malcolm)]: [Genealogical notices of the Napiers of Kilmahew, in Dunbartonshire.] Glasgow, 1849. *Glas. Mit.; Edin. P.; Edin. L.L.; Glas. U.*

RIDDELL (John), & *others, comps.*: The Pedigree of Her Royal and Most Serene Highness the Duchess of Mantua . . . her descent from . . . the houses of . . . Lennox, Napier, etc. New ed., London, 1885. *Edin. P.*

Napier of Merchiston

HISTORY of the Napiers of Merchiston, shewing their descent from the Earls of Lennox of auld and their marriage into the family of the Scotts of Thirlestane; comp. from old records. [London], 1921. *Edin. S.; Glas. Mit.*

NAPIER (Mark): Memoirs of John Napier of Merchiston, his lineage, life and times. Edinburgh, 1834. *Glas. U.; Edin. P.; Edin. S.; Glas. Mit.; Edin. L.L.*

Neilson, *see* **Nelson**

Neish

McNISH (David) & TOD (William A.): The History of the Clan Neish or McNish of Perthshire and Galloway. Edinburgh, 1925. *Dund. P.; Ab. P.; Dumf. C.; Per. C.; Per. P.; Edin. U.; St.A. U.; Ab. U.; Dund. Q.; Kirkcud. C.; Glas. U.; Edin. P.; Edin. S.; Glas. Mit.; Edin. L.L.; Edin. Ant.*

Nelson

NELSON (William): Contributions towards a Nelson genealogy. Pt. 1. Some Neilsons of Scotland. Paterson, N.J., 1904. *Edin. S.*

Newburgh, Earldom of

BANDINI (Cecilia . . .), *Marchioness*: Case on behalf of Cecilia . . . Marchioness Dowager Bandini claiming . . . Countess of Newburgh in the peerage of Scotland. *Edin. L.L.*

— Supplementary case . . . *Edin. L.L.*

MINUTES of evidence . . . 1857-58. *Edin. L.L.*

Nicholson

NICHOLSON (Francis): Memorials of the family of Nicholson of Blackshaw, Dumfriesshire, Liverpool & Manchester; ed. by E. Axon. Kendal, 1928. *Dumf. C.; Glas. U.; Glas. Mit.; Edin. P.*

NICHOLSON (John Gibb): Clan Nicolson. [Edinburgh, 1938.] *Inv. P.; Edin. U.; Ab. U.; Ab. P.; Ham. P. ([1920]); Cai. C.; Edin. P.; Edin. S.; Glas. Mit.; Edin. L.L.*

Nicol of Ballogie

NICOL (W. E.): The Genealogy of the Nicol family, the Kincardineshire branch. London, 1909. *Ab. P.; Edin. P.; Edin. S.*

Nisbet of Carfin, Carphin

INGLIS (John A.): The Nisbets of Carfin. London, 1916. (Repr. from *Miscellanea Genealogica and Heraldica*, June 1916.) *Edin. S.; Edin. Ant.*

Nisbet of Dean

[WOOD (John Philip)]: Some notes about . . . Nisbet of Dean . . . (In his *Memorials of various families* . . . c. 1830. (*MS.*).) *Edin. P.*

Nisbet of Nisbet

MITCHELL (J[ohn] O[swald]): Sir Philip Nisbet. (Repr. from the *Glasgow Herald*, 25th July 1891.) *Glas. Mit.; Edin. L.L.*

NESBETT (Robert Chancellor): Nisbet of that ilk. London, 1941. *S.C.L.; Sti. P.; Ber. C.; Rox. C.; Edin. U.; Ab. U.; St.A. U.; Glas. U.; Air. P.; Edin. P.; Edin. S.; Glas. Mit.; Edin. Ant.*

Nisbit

DOWLING (J. N.), *comp.*: Chart of the descent of the family of Nisbit. 1926. (*MS.*) *Glas. Mit.*

Nithsdale, Earldom of

MAXWELL (William) of Carruchan: Case for William Maxwell of Carruchan, Esq., claiming to be Earl of Nithsdale, Lord Maxwell, Eskdale and Carlyle and Lord Herries in the peerage of Scotland. n.p., n.d. *Edin. Ant.*

see also **Maxwell,** Earl of Nithsdale

Ochiltree

RAILEY (Mrs. Clementine Brown): History of the house of Ochiltree of Ayrshire, Scotland, with the genealogy of the families of those who came to America, and of some of the allied families, 1124-1916. Sterling, Kan., 1916. *Glas. Mit.*

Ochterloney

WATKINS (Walter Kendall): The Ochterloney family of Scotland, and Boston in New England. Boston, Mass., 1902. *Arb. P.; Edin. P.; Edin. L.L.*

Ogilvie of Banff

ABERCROMBY (Cavendish Douglas): The Ogilvies of Banff. n.p., 1939. *Ab. P.; Ab. C.; Edin. P.*

Ogilvie of Barras

BARRON (Douglas Gordon): In defence of the regalia, 1651-52. Selections from the family papers of the Ogilvies of Barras. London, 1910. *Ang. C.; Arb. P.; Mont. P.; Ab. P.; Glas. U.; Dund. P.; Edin. P.; Edin. S.; Glas. Mit.*

Ogilvie of Milton

WELSH (G. C.): Keith and its lairds. Keith, 1958. *Banff C.; Edin. L.L.*

Ogilvie of Ternemny

[OGILVIE (Alex. John)]: The Ogilvies of Ternemny, Rothiemay: [a famous scholastic family]. Edinburgh, 1938. *Ab. P.; Edin. P.* (1937).

Ogilvie-Grant, Earl of Seafield

SEAFIELD (Ian Charles Grant), *8th Earl of*: In memoriam, Ian Charles, 8th Earl of Seafield, 27th chief of Clan Grant. [Inverness], 1884. *Mor. C.; Edin. P.*

SEAFIELD (Caroline Ogilvie-Grant), *Countess of*: The Right Hon. Caroline, Countess of Seafield. Born 30th June, 1830, died 6th October, 1911. [Volume of tributes to Caroline, Countess of Seafield.] *Inv. P.*

see also **Grant**

Ogilvy

THE BOOK of Ogilvy. [Two *MS.* volumes on the Ogilvys.] *Forf. P.*

RAMSAY (Sir James Henry): Early Ogilvy pedigrees, 1366/7-1628. [Ogilvy of Auchterhouse, of Inverquharity, of Clova.] 1919. (Repr. from *The Genealogist*, n.s., v. XXXV.) *Edin. P.; Edin. Ant.; S.C.L.* (Photocopy).

Ogilvy, Earl of Airlie

WILSON (William): The House of Airlie. 2 v. London, 1924. *S.C.L.; Dund. P.; Coat. P.; Pet. P.; Ang. C.; Sti. P.; Per. C.; Ham. P.; Arb. P.; Gala. P.; Ab. U.; St.A. U.; Haw. P.; Forf. P.; Ab. P.; Glas. U.; Edin. U.; Edin. P.; Edin. S.; Glas. Mit.; Edin. L.L.*

Ogilvy of Auchterhouse, *see* **Ogilvy**

Ogilvy of Boyne

OGILVY-BETHUNE marriage contract, 1566. n.d. *Glas. Mit.*

TAYLER (Alistair) & TAYLER (Henrietta): The Ogilvies of Boyne. Aberdeen, 1933. *Ab. P.; St.A. U.; Edin. P.; Edin. S.; Glas. Mit.; Edin. L.L.; Edin. Ant.; Ab. U.*

Ogilvy of Clova, *see* **Ogilvy**

Ogilvy in Cornton

STEUART (Katherine) [i.e. *Agnes Maciver Logan*]: By Allan Water: the true story of an old house. Edinburgh, 1901. *St.A. U.*

Ogilvy of Eastmiln

ROUGHEAD (William), *ed.*: Trial of Katherine Nairn. Edinburgh, 1926. *S.C.L.; Glas. Mit.*

Ogilvy, Earl of Findlater

MAIDMENT (James): Genealogical fragments relating to the families of Findlater, Gardner, Douglas, Keith, Auchinlechs, Vetch and Duguid. Berwick, 1855. *Inv. P.; Glas. U.; Edin. P.; Edin. S.; Glas. Mit.; Edin. Ant.*

Ogilvy of Inverquharity, *see* **Ogilvy**

Ogilvy, Earl of Seafield, *see* **Ogilvie-Grant,** Earl of Seafield

Ogstoun of Ogstoun

[OGSTON (Alexander)]: A genealogical history of the family of Ogstoun from . . . c. 1200. Edinburgh, 1876. *Ab. P.; Edin. L.L.*
— — Supplement. 1897. *Ab. P.*

Oliphant

ANDERSON (Joseph), *ed*: The Oliphants in Scotland, with a selection of original documents from the charter chest at Gask. Edinburgh, 1879. *Cai. C.; Per. C.; Fife C.; Per. P.; St.A. U.; Ab. U.; Glas. U.; Edin. P.; Edin. S.; Glas. Mit.; Edin. L.L.; Edin. Ant.*

MACLAGAN (Bessie): The Story of Williamston: an old Jacobite home of Strathearn. Perth, 1924. *Per. C.; Per. P.*

Oliphant of Gask

FAMILY of Oliphant of Fingask, Condie, Gask, Rossie . . . [Genealogical MSS.] n.d. *Glas. Mit.*

GRAHAM (Ethel Maxtone): The Oliphants of Gask: records of a Jacobite family. London, 1910. *Inv. P.; Ang. C.; Per. C.; Per. P.; Dumb. P.; Ab. U.; Dund. P.; Edin. P.; Glas. Mit.; Edin. S.; Edin. Ant.*

OLIPHANT (Thomas Lawrence Kington): The Jacobite lairds of Gask. London, 1870. (Grampian Club, 2.) *S.C.L.; Inv. P.; Sti. P.; Per. C.; Ab. P.; Glas. U.; Kirkcud. C.; Edin. P.; Dund. P.; Glas. Mit.; Edin. S.; Edin. L.L.; Edin. Ant.*

STIRTON (John): Links with Lady Nairne and the house of Gask. Forfar, 1930. *Per. C.*

Omey

McKERRAL (Andrew): Two old Kintyre lawsuits, with some notes on . . . Omeys of Kilcolmkill, etc. n.p., 1941. *Glas. Mit.*

Orkney, Earldom of

CLOUSTON (J. Storer), *ed.*: Records of the Earldom of Orkney, 1299-1614. Edinburgh, 1914. (Scottish Hist. Soc., 2nd ser. v. 7.) *S.C.L.; Ork. C.; Edin. L.L.*

Ormiston

ORMISTON (Thomas Lane): The Ormistons of Teviotdale. Exeter, 1951. *S.C.L.; Edin. U.; St.A. U.; Edin. P.; Edin. S.; Edin. L.L.*

— Ormistons in Scotland before 1854. 1936. (*Typescript.*) *Edin. L.L.*

— An index of Ormistons in Scotland, 1855-1933. 1937. (*Typescript.*) *Edin. L.L.*

— Registration of births, deaths and marriages of Ormistons in Scotland, 1855-1940. 1948. (*Typescript.*) *Edin. L.L.*

ORMSTON (W. J.): Ormistons of that ilk. n.p., 1933. *Edin. S.; Edin. L.L.*

Orr

McCALL (Hardy Bertram): Some old families: a contribution to the genealogical history of Scotland. Birmingham, 1890. *S.C.L.; Edin. P.; Edin. S.; Sel. P.; Edin. Ant.; Edin. L.L.*

Orrok of Orrok

ORROK (John): Letters, comp. by Lady H. Forbes, and ed. by A. and H. Tayler. Aberdeen, 1927. *Glas. Mit.*

Osler

OSLER (James Couper): Osler tree [chart pedigree] with some supplementary notes on Oslers, Fentons, Spences, Eassons, Sinclairs and Coupers by David Couper Thomson. [Dundee], 1924. *Edin. L.L.; Edin. Ant.*

144

Park

DEUCHAR (A.): Genealogical collections relative to the family of Park. (*MS.*) *Glas. Mit.*

Parker, see **Patterson**

Paterson

PATERSON (James): Scottish surnames: a contribution to genealogy. Edinburgh, 1866. *Arb. P.; Glas. Mit.; Ab. P.; Dund. Q.*

Paterson-Anstruther, *see* **Polwarth,** Lord

Patterson

PARKER (Donald Dean): The Graham-Patterson family history. [Includes Parker family history.] [Brookings, S. Dakota,] 1947. *Dumf. C.*

RIX (Guy Scoby): Patterson genealogy: descendants of John Patterson of Argyleshire, Scotland. Concord, N.H., 1914. *Edin. P.* (micard).

Paul

PAUL (Sir James Balfour): Some Pauls of Glasgow and their descendants . . . the scanty record of an obscure family. Edinburgh, 1912. (*Photocopy.*) *S.C.L.*

Pearson, Peirson, (*see also* **Pierson** of Balmadies)

BAXTER (Angus): The History of the Pearson family, 1296-1949. [1949.] *Dumf. C.*

PEARSON (David Ritchie): A condensed account of the family of Pe-rson in Scotland from A.D. 1296. 1891. (*Typescript.*) *Edin. L.L.*

Percy in Scotland

BAIN (Joseph): The Percies in Scotland. n.p., [1884]. (Repr. from *Archaeological Journal,* v. XLI.) *Edin. L.L.*

Perth, Earldom of

[BANKS (Thomas Christopher)]: The Detection of infamy earnestly recommended to the justice and deliberation of the Imperial Parliament of Great Britain by an unfortunate nobleman. (Cont. Appeal of Charles Edward, Duke of Melfort, etc., heir-male and chief representative of the house of Drummond of Perth, submitted to the two Houses of Parliament . . .) London, 1816. *Edin. L.L.*

DRUMMOND (Thomas): An interesting statement of the claims of Thomas Drummond of New Painshaw, co. Durham, to the . . . Earldom of Perth. Newcastle upon Tyne, 1831. *Inv. P.; Edin. P.* (1830)*; Glas. Mit.* (1830).

HISTORICAL facts and explanations regarding the succession to the Lordships, Baronies and Regality of Drummond and Earldom of Perth. Paris, 1866. *Edin. L.L.*

MELFORT (George Drummond), *Duc de*: Case on behalf of George Drummond, Duke de Melfort in France, claiming to be Earl of Perth, in the Peerage of Scotland. n.p., n.d. *Forf. P.; Edin. L.L.*

— Case on behalf of George Drummond, Duke de Melfort in France, claiming to be Earl of Perth and Earl of Melfort in the Peerage of Scotland. n.p., n.d. *Forf. P.; Edin. L.L.*

MINUTES of evidence . . . 1846. *Edin. L.L.*

Pierson of Balmadies (*see also* **Pearson, Peirson**)

PIERSON (Dr John): Familien chronik der Pierson von Balmadies. Berlin, 1901. *Edin. L.L.*

Pike, Pyke

MACPIKE (E. H.): Pyke and MacPike families. 1927. (Repr. from *Scottish Notes & Queries*.) *Dund. Q.*

Pitcairn

[BOASE (Edward R.)]: The Family of Pitcairn of Kinninmont and Pitcairn of Kinnaird. Edinburgh, [1938]. (*Typescript.*) *Dund. P.; Edin. P.; Edin. S.*

PITCAIRN (Constance): The History of the Fife Pitcairns. Edinburgh, 1905. *Kir. P.; Fife C.; Ab. U.; Dunf. P.; St.A. U.; Edin. P.; Edin. S.; Glas. Mit.; Edin. L.L.; Edin. Ant.*

Pitman

PITMAN (Charles Edward): History and pedigree of the family of Pitman of Dunchideock, Exeter, and their collaterals, and of the Pitmans of Alphington, Norfolk, and Edinburgh. London, 1920. *Edin. S.*

PITMAN (Harry Anderson): Frederick Cobbe Pitman and his family. [London], 1930. *Edin. S.; Edin. L.L.*

Playfair

PLAYFAIR (Arthur Grace): Playfair book; or, Notes on the Scottish family of Playfair. 4th ed. Tunbridge Wells, 1932. *Glas. U.; Edin. U.; Edin. P.; Edin. L.L.* (1913).

146

ROGER (James Cruikshank): Some account of the Rogers in Coupar-Grange, with a synopsis . . . of the family of Playfair, with whom they intermarried. London, 1877. *Ang. C.; Edin. P.; Edin. L.L.*

ROGERS (Charles): Four Perthshire families: Roger, Playfair, Constable and Haldane of Barmony. Edinburgh, 1887. *Sti. P.; Glas. U.; Per. P.; Dunf. P.; St.A. U.; Dund. P.; Edin. S.; Edin. L.L.; Edin. Ant.*

— The Scottish branch of the Norman house of Roger, with a genealogical sketch of the family of Playfair. London, 1872. *Dunf. P.; Sti. P.*

— The Scottish house of Roger, with notes respecting the families of Playfair and Haldane of Barmony. 2nd ed. Edinburgh, 1875. *Dunf. P.; Edin. P.; Edin. S.; Glas. Mit.*

Plenderleath

LANG (Patrick Sellar), *comp.*: The Langs of Selkirk, with some notes on other families. Melbourne, 1910. *Edin. P.; Edin. S.*

Polwarth, Lord

ANSTRUTHER (Anne Paterson): Case of Dame Anne Paterson Anstruther . . . claiming the title . . . of Baroness Polewart or Polwarth. *Edin. L.L.*

JUDGEMENT. 1835. *Edin. L.L.*

MS. notes of the Lord Chancellor's speech. 1831, 1835. *Edin. L.L.*

MINUTES of evidence . . . 1818. *Edin. L.L.*

SCOTT (Hugh): Case of Hugh Scott of Harden, Esq., claiming the title . . . Baron Polewart or Polwarth. *Edin. L.L.*

— Additional case for above . . . [1835.] *Edin. L.L.*

Porteous

DEUCHAR (A).: Genealogical collections relative to the family of Porteous. n.d. (*MS.*) *Glas. Mit.*

Preston

MS. notes and press cuttings on the family of Preston. n.d. . . . . *Edin. P.*

Preston of Fyvie

STIRLING (Anna Maria D. W. Pickering), *Mrs. Stirling*: Fyvie Castle, its lairds and their times. London, 1928. *S.C.L.; Elg. P.; Mid. C.; Ren. C.; Fife C.; Ab. P.; West L. C.; Banff C.; Fras. P.; Dunb. C.; Edin. U.; Glas. Mit.*

Primrose

> GIBSON (John C.): Lands and lairds of Dunipace. Stirling, 1903. *Edin. P.; Edin. S.; Glas. Mit.*

Primrose, Earl of Roseberry

> FORBES (J. Macbeth): History of the Primrose-Roseberry family, 1500-1900. London, 1907. *Edin. L.L.*

Pringle

> PRINGLE (Alexander): Records of the Pringles or Hoppringles of the Scottish border. Edinburgh, 1933. *S.C.L.; Ber. C.; Edin. U.; Haw. P.; Gala. P.; St.A. U.; Ab. P.; Edin. P.; Edin. S.; Glas. Mit.; Edin. L.L.; Edin. Ant.*

> PRINGLE (Veronica): Veronica Pringle, widow, and Robert, Andrew and Mark Pringle . . . appellants; John Pringle of Crichton, respondent. n.p., 1767. *Edin. P.*

Pringle in South Africa

> PRINGLE (Eric), *and others*: Pringles of the Valleys: their history and genealogy. Adelaide, Cape Prov., 1957. *Edin. L.L.*

Purves of Purves

> PURVES (Sir William): Revenue of the Scottish crown, 1681; ed. by D. Murray Rose, [with genealogy of the family of Purves]. Edinburgh, 1897. *S.C.L.; Edin. P.*

Pyke, *see* **Pike**

Pyott

> BONAR (Horatius): Notes to genealogical chart or pedigree of the descendants of James Pyott, merchant, Montrose. n.p., 1914. *Ab. U.; Edin. P.; Edin. S.; Edin. L.L.*

Queensberry, Marquessate of

> CASE of Charles, Marquess and Earl of Queensberry, etc., formerly Sir Charles Douglas of Kelhead, Bt., claiming to be enrolled in his due place among the peers of Scotland and to have his right to the above titles . . . recognised and established. [1812.] *Edin. L.L.*

Ramsay

> RAMSAY (Sir James Henry): Notes on early Ramsay pedigrees, 1200-1600. 1914. (Repr. from *The Genealogist*, n.s. XXXI.) *Edin. S.*

Ramsay of Bamff

RAMSAY (Sir James Henry), *ed.*: Bamff charters, 1232-1703, with introduction, biographical summary and notes. Oxford, 1915. *Clack. C.; Per. C.; Dund. P.; Edin. P.; Glas. Mit.; Edin. S.; Edin. Ant.*

Ranald, the Clan, *see* **Macdonald**

Ranken of Colden

McCALL (Hardy Bertram): Some old families: a contribution to the genealogical history of Scotland. Birmingham, 1890. *S.C.L.; Edin. P.; Edin. S.; Sel. P.; Edin. L.L.; Edin. Ant.*

Rankin

WHYTE (Henry): The Rankins, pipers to the Macleans of Duart, and . . . Macleans of Coll. Glasgow, 1907. *Glas. Mit.*

Rede

READE (Compton): A record of the Redes of Barton Court, Bucks., and other lines of the name. Hereford, 1899. *Inv. P.*

Reid

REID (Herbert): The Reids of Kittochside. Pt. 1. Glasgow, 1943. *Lan. C.; Ruth. P.; Ham. P.; Glas. U.; Edin. P.; Glas. Mit.; Edin. S.*

—— Pt. 2. Glasgow, 1945. *Lan. C.; Ruth. P.; Glas. Mit.*

Reid-Robertson

ROBERTSON (James): Historical account of the Barons Reid-Robertson of Straloch. Blairgowrie, 1887. *Ab. P.; Per. P.; Dund. Q.; Glas. U.; Edin. P.; Glas. Mit.*

Reith

BULLOCH (John Malcolm): The Family of Reith. Aberdeen, 1937. (*Newspaper cuttings and typescript.*) *Ab. P.*

— The Reith family. 1935. *Ab. P.*

Renny

[RENNY (James)], *d. 1797*: Papers relative to the Renny family, with particular reference to James Renny, jun., . . . n.d. (*MS.*) *Arb. P.*

Renton

RENTON [family history]. n.p., n.d. *Edin. P.*

Richardson

[MSS., and miscellaneous information.] *Dumf. C.*

McMILLAN (William): Gabriel Richardson and his family. n.p., n.d. *Dunf. P.*

Riddell, Riddle

RIDLON (G. T.): History of the ancient Ryedales . . . 860 to 1884 . . . Riddell, Riddle, Ridlon, Ridley, etc. Manchester, N.H., 1884. *Ab. P.; Dumf. C.; Sel. P.; Edin. P.; Edin. S.*

Ridley, *see* **Riddell**

Ridlon, *see* **Riddell**

Ridpath

LE HARDY (William): History of the family of Ridpath of Redpath and Angelraw, in the county of Berwick and subsequently of London. n.d. (*Typescript.*) *Edin. P.*

Rintoul

SPENCER (C. L.): Some notes on the Spencers, Jarvies and Rintouls in Glasgow, comp. from family tradition and public records. 1935. (*Typescript.*) *Glas. Mit.*

Robertson

CLAN DONNACHAIDH ANNUAL, 1951—date. Edinburgh, 1951-. *Edin. P.*

IN MEMORIAM: descent of Catherine MacDiarmid, wife of J. N. Paton, Dunfermline. n.p., n.d. *Dunf. P.*

MONCREIFFE (Iain): The Robertsons: Clan Donnachaidh of Atholl. Edinburgh, [1954]. *Inv. P.; Edin. U.; Lan. C.; Dunf. P.; Ab. P.; Per. C.; Dund. P.; Pai. P.; Edin. P.; Glas. Mit.; Cai. C.; Ber. C.; Edin. L.L.; Edin. Ant.*

REID (James Robertson): A short history of the Clan Robertson. Stirling, 1933. *S.C.L.; Ross C.; Inv. P.; Sti. C.; Ab. U.; Inv. C.; Dunf. P.; Ab. P.; Dund. Q.; Ren. C.; Edin. P.; Edin. S.; Edin. L.L.; Edin. Ant.; Glas. Mit.*

ROBERTSON (David): A brief account of the Clan Donnachaidh. Glasgow, 1894. *Dunf. P.; Inv. P.; Ab. U.; Glas. U.; Glas. Mit.; Edin. P.; Edin. S.; Edin. L.L.; Edin. Ant.*

ROBERTSON (Herbert): Stemmata Robertson et Durdin. London, 1893-95. *Edin. P.; Edin. L.L.*

ROBERTSON (James): Chiefs of Clan Donnachaidh, 1275-1749, and the Highlanders at Bannockburn. Perth, 1929. *Dunf. P.; Sti. P.; Per. C.; Ab. U.; Dund. Q.; Dund. P.; Edin. P.; Edin. S.; Glas. Mit.; Edin. L.L.*

ROBERTSON (James Alexander): Comitatus de Atholia: the Earldom of Atholl . . . and their descendants, the Robertsons, with proofs. [Edinburgh], 1860. *Per. P.; Glas. U.; Edin. P.; Edin. S.; Edin. L.L.; Edin. Ant.*

Robertson of Cray

W[ILLIAMSON] (Henry McIree): The Robertsons of Cray. Edinburgh, 1935. *Edin. P.; Edin. S.*

Robertson of Inshes

THE ROBERTSONS of Inshes. n.d. (*Press cuttings.*) *Nai. C.*

Robertson of Kindeace

[AIRD (Gustavus)]: Genealogy of the families of Douglas of Mulderg and Robertson of Kindeace. Dingwall, 1895. *Ross C.; Cai. C.; Inv. P.; Nai. C.; Ab. U.; Ork. C.; Ab. P.; Edin. P.; Glas. Mit.; St.A. U.*

Robertson of Prenderguest

[EUSTACE (S.), *comp.*:] The Family of Robert Robertson of Prenderguest and Brownshank and Margaret Home his wife. n.p., 1931. *Edin. L.L.*

Robertson of Straloch

NEWSPAPER cuttings relating to the Robertsons of Straloch in Strathardle. *Inv. P.*

ROBERTSON (James): Historical account of the Barons Reid-Robertson of Straloch. Blairgowrie, 1887. *Ab. P.; Per. P.; Ab. U.; Edin. P.; Edin. S.*

Robertson of Strowan

PATON (Sir Joseph Noel): Genealogy of the Celtic Earls of Atholl, the immediate descendants of Duncan I, King of Scotland; with chart of the descendants of Conon . . . founder of the De Atholia family, aft. known as Robertsons of Strowan, etc. n.p., 1873. *Ab. U.; Dunf. P.; Glas. Mit.; Edin. L.L.*

ROBERTSON (Alexander) of Strowan: The History and martial achievements of the Robertsons of Strowan. Edinburgh, [1771-1785]. *Inv. P.; St.A. U.; Glas. U.; Edin. P.; Glas. Mit.; Edin. Ant.*

Rochead

DEUCHAR (A.): Genealogical collections relative to the family of Rochead. n.d. (*MS.*) *Glas. Mit.*

Roger

ROGER (James Cruickshank): An historical summary of the Roger tenants of Coupar. London, 1879. *Glas. U.; Edin. P.; Edin. S.; Edin. L.L.*

— Some account of the Rogers in Coupar-Grange, with a synopsis of the more prominent members of the family of Playfair, with whom they intermarried. London, 1877. *Ang. C.; Edin. P.; Edin. L.L.; Edin. Ant.*

ROGERS (Charles): Four Perthshire families: Roger, Playfair, Constable and Haldane of Barmony. Edinburgh, 1887. *Sti. P.; Dunf. P.; Per. P.; St.A. U.; Glas. U.; Dund. P.; Edin. S.; Edin. L.L.; Edin. Ant.*

— The Scottish branch of the Norman house of Roger, with a genealogical sketch of the family of Playfair. London, 1872. *Dunf. P.; Sti. P.; Edin. L.L.; Edin. Ant.*

— The Scottish house of Roger. 2nd ed. Edinburgh, 1875. *Dunf. P.; Edin. P.; Edin. S.; Glas. Mit.; Edin. L.L.; Edin. Ant.*

ROGERS (Kenneth): The Family of Roger in Aberdeenshire. n.p., 1920. *S.C.L.*

Roger of Westmeon

ROGER (Julian C.): A history of our family (Rogers of Westmeon) 1451-1902. Compiled from authoritative documents. London, 1902. *Kirkcud. Bro.*

Rolland of Disblair

WALKER (Alexander): Disblair, 1634-1884, or, An old oak panel and something thereon. Aberdeen, 1884. *Edin. Ant.*

Rose

[ROSE (David Murray)]: Roses of Earlsmiln and Cullisse. Dingwall, n.d. (Repr. from the *North Star*, 1898.) *Inv. P., Ab. P.*

ROSE (Eric Hamilton): History of the family of de Ros, de Rose, Rose of Kilravock. Frome, 1939. *Edin. S.*

Rose of Holme Rose

ROSE (Henry): Genealogy of the family of Rose of Holme Rose. Nairn, 1929. *S.C.L.; Ab. P.; Inv. P.; Ab. U.; Dund. Q.; Edin. P.; Edin. S.; Glas. Mit.; Edin. L.L.; Edin. Ant.*

Rose of Kilravock

ROSE (Hew) & SHAW (Lachlan): A genealogical deduction of the family of Rose of Kilravock; ed. by Cosmo Innes. Edinburgh, 1848. (Spalding Club, 18.) *S.C.L.; Inv. C.; Ab. C.; Elg. P.; Haw. P.; Inv. P.; Edin. U.; Ab. P.; Glas. U.; Edin. P.; Dund. P.; Glas. Mit.; Edin. S.; Edin. L.L.*

SKELTON (J.): The Roses of Kilravock. 1883. *Nai. C.*

Rose of Montcoffer

TAYLER (Alastair) & TAYLER (Henrietta), *eds.*: The Domestic papers of the Rose family. Aberdeen, 1926. *Ab. U.; Ab. P.; Edin. P.; Glas. Mit.; Edin. S.*

Rosebery, Earl of, *see* **Primrose,** Earl of Rosebery

Ross

MACKINNON (Donald): The Clan Ross. Edinburgh, 1957. *Dund. P.; Edin. P.; Glas. Mit.; Inv. P.; Cai. C.; Ber. C.*

ROSS (Alexander M.): History of Clan Ross, with genealogies of the various families. Dingwall, 1932. *S.C.L.; Ross C.; Ab. P.; Inv. P.; Edin. U.; Ab. U.; St.A. U.; Edin. P.; Edin. S.; Glas. Mit.; Suth. C.; Edin. Ant.*

ROSS (Donald): The Massacre of the Rosses of Strathcarron. Inverness, 1886. *Inv. P.*

ROSS (Richard): Genealogy of R. R. [ancestor of Charles B. Boog Watson]. n.p., n.d. *Edin. P.*

WATSON (Charles Brodie Boog): Traditions and genealogies of some members of the families of Boog, Heron, Leishman, Ross and Watson. Perth, 1908. *St.A. U.; Edin. P.; Edin. S.; Edin. Ant.; Edin. L.L.*

Ross, Earldom of

ANE BREVE cronicle of the Earlis of Ross, including notices of the Abbots of Fearn, and of the family of Ross of Balnagown; ed. by W. R. B[aillie]. Edinburgh, 1850. *Inv. P.; Ab. U.; Edin. P.; Glas. Mit.; Edin. L.L.*

THE EARLDOM of Ross and lordship of Ardmanach. MS. of memorandum by John Horne Stevenson. 1934. (*Typescript.*) *Edin. L.L.*

REID (Francis Nevile): The Earls of Ross and their descendants. Edinburgh, 1894. *Cai. C.; Inv. P.; St.A. U.; Ab. U.; Edin. P.; Edin. S.; Glas. Mit.*

ROSE (David Murray): The Earldom of Ross. n.p., n.d. *Ab. U.*

Ross of Balnagown, *see* **Ross,** Earldom of

Ross of Dalton

KNOWLES (George Parker): A genealogical account of the Rosses of Dalton, in the county of Dumfries. London, 1855. *S.C.L.; Edin. L.L.*

Ross of Glencalvie

ROBERTSON (John): Rosses of Glencalvie. n.p., 1844. *Inv. P.*

Row of Carnock

MAIDMENT (James): Memorials of the family of Row. Edinburgh, 1828. *Dunf. P.; St.A. U.; Edin. P.; Glas. Mit.*

Roxburghe, Lord, Earl of, Duke of

KER (Sir James Innes): Case of Sir James Innes Ker, Bt., . . . 1808. *Edin. L.L.*

— Additional case of the above . . . *Edin. L.L.*

KER (John Bellenden): Case of John Bellenden Kerr and others . . . 1808. *Edin. L.L.*

— Tree showing propinquity of Mr. Bellenden Ker to the family of Roxburghe. n.p., n.d. *Glas. Mit.*

KER (Walter): Case of Colonel Walter Ker of Littledean . . . *Edin. L.L.*

MINUTES of evidence . . . 1808. *Edin. L.L.*

ROXBURGHE (James Innes Ker), *5th Duke of*: Additional appendix for James, Duke of Roxburgh against General Walter Ker of Littledean. 1819. *Edin. L.L.*

— Petition, answers, and duplies anent feu duties of the entailed estate of Roxburghe, Jan.-Nov. 1817. Edinburgh, 1817. *Edin. P.*

Ruddiman

JOHNSTON (George Harvey): Notes on the Ruddimans, and genealogical tables. Edinburgh, 1887. *Edin. P.; Edin. S.* (1901); *Edin. L.L.*

— The Ruddimans in Scotland: their history and works. Edinburgh, 1901. *St.A. U.; Edin. P.; Edin. S.*

Russell

THOMSON (David Couper), *comp.*: [Genealogical chart of] McCulloch, Turner, McCormick, and Russell. Dundee, 1943. *Edin. L.L.; Edin. Ant.*

Russell of Kingseat and Slipperfield

PATERSON (James): Scottish surnames: a contribution to genealogy. Edinburgh, 1866. *Ab. P.; Glas. Mit.; Ab. P.; Dund. Q.*

Rutherford

FACTS and data relating to the Rutherford family or clan, more especially the Rutherfords of Nisbet. Comp. from various sources and herein collated. 1885. (*MS.*) *St.A. U.*

154

Rutherfurd in Aberdeen

RUTHERFURD (James H.): The Rutherfurds in Aberdeen. [Kelso?], c. 1900. *Ab. P.*

Rutherfurd of Rutherfurd

COCKBURN-HOOD (Thomas H.): Rutherfurds of that ilk and their cadets. Edinburgh, 1884. *S.C.L.; Sel. P.; Ab. U.; Glas. U.; Glas. Mit.; Edin. P.; Edin. S.; Edin. L.L.*

—— [Additions and corrections by C. H. E. Carmichael.] Edinburgh, 1884-99. *St.A. U.; Edin. L.L.*

— The Rutherfurds of that ilk, and their cadets . . . [Additions and corrections by C. H. E. Carmichael and others.] Edinburgh, 1884-1903. *St.A. U.*

Rutherfurd, Lord Rutherfurd

RUTHERFORD (John): Case of John Rutherford, claiming the title of Baron Rutherford of Rutherford (with pedigree). 1839. *Edin. L.L.*

Ruthven

COWAN (Samuel): The Ruthven family papers. London, 1912. *Cai. C.; Per. C.; Fife C.; Dumb. P.; Ab. U.; Ab. P.; Kirkcud. C.; Ham. P.; Pai. P.; Edin. P.; Edin. S.; Glas. Mit.; Edin. L.L.*

FORTH & BRENTFORD (Patrick Ruthven), *Earl of*: Ruthven correspondence . . . A.D. 1615-62. London, 1868. (Roxburghe Club, 90.) *Glas. U.; Edin. P.; Edin. Ant.*

Ruthven, Earl of Gowrie

[BRUCE (John), *ed.*]: Papers relating to William, first Earl of Gowrie and Patrick Ruthven, his fifth and last surviving son. London, 1867. *Glas. U.; Dund. P.; Edin. P.; Glas. Mit.; Edin. L.L.; Edin. Ant.*

Ruthven, Lord Ruthven of Freeland

FRASER (Sir William): Memorials as to the Ruthven (of Freeland) peerage. n.p., n.d. *Edin. L.L.*

STEVENSON (John Horne): The Ruthven of Freeland peerage, and its critics. Glasgow, 1905. *S.C.L.; Ham. P.; Ab. P.; Glas. U.; Edin. P.; Glas. Mit.; Edin. S.; Edin. L.L.*

Ryedale, *see* **Riddell**

155

St Clair, (*see also* **Sinclair**)

SAINT-CLAIR (Louis Anatole de): Histoire généalogique de la famille de Saint-Clair et de ses alliances (France-Ecosse). Paris, 1905. *Edin. P.*

SAINT CLAIR (Roland William): The Saint Clairs of the Isles: a history of the Sea Kings of Orkney and their Scottish successors of the surname of Sinclair. Auckland, N.Z., 1898. *Cai. C.; Mid. C.; Ork. C.; Edin. P.; St.A. U.; Ab. U.; Glas. U.; Edin. S.; Glas. Mit.; Edin. L.L.; Edin. Ant.*

St Clair of Roslin, Rosslyn

HAY (Richard Augustin): Genealogie of the Sainteclaires of Rosslyn. Edinburgh, 1835. *S.C.L.; Mid. C.; Inv. P.; St.A. U.; Kir. P.; Glas. U.; Edin. P.; Edin. S.; Glas. Mit.* (1898); *Edin. Ant.*

Sandeman

THE CLAN: the Sandeman family magazine. (New series.) 5 v. Hove; [later at] Edinburgh, 1893-1899. *Per. P.*

SANDEMAN (John Glas), *comp.*: The Sandeman genealogy . . . from family notes, memoranda, and the original MS. by David Peat. Edinburgh, 1895. *Per. P.; Edin. P.; Edin. S.; Glas. Mit.; Edin. L.L.*

—— Brought up to date by G. L. Sandeman. Edinburgh, 1950. *Per. P.; Edin. P.; Edin. S.; Edin. L.L.*

SANDEMAN (Walter Albert): The Sandeman family of Perth. n.p., 1926. *Ab. U.*

Sandilands

MEMOIR and genealogy of the family of Sandilands of Crabstone & Cotton in Aberdeenshire. n.p., 1863. *Edin. S.*

Saunders

SAUNDERS (Herbert Clifford), *comp.*: Saunders pedigree. London, 1883. *Edin. P.*

Schevez of Kemback

SCHIVAS of Kemback. [A collection of extracts from printed sources.] [c. 1937.] *Edin. Port.*

Scollay

MARWICK (Hugh): Some notes on an old Orkney family—the Scollays. (In *Orkney Miscellany*, v. 1, 1953, pp. 29-47.) *Ork. C.; Zet. C.*

Scott

DUNLOP (Jean [Mary]): The Scotts. Edinburgh, 1957. *Dund. P.; Edin. P.; Glas. Mit.; Inv. P.; Cai. C.; Ber. C.*

SCOT (Walter): Metrical history of the honourable families of the names of Scot and Elliot in the shires of Roxburgh and Selkirk. Edinburgh, 1892. *Haw. P.; Glas. U.; Edin. S.; Edin. P.; Glas. Mit.*

— A true history of several honourable families of the right honourable name of Scot. Edinburgh, 1776. *Haw. P.; Edin. S.; Edin. L.L.*

— — Hawick, 1786. *Ab. P.* (+1688).

— — Ed. by J. G. Winning. Hawick, 1894. *Dumf. C.; St.A. U.; Edin. P.; Edin. S.; Haw. P.; Kirkcud. C.; Glas. Mit.*

SCOTT (Keith S. M.): Scott, 1118-1923, being a collection of Scott pedigrees, containing all male descendants from Buccleugh, Sinton, Harden, Balweary, etc. London, 1923. *Gala. P.; St.A. U.; Ab. U.; Haw. P.; Edin. P.; Edin. S.; Glas. Mit.; Edin. L.L.; Edin. Ant.*

SHARPE (Charles Kirkpatrick): [Scott family: some biographical notes, 1663-1723]. 1849. (*MS.*) *St.A. U.*

Scott of Abbotsford

ROGERS (Charles): Genealogical memoirs of the family of Sir Walter Scott of Abbotsford; with a reprint of his *Memorials of the Haliburtons*. London, 1877. (Grampian Club, 13.) *S.C.L.; Ab. P.; Dund. P.; Kil. P.; Dunf. P.; Dumf. C.; Haw. P.; Inv. P.; Sti. P.; Rox. C.; Edin. U.; Kirkcud. C.; Edin. S.; Glas. Mit.; Edin. L.L.; Edin. Ant.*

Scott of Aikwode, *see* Scott of Wamphray

Scott of Balwery

FAMILY of Scott of Balwery, Jawcraig, Aberdeenshire, etc. [Genealogical MSS.] *Glas. Mit.*

Scott of Bavelaw

[WOOD (John Philip)]: Scott of Bavelaw. (In his *Memorials of various families* . . . c. 1830. (*MS.*).) *Edin. P.*

Scott of Bowhill, *see* Scott of Wamphray

Scott of Branxholme

LOCKHART (William Eliott): Historical notes relating to Branxholme, plates, plan, etc. n.p., n.d. *Edin. L.L.*

Scott, Earl of, Duke of Buccleuch

[CRICHTON (Andrew)]: A short genealogical and historical account of the noble family of Buccleuch as it appeared in the *Dumfries Weekly Journal*, 18th Dec. 1827. Dumfries, 1827. *Dumf. C.*

FRASER (Sir William): The Scotts of Buccleuch. 2 v. Edinburgh, 1878. *S.C.L.; Haw. P.; Mid. C.; Dumf. C.; Rox. C.; Sel. P.; Moth. P.; St.A. U.; Ab. U.; Glas. U.; Dund. P.; Edin. P.; Edin. S.; Glas. Mit.; Edin. L.L.; Edin. Ant.*

— The Two heiresses of Buccleuch, Ladies Mary and Ann Scott, and their husbands, 1647-1732. 2 v. Edinburgh, 1878-80. (Repr. from his *Scotts of Buccleuch.*) *Ab. U.; Edin. L.L.; Edin. Ant.* (1 v. 1880).

GALLOWAY (George): Elegy on His Grace Henry, Duke of Buccleuch, . . . born . . . 1746 . . . died . . . 1812. Edinburgh, 1812. *Edin. P.*

MEMORIAL of the majority of the Earl of Dalkeith. Dalkeith, 1852. *Haw. P.; Edin. P.*

OLIVER (J. Rutherford Scott): Upper Teviotdale and the Scotts of Buccleuch. Hawick, 1887. *Rox. C.; Haw. P.; Dumf. C.; Gala. P.; Ayr P.; Ab. U.; Edin. U.; Mid. C.; Ab. P.; Kirkcud. C.; Glas. U.; Dund. P.; Pai. P.; Edin. P.; Edin. S.; Glas. Mit.; Edin. L.L.*

Scott of Ewisdale

CARLYLE (Thomas J.): The Scotts of Euisdail. Hawick, 1884. *Haw. P.; Dumf. C.; Glas. Mit.; Edin. L.L.; Edin. Ant.*

Scott in Greenock

SCOTT's Shipbuilding & Engineering Co. Ltd. Two centuries of shipbuilding by the Scotts at Greenock. London, 1906. *S.C.L.; Edin. P.* (2/1920); *Gree. P.* (+2/1920, 3/1950).

Scott of Harden, *see* **Polwarth,** Lord

Scott of Harperrig

INGLIS (John Alexander): The Scotts of Harperrig. London, 1914. *Edin. S.; Edin. Ant.*

Scott of Milsington

SCOTT (William): Pedigree of the family of Scott of Stokoe, and also the pedigree of the Scotts in Milsington, etc. 2nd ed. Hawick, 1898. *Haw. P.*

Scott of Scots-Hall

SCOTT (James R.): Memorials of the family of Scott of Scots-Hall. London, 1876. *Edin. L.L.*

Scott of Stokoe

SCOTT (William): Pedigree of the family of Scott of Stokoe, London, 1852. *Sel. P.; St.A. U.; Kirkcud. C.* (1842); *Edin. P.; Edin. L.L.*

—— Also the pedigree of the Scotts in Milsington, etc. Hawick, 2nd ed., 1898. *Haw. P.*

Scott of Thirlestane

HISTORY of the Napiers of Merchiston, shewing . . . their marriage in to the family of the Scotts of Thirlestane; comp. from old records. [London], 1921. *Edin. S.; Glas. Mit.*

SCOTT (John): Memoirs of Scott of Thirlestane and other families of the name of Scott. 2 v. n.p., n.d. (*Typescript.*) *Edin. P.; Edin. L.L.; Edin. Ant.*

MCCALL (Hardy Bertram): Some old families: a contribution to the genealogical history of Scotland. Birmingham, 1890. *S.C.L.; Sel. P.; Edin. P.; Edin. S.; Edin. L.L.; Edin. Ant.*

Scott of Wamphray

REID (Robert Corsane): Scott of Wamphray and their kinsmen: [Scott of Aikwode and Bowhill]. (Repr. from *Trans. Dumfriesshire & Galloway Nat. Hist. & Antiquarian Soc.*, 3rd ser., v. XXXIII, 1956.) *Edin. L.L.*

Scrymgeour

THOMSON (John Maitland), *ed.*: Inventory of documents [c. 1327-1611], relating to the Scrymgeour family estates, 1611. Edinburgh, 1912. (Scottish Record Soc., 42.) *S.C.L.; Glas. U.; Dund. P.; Edin. P.; Edin. S.; Glas. Mit.*

WARDEN (A. J.): History of the Scrymgeours. 1886. (*MS.*) *Dund. P.*

Scrymgeour of Glassarie

WRITS relating chiefly to the lands of Glassarie and their early possessors. (In *Highland Papers*; ed. by J. R. N. Macphail, v. II, Scottish Hist. Soc., 2nd ser. v. XII.) *S.C.L.*

Scrymgeour-Wedderburn, *see* **Dudhope**, Viscount; **Dundee**, Earldom of

Seafield, Earl of, *see* **Ogilvie-Grant**, Earl of Seafield

Seaforth, Earl of, *see* **Mackenzie**, Earl of Seaforth

Selcraig, *see* **Selkirk**

Selkirk

SELCRAIG (Thomas): Chronology of the family of John Selcraig, father of Alexander Selcraig or Selkirk (the prototype of Robinson Crusoe). n.p., 1869. (*Broadsheet.*) *Edin. P.*

Sellar

LANG (Patrick Sellar), *comp.*: The Langs of Selkirk with some notes on other families. Melbourne, 1910. *Edin. P.; Edin. S.*

Sempill

ARCHAEOLOGICAL and historical collections relating to the county of Renfrew; charters and documents relating to the parish of Lochwinnoch and the house of Sempill. 2 v. Paisley, 1885-90. *Ren. C.; Glas. U.; Edin. P.; Edin. S.*

Sempill of Beltries

PATERSON (James): Poems of the Sempills of Beltrees with notes and biographical notices of their lives. Edinburgh, 1849. *Glas. U.; Dund. P.; Edin. P.; Edin. S.; Glas. Mit.*

Semple

SEMPLE (William Alexander), *comp.*: Genealogical history of the family from 1214 to 1888. Hartford, Conn., 1888. *Edin. S.*

Seton

MAITLAND (Sir Richard): The Genealogy of the house and surname of Setoun; with the chronicle of the house of Setoun, comp. in metre by James Kamington, alias Peter Manye. Edinburgh, 1830. *Inv. P.; Ayr P.; Edin. U.; St.A. U.; Kirkcud. C.; Edin. P.; Edin. S.*

— The History of the house of Seytoun to the year 1559; with the continuation by Alexander, Viscount Kingston, to 1687. Glasgow, 1829. (Bannatyne Club, 31.) *Dunf. P.; Inv. P.; Glas. U.; Dund. P.; Edin. P.; Edin. S.; Glas. Mit.; Edin. L.L.*

SETON (Sir Bruce Gordon): The House of Seton: a study of lost causes. 2 v. Edinburgh, 1939-41. *S.C.L.; St.A. U.; Ab. U.; Glas. U.; Edin. U.; Edin, P.; Glas. Mit.*

SETON (Sir George): A history of the family of Seton during eight centuries. 2 v. Edinburgh, 1896. *S.C.L.; Dunf. P.; Rox. C.; St.A. U.; Ab. U.; Glas. U.; Edin. P.; Edin. S.; Glas. Mit.; Edin. L.L.; Edin. Ant.*

SETON (Robert): An old family, or, the Setons of Scotland and America. New York, 1899. *S.C.L.; Ab. U.; Edin. P.; Edin. S.; Glas. Mit.; Edin. L.L.*

Seton of Abercorn, *see* **Gordon,** Lord Gordon

Seton, Earl of Dunfermline

SETON (George): Memoir of Alexander Seton, Earl of Dunfermline . . . With an appendix cont., a list of the various presidents of the court, and genealogical tables of the legal families of Erskine, Hope, Dalrymple and Dundas. Edinburgh, 1882. *Dunf. P.; Glas. Mit.; Edin. L.L.*

Seton, Lord Fyvie

STIRLING (Anna Maria D. W. Pickering), *Mrs. Stirling*: Fyvie Castle: its lairds and their times. London, 1928. *S.C.L.; Elg. P.; Mid. C.; Ren. C.; Fras. P.; Dunb. C.; Fife C.; Banff C.; Ab. C.; West L. C.; Edin. U.; Glas. Mit.*

Seton of Parbroath

MARSHALL (Col. Robert Seton): The Last of the Setons of Parbroath, in Fife, and their cadets, the Setons of Dumbarrow in Fife and other Setons descended therefrom, etc. Corrections, additions and notes for the hitherto printed accounts concerning this branch of the Setons. Edinburgh, 1925. *Edin. L.L.*

Shand

SHAND (Rev. George): Some notices of the surname of Shand, particularly of the county of Aberdeen. Norwich, 1877. *Ab. P.; Edin. P.; Edin. S.; Glas. Mit.; Edin. L.L.*

Shaw

EXTRACTS from Baptism, Marriage and Death records for the parishes of Alvie, Croy, Inverness, Kingussie & Inch, and Petty, relating to the name of Shaw. 17th and 18th centuries. (*MSS.*) *Inv. P.*

MACKINTOSH (Alexander Mackintosh), *formerly A. M. Shaw*: A genealogical account of the Highland families of Shaw. London, 1877. *Inv. P.; Nai. C.; Ab. U.; Glas. Mit.; Edin. L.L.*

SHAW (Norman): History of the Clan Shaw. Oxford, 1951. *Inv. P.; Per. C.; Ross C.; Elg. P.; Ang. C.; Edin. U.; St.A. U.; Ab. U.; Ab. P.; Glas. U.; Arg. C.; Edin. P.; Glas. Mit.; Edin. L.L.*

SHAW (William G.): History and memorials of the Clan Shaw. Dundee, 1868. *Inv. P.; Glas. U.* (+1871)*; Edin. P.* (1871)*; Edin. S.* (1871)*; Edin. L.L.* (+1871).

Shaw of Sauchie

BROWN-MORISON (John Brown): Genealogical notes anent some ancient Scottish families. Perth, 1884. *Clack. C.; Dunf. P.; Edin. S.*

Sibbald

SIBBALD (William): Summons of proving the tenor, Sir William Sibbald, against Officers of State, Aug. 5, 1834. n.p., 1834. *Edin. P.*

Sibbald of Roxburghshire

SIBBALD (Susan Mein), *Mrs. Sibbald*: Memoirs (1783-1812); ed. by F. P. Hett. London, 1926. *Glas. Mit.*

Sibbald of Whitelaw

LANG (Patrick Sellar), *comp.*: The Langs of Selkirk, with some notes on other families. Melbourne, 1910. *Edin. P.; Edin. S.*

Simson

LANG (Patrick Sellar), *comp.*: The Langs of Selkirk, with some notes on other families. Melbourne, 1910. *Edin. P.; Edin. S.*

SIMSON (Archibald): Annals of such patriots of the distinguished family of Fraser, Frysell, Sim-son, or Fitz-simon . . . Edinburgh, 1795. *Inv. P.; Edin. P.; Edin. S.; Glas. Mit.*

— — 2nd ed. edited by A. Fraser. Edinburgh, 1805. *Inv. P.; Haw. P.; Inv. C.; St.A. U.*

STEVENSON (Robert): The Simsons. n.p., 1867. *Edin. P.; Glas. Mit.*

Sinclair (*see also* **St Clair**)

MORRISON (Leonard Allison): The History of the Sinclair family in Europe and America. Boston, 1896. *Cai. C.*

OSLER (James Couper): Osler tree [chart pedigree] with some supplementary notes on . . . Sinclairs . . . [Dundee], 1924. *Edin. L.L.; Edin. Ant.*

SINCLAIR (James): Information for James Sinclair against William Sinclair of Ratter. n.p., 1769. *Edin. P.; Edin. S.*

THOMSON (D. C.): Thomson, Couper, Yule, Sinclair genealogical chart. Dundee, [1937]. *Dund. P.*

Sinclair of Brabsterdorran

ST CLAIR (Roland William): Sinclairs of Brabsterdorran, Caithness. (In *Viking Club Miscellany*, v. 4, 1911, pp. 194-200.) *Zet. C.; Ork. C.*

Sinclair of Brecks

CLOUSTON (J. Storer): James Sinclair of Brecks. (In *Proceedings Orkney Antiquarian Soc.*, v. 15, 1939, pp. 61-68.) *Ork. C.*

Sinclair in England

[SINCLAIR (Thomas)]: The Sinclairs of England. London, 1887. *Cai. C.; Haw. P.*

Sinclair of Lybster

St Clair (Roland William): Sinclairs of Lybster. (In *Viking Club Miscellany*, v. 3, 1910, pp. 226-229.) *Zet. C.; Ork. C.*

Sinclair of Mey

Donaldson (John E.): The Sinclairs of Mey. (In his *Caithness in the 18th century*, 1938.) *S.C.L.; Glas. Mit.*

Sinclair of Olrig

Information for Henrietta Sinclair, lawful daughter and executrix decerned to the deceased Donald Sinclair of Olrick, and Benjamin Moody of Melsetter, Esq., her husband, for his interest, pursuers *v.* Charles Sinclair of Olrick, defender. 1767. *Edin. Ant.*

Information for Charles Sinclair of Olrick *v.* Henrietta Sinclair, daughter of the deceased Donald Sinclair of Olrick, and Benjamin Moodie of Melsetter, her husband, for his interest. *Edin. Ant.*

Sinclair, Earl of Orkney

Tulloch (Thomas), *Bishop of Orkney*: Diploma of Thomas . . . addressed to Eric, King of Norway, respecting the genealogy of William St. Clair, Earl of Orkney; with a transl. by Dean Thomas Guild . . . 1554. (In *Bannatyne Miscellany*, v. 3, 1855.) *Ork. C.; Glas. Mit.*

see also **Orkney,** Earldom of

Sinclair of Ratter

MacDonald (Kenneth): The Castle of Girnigoe, and the Sinclairs of Ratter. Inverness, 1889. *Inv. P.; Edin. P.*

Sinclair, Lord Sinclair

St Clair (Charles): The Case of Charles St Clair, Esq., claiming the title and dignity of Lord Sinclair. 1782. *Glas. Mit.*

Sinton

Sinton (Rev. Thomas): Family and genealogical sketches. Inverness, 1911. *Ab. P.; Inv. P.; Ab. U.; Edin. S.; Edin. P.; Dund. Q.*

Skene

[Descent of the family of Skene.] [Folding pedigree table.] n.p., n.d. *St.A. U.; Ab. P.; Edin. P.; Edin. L.L.*

The Family of Skene of Auchtertool, Dyce, Rubislaw, etc. (*Genealogical MSS.*) *Glas. Mit.*

163

SKENE (William Forbes): Memorials of the family of Skene of
Skene, from the family papers, with other illustrative docu-
ments. Aberdeen, 1887. (New Spalding Club, 1.) *S.C.L.;
Inv. P.; Elg. P.; Ab. C.; Dund. Q.; Ab. P.; Glas. U.; Dund. P.;
Edin. P.; Edin. S.; Glas. Mit.*

Smith

GRAZEBROOK (Henry Sydney): The Heraldry of Smith. London, 1870. *Glas. U.; Edin. P.; Edin. S.; Glas. Mit.; Edin. L.L.*

READE (Compton): The Smith family: a popular account of
most branches of the name, however spelt, from the 14th
century downwards. London, 1902. *S.C.L.* (1904); *Ab. P.;
Glas. Mit.* (1904).

SCOTT (M. P.): [Three MS. letters on Adam Smith to Charles
B. Boog Watson. Glasgow, 1935]. *Edin. P.*

[SMITH (Francis Montagu)]: The Heraldry of Smith in Scotland:
supplement to Grazebrook's *Heraldry of Smith.* London,
1873. *Glas. U.; Edin. P.; Edin. S.; Glas. Mit.; Edin. L.L.*

Smith of Aberdeen

SMITH (James): Genealogies of an Aberdeen family, 1540-1913.
Aberdeen, 1913. *Ab. P.; Ab. C.; St.A. U.; Edin. P.; Edin. U.;
Edin. Ant.; Glas. U.*

Smith of Tormiston, Orkney

LEITH (Peter): The Smiths of Tormiston. (In *Proceedings
Orkney Antiquarian Soc.*, v. 13, 1935, pp. 9-13.) *Ork. C.*

Smollett

WATSON (Charles Brodie Boog): Traditions and genealogies of
some members of the families of Boog, Heron, Leishman,
Ross, Watson. Perth, 1908. *St.A. U.; Edin. P.; Edin. S.*

Smollett of Bonhill

SMOLLETT (Tobias): Some account of the family of Smollett of
Bonhill; with a series of letters hitherto unpublished; . . .
arr. by J. Irving. Dumbarton, 1859. *Edin. P.; Glas. Mit.*

Sobieski-Stuart

BEVERIDGE (Hugh): The Sobieski-Stuarts: their claim to be
descended from Prince Charlie. Inverness, 1909. *S.C.L.;
Inv. P.; Ab. U.; Ab. P.; Edin. P.; Edin. S.; Glas. Mit.*

CRAIG (Archibald): The Sobieski Stuarts: a short sketch of
their remarkable career. Edinburgh, 1922. *Edin. P.; Edin. S.;
Glas. Mit.*

Somerville

SOMERVILLE (James), *comp.*: The Baronial house of Somerville
. . . Glasgow, 1920. *Per. P.; Edin. P.; Edin. S.; Glas. Mit.*

SOMERVILLE (James Somerville), *11th Baron*: Memorie of the
Somervills. [1066-1677.] [1679?] (*MSS.*) *Edin. P.*

— Memorie of the Somervilles; ed. by Sir W. Scott. 2 v.
Edinburgh, 1815. *Mont. P.; Ham. P.; Glas. U.; Edin. P.;
Glas. Mit.; Edin. S.; Edin. L.L.; Edin. Ant.*

Somerville of Drum

NISBETT (Hamilton More): Drum of the Somervilles. Edinburgh, 1928. *Ab. P.; Mid. C.; Dund. Q.; Edin. P.; Edin. S.;
Glas. Mit.*

Somerville, Lord Somerville

BAIN (Joseph): The Dormant Barony of Somerville, a claim
disposed of. n.d. (Repr. from *Genealogist*, n.s. v. IX, 1-4.)
Glas. Mit.

Southesk, Earldom of

CARNEGIE (Sir James): An act to relieve Sir James Carnegie of
Southesk, etc., from the Effect of the Attainder of James,
Fifth Earl of Southesk . . . 2nd July, 1855. *Forf. P.*

— Case of Sir James Carnegie of Southesk, Kinnaird and
Pittarrow, Bart., on his claim to the titles, honour and
dignities of Earl of Southesk, etc. 1848. *Forf. P.; Edin. L.L.*

— Supplemental case. *Forf. P.; Edin. L.L.*

— Case . . . n.p. 1855. *Forf. P.*

— Minutes of evidence in the petition of Sir James Carnegie
of Kinnaird, Bt., claiming the Earldom of Southesk. 1855.
Forf. P.

Spalding

S (F. J.) & S (M.): Notes and traditions concerning the family
of Spalding. Liverpool, 1914. *Edin. P.*

SPALDING (Eduard): Geschichtliches Urkunden, Stamm-tafeln
der Spalding in Schottland, Deutschland und Schweden.
Greifswald, 1898. *Edin. L.L.*

Speirs of Elderslie

MITCHELL (John Oswald): . . . The Two Elderslies. Glasgow,
1884. (Repr. from the *Glasgow Herald*, 13th Sept. 1884.)
Glas. Mit.

Spence

OSLER (James Couper): Osler tree [chart pedigree] with some supplementary notes on . . . Spences . . . [Dundee], 1924. *Edin. L.L.; Edin. Ant.*

Spencer

SPENCER (C. L.): Some notes on the Spencers, Jarvies and Rintouls in Glasgow, comp. from family tradition and public records. 1935. (*Typescript.*) *Glas. Mit.*

Spottiswoode

GIBSON (John C.): Lands and lairds of Dunipace. Stirling, 1903. *Edin. P.; Edin. S.; Glas. Mit.*

Spottiswoode of Spottiswoode

HAY (Father Augustin): Genealogy, from the MS. collection . . . of the family of Spottiswoode. [1844.] *Glas. U.; Edin. P.; Glas. Mit.*

Spreull

BUCHANAN (Leslie): Cowdonhill mansion and the Glasgow family of Spreull, misc. notes, letters, prints, etc. c. 1924-27. (*MS.*) *Glas. Mit.*

S[PREULL] (J. M.) & S[PREULL] (G. J.): Notes on the family of Spreull. Glasgow, 1915. *Glas. Mit.; Edin. L.L.*

Spynie, Lord Spynie

MAIDMENT (James), *ed.*: Reports of claims . . . to the House of Lords . . . of the Cassilis, Sutherland, Spynie and Glencairn peerages, 1760-1797. Edinburgh, 1882. *Glas. U.; Dund. P.* (1840)*; Edin. P.; Edin. S.; Glas. Mit.; Edin. Ant.; Edin. L.L.* (1840).

Stair, Earl of, *see* **Dalrymple,** Earl of Stair

Steel

[KERR (Robert Malcolm)]: Nugae antiquae. Glasgow, 1847-49. *Glas. U.; Glas. Mit.*

Steel of Annathill

BLACK (William George): A note on the family of Black of Over Abington . . . with memoranda on . . . Steel of Annathill. [2nd ed.] Glasgow, 1924. *Glas. Mit.; Ab. P.; Glas. U.* (+ 1908)*; Edin. P.; Edin. S.; Glas. Mit.; Edin. Ant.; Edin. L.L.* (+ 1908).

Steele

STEVENSON (Robert): The Simsons. n.p., 1867. *Edin. P.*

Stein, Stiven, Clackmannanshire

BOASE (Edward R.): The Family of Stein, or Stevin, Clackmannanshire from notes by Miss Margaret Haig, Lochrin, 1841, with additions by C. E. Haig and Mrs M. Stuart, Lochrin House and further additions by E. R. Boase. n.p., n.d. *Edin. L.L.*

Stephen of Linthouse

CARVEL (John Lees), *"Iain C. Lees"*: Stephen of Linthouse: a record of two hundred years of shipbuilding, 1750-1950. Glasgow, 1950. *Gree. P.*

STEPHEN (Alexander), & *Sons, Ltd.*: A shipbuilding history, 1750-1932: a record of the business founded about 1750, by Alex. Stephen at Burghead, & subsequently carried on at Aberdeen, Arbroath, Dundee and Glasgow. London, 1932. *Gree. P.*

Steuart (*see also* **Stewart**)

STEUART (Katherine): By Allan water: the story of an old house. Edinburgh, 1901. *Kil. P.; Pai. P.*

Steuart of Steuarthall

STEUART (George): Pedigree shewing the descent of the family of Lt. Gen. George Mackenzie Steuart . . . Edinburgh, 1855. *Edin. P.; Edin. L.L.*

Stevenson

STEVENSON (Robert): The Simsons. n.p., 1867. *Edin. P.*

STEVENSON (Robert Louis): Records of a family of engineers. London, 1912. *S.C.L.; Kil. P.; Per. C.; Fife C.; West L. C.; Arb. P.; Dunb. C.; Lan. C.; Kir. P.; Ab. P.; Glas. U.; Pai. P.; Edin. P.; Glas. Mit.*

Stewart or Stuart, The Royal House of

AHAB'S evil: secret history of the family of the Stuarts. London, 1720. *Inv. P.*

BROWNE (Sir Anthony): The Right of succession to the crown of England, in the family of the Stuarts, exclusive of Mary, Queen of Scots, learnedly asserted . . . by Sir Nicholas Bacon . . . against Sir A. Brown . . . published from the original MS. by Nathaniel Boothe, etc. London, 1723. *Edin. P.*

CAMPANA ( ), *Marquise de Cavelli*: Les derniers Stuarts à Saint-Germain en Laye. 2 v. Paris, 1871. *S.C.L.; Glas. Mit.*

COISSAC DE CHAVREBIÈRE ( ): Histoire des Stuarts. Paris, 1930. *Edin. P.; Edin. S.*

COWAN (Samuel): The Royal house of Stuart; from its origin to the accession of the House of Hanover. London, 1908. *S.C.L.; Per. P.; Ab. P.; Per. C.; Edin. P.; Edin. S.; Glas. Mit.*

CRAWFURD (George): . . . Genealogical history of the royal and illustrious family of the Stewarts, 1034-1710. Edinburgh, 1710. *Gree. P.; Ab. U.; Glas. U.; Pai. P.; Edin. P.; Edin. S.; Glas. Mit.*

—— 2nd ed. contin. by W. Semple. Paisley, 1782. *Glas. Mit.; Edin. S.*

—— 3rd ed. contin. to present time by G. Robertson. Paisley, 1818. *Glas. Mit.; Edin. S.; Edin. L.L.*

EDINBURGH "Royal Stuart" exhibition, 1949. [Catalogue.] *Edin. P.*

FOSTER (Joshua James): The Stuarts: outlines of the personal history of the family. Illus. from portraits in the most celebrated collections. London, 1907. *Dund. P.; Ab. U.* (1902); *Edin. P.* (1902); *Glas. Mit.; Edin. S.* (1902).

FRANCIS (Grant R.): Scotland's royal line: the tragic house of Stuart. London, 1928. *S.C.L.; Clack. C.; Per. C.; Coat. P.; Ham. P.; Cly. P.; Ab. U.; Ab. P.; Edin. P.; Glas. Mit.*

A GENEALOGICAL history of the royal family of Scotland, England and Ireland . . . name of Stuart . . . to . . . 1754. London, 1755. *Edin. P.*

HAY (Richard): An essay on the origine of the royal family of the Stewarts. Edinburgh, 1793. *Glas. U.; Edin. P.; Edin. S.* (+1722); *Glas. Mit.* (1722).

HENDERSON (Thomas Finlayson): The Royal Stewarts. Edinburgh, 1914. *Cai. C.; Coat. P.; Per. C.; Ab. U.; Ab. P.; Edin. S.; Edin. P.; Glas. Mit.*

KENNEDY (Matthew): A chronological genealogical and historical dissertation of the Royal Family of Stewarts. Paris, 1705. *Pai. P.; Edin. P.; Edin. S.; Glas. Mit.*

LINDSAY (W. A.): Pedigree of the house of Stewart. [1891.] *Edin. L.L.*

LONDON, New Gallery. [Catalogue of] exhibition of the royal house of Stuart. [London, 1889.] *S.C.L.*

MACKENZIE (Agnes Mure): The Passing of the Stewarts. London, 1937. *S.C.L.; Coat. P.; Cly. P.*

168

— The Rise of the Stewarts. London, 1935. *S.C.L.; Clack. C.; Cly. P.; Coat. P.*

MACKENZIE (Sir George): The Antiquity of the royal line of Scotland defended. London, [?1686]. *Inv. P.*

MARCHAND (Pierre Joseph Abel): Les Stuarts à Avignon. Avignon, 1895. *Ab. U.*

MURDOCH (W. G. Blaikie): The Royal Stuarts in their connection with art and letters. Edinburgh, 1908. *Glas. U.; Edin. P.; Ab. P.; Edin. S.*

NOBLE (Mark): A historical genealogy of the royal house of Stuart . . . London, 1795. *Ab. U.; Ab. P.; Dund. P.; Edin. P.; Edin. S.; Glas. Mit.*

RAIT (Sir Robert Sangster): Five Stuart princesses. London, 1902. *Glas. U.; Glas. Mit.; Edin. P.; Edin. S.*

RIDDELL (John): Stewartiana, containing the case of Robert II and Elizabeth Mure and question of legitimacy of their issue. Edinburgh, 1843. *Glas. U.; Glas. Mit.; Edin. P.; Edin. L.L.*

— Tracts legal and historical, etc. Edinburgh, 1835. *S.C.L.; Edin. P.; Edin. S.; Edin. L.L.*

THE ROYAL house of Stuart. Illus. . . . by Wm. Gibb. Intro. by John Skelton, and notes by W. H. St. John Hope. London, 1890. *S.C.L.; Ab. U.; Ab. P.; Glas. U.* (1900)*; Haw. P.; Edin. P.* (1900)*; Glas. Mit.*

SCOTTISH NATIONAL PORTRAIT GALLERY. The Royal house of Stewart. Edinburgh, 1958. *Edin. P.*

SKEET (Francis John Angus), *ed.*: Stuart papers, pictures, relics, medals and books in the collection of Miss Maria Widdrington. Leeds, 1930. *Glas. U.* (1938)*; Ab. P.; Dund. P.; Edin. P.*

[STEUART (Sir Henry)]: The Genealogy of the Stewarts refuted: in a letter to Andrew Stuart, etc. Edinburgh, 1799. *Ab. U.; Ab. P.; Glas. U.; Glas. Mit.; Edin. P.; Dumf. C.; Edin. L.L.*

STEWART (Duncan): Short historical and genealogical account of the royal family of Scotland . . . and of the surname of Stewart. Edinburgh, 1739. *S.C.L.; Inv. P.; Glas. U.; Edin. P.; Edin. S.; Glas. Mit.; Edin. L.L.*

STEWART (Helen Catherine), *ed.*: The Exiled Stewarts in Italy, 1717-1807. (In *Scottish Hist. Soc., Misc.*, 3rd ser. v. XXXV, 1941.) *S.C.L.; Glas. Mit.*

STRICKLAND (Agnes): Lives of the last four princesses of the royal house of Stuart. London, 1872. *Glas. Mit.*

STUART (Andrew): Genealogical history of the Stuarts, from the earliest period of their authentic history. London, 1798. *S.C.L.; Inv. P.; Per. C.; St.A. U.; Glas. Mit.; Nai. C.; Edin. S.; Dumb. P.; Kirkcud. C.; Glas. U.; Edin. P.; Dumf. C.; Edin. L.L.; Edin. Ant.*

—— Supplement with corrections and additions, etc. London, 1799. *Dumf. C.; St.A. U.*

SYMSON (David): Genealogical and historical account of the illustrious name of Stuart. Edinburgh, 1712. *Inv. P.; Gree. P.* (1726); *Ab. U.; Edin. P.; Edin. S.; Glas. Mit.*

TAITT (Alexander): Right of the house of Stewart to the crown of Scotland; 2nd ed. [Edinburgh], 1746. *Glas. U.; Edin. P.; Glas. Mit.*

THORNTON (Percy Melville): Stuart dynasty: short studies drawn from papers . . . at Windsor Castle. London, 1890. *Edin. P.; Glas. Mit.; Ab. P.; Edin. S.; Edin. L.L.*

TOWNEND (William): The Descendants of the Stuarts. London, 1858. *Inv. P.; Ab. U.; Glas. U.; Edin. P.; Glas. Mit.; Edin. S.; Edin. L.L.*

A TREWE description of the nobill race of the Stewards. Amsterdam, 1603. *Edin. P.*

UDALL (William): The Historie of the life and death of Mary Stuart, Queene of Scotland. London, 1636. *Edin. P.; Glas. U.; Edin. S.*

VAUGHAN (Robert): Memorials of the Stuart dynasty . . . 2 v. London, 1831. *Glas. Mit.*

WALLACE (Harold Frank): A Stuart sketch book, 1542-1746. London, 1933. *Per. C.; Ab. P.; Glas. U.; Edin. P.*

WATERHOUSE (Thomas): A genealogical account of the royal house of Stuart from 1043. Grantham, 1816. *Ab. U.; Glas. U.; Edin. P.; Glas. Mit.*

WATSON (Rev. John): Memoires of the family of the Stuarts . . . London, 1683. *Edin. P.; Glas. Mit.*

Stewart, (*see also* **Stuart**)

THE CLAN STEWART SOCIETY, Glasgow. Constitution and rules. n.d. *Glas. Mit.*

— 1st-4th annual report and list of members, 1900-1902-3; 6th annual report. n.d. *Glas. Mit.*

JOHNSTON (George Harvey): The Heraldry of the Stewarts, with notes on all the males of the family, etc. Edinburgh, 1906. *Dund. P.; Edin. P.; Glas. Mit.; Edin. S.; Edin. L.L.*

STEWART (Charles W. A.): A short account of Clann Mhic Alastair (the children or descendants of Alexander) Cam Chasach (Cross-legged) Leonac (Lennox) Stewart. Perth, 1898. *Per. C.*

STEWART (J. K.): Address in response to the toast of "The Stewart Society" at the annual dinner, 1904. *Glas. Mit.*

— The Story of the Stewarts. Edinburgh, 1901. *Nai. C.; Fife C.; Ab. U.; Kirkcud. C.; Edin. P.; Edin. S.; Glas. Mit.; Edin. L.L.*

STEWART (John): The Stewarts: the highland branches of a royal name. Edinburgh, 1954. *Inv. P.; Edin. U.; Lan. C.; Dunf. P.; Mid. C.; Ab. P.; Dund. P.; Pai. P.; Per. C.; Edin. P.; Glas. Mit.; Cai. C.; Ber. C.; Edin. L.L.*

STEWART (John Alexander): Stewart arms; recent matriculations and grants. Glasgow, 1924. *Edin. P.; Edin. Ant.*

THE STEWART SOCIETY, Edinburgh. Annual report and list of members. 1902-1904, 1906-1912, 1914, 1953-1955. *Glas. Mit.; Edin. U.* (1906-1913).

— Roll of honour. Edinburgh, 1914-16. *Edin. P.*

THE STEWARTS: a historical and general magazine for the Stewart Society. Edinburgh, Vol. 1, [1902-]. *S.C.L.* (v. 1-4 imp.); *Edin. P.; Edin. S.* (v. 8-); *Edin. U.* (v. 3-6 imp.); *Glas. Mit.* (v. 1-3); *Per. P.* (v. 3-4 imp.); *Edin. L.L.*

WALTER STEWART, crusader . . . and his descendants. n.p., n.d. *Edin. P.*

Stewart, Duke of Albany

FRASER (Sir William): The Dukes of Albany and their castle of Doune. Edinburgh, 1881. (Repr. from his *Red Book of Menteith*, 2 v. 1880.) *St.A. U.; Edin. P.; Glas. Mit.*

Stewart of Allanton

DENHAM (Sir Archibald Stewart): Coltness collections: memorials of the Stewarts of Allanton, Coltness and Goodtrees, 1608-1840. Ed. by James Dennistoun. Edinburgh, 1842. (Maitland Club, 58.) *Mid. C.; Inv. P.; Glas. U.; Dund. P.; Edin. P.; Edin. S.; Glas. Mit.; Edin. L.L.*

RIDDELL (John): The Salt-foot controversy as it appeared in Blackwood's Magazine. Edinburgh, 1818. *Ab. U.* [1819]; *Glas. U.; Edin. P.; Edin. S.; Glas. Mit.; Edin. L.L.* (n.p., n.d.)

Stewart of Appin

STEWART (John H. J.) & STEWART (Duncan): The Stewarts of Appin. Edinburgh, 1880. *Inv. C.; St.A. U.; Ab. U.; Glas. U.; Edin. P.; Glas. Mit.; Edin. L.L.; Edin. Ant.*

Stewart of Ballechin, *see* **Stewart** of Kynachan

Stewart of Balloan

[STEWART (C. Poyntz)]: The Legend of Balloan [the Wolf of Badenoch and his descendants]: extracts from *The Stewarts,* v. 3, 1912-1916. *Edin. L.L.; Edin. Ant.*

Stewart, Earl of Carrick, *see* **Carrick,** Earldom of

Stewart of Coltness, *see* **Stewart** of Allanton

Stewart of Craigiehall

STEWART (William Burton), *comp.*: Records of the Stewarts of Craigiehall, Newhalls and the Leuchold. Alnmouth, 1933. (*Typescript.*) *Edin. L.L.*

Stewart of Darnley

STUART (Andrew): Genealogical history of the Stewarts . . . London, 1798. *S.C.L.; Inv. P.; Per. C.; St.A. U.; Glas. Mit.; Nai. C.; Edin. S.; Dumb. P.; Kirkcud. C.; Glas. U.; Edin. P.; Dumf. C.; Edin. L.L.; Edin. Ant.*

TYTLER (Patrick Fraser): Historical notes on the Lennox or Darnley jewel; the property of the Queen. [London], 1843. *Glas. U.; Edin. P.*

[WILLIAMS (E.)]: Abstract of the evidence adduced to prove that Sir William Stewart, of Jedworth, the paternal ancestor of the present Earl of Galloway, was the second son of Sir Alex. Stewart, of Darnley. London, 1801. *Dumf. C.; St.A. U.; Glas. Mit.*

— — A view of the evidence for proving that the present Earl of Galloway is the lineal heir-male and lawful representative of Sir William Stewart of Jedworth, so frequently mentioned in history, from the year 1385 to the year 1429. (*No title-page.*) [1796.] *Kirkcud. Bro.*

Stewart of Drumlin

MATHESON (W. S.): The Stewarts of Drumlin. 1933. (*MS.*) *Ab. P.*

Stewart in England

STEWARD (Sir Henry): Record of a branch of the Stewart family; ed. by Lady G. S. Steward. n.p., 1954. *Edin. L.L.*

Stewart of Forthergill

STEWART (Charles Poyntz), *ed.*: Historic memorials of the Stewarts of Forthergill, Perthshire, and their male descendants . . . Edinburgh, 1879. *Per. P.; St.A. U.; Ab. U.; Glas. U.; Edin. P.; Glas. Mit.; Edin. S.; Edin. L.L.; Edin. Ant.*

Stewart in Galloway

STEWART (G. Macleod): Galloway records. Vol. 1: the Stewart family in Galloway. Dumfries, 1914. *Wig. C.; Edin. P.; Edin. S.*

— The Stewart family. n.d. *Wig. C.* ([1920]); *Dumf. C.*

Stewart of Goodtrees, *see* **Stewart** of Allanton

Stewart of Grandtully

Fraser (Sir William): The Red book of Grandtully. 2 v. Edinburgh, 1868. *S.C.L.; St.A. U.; Ab. U.; Glas. U.; Per. C.; Edin. P.; Edin. S.; Glas. Mit.; Edin. L.L.; Edin. Ant.*

Stewart of Jedworth, *see* **Stewart** of Darnley

Stewart of Kynachan

SINTON (Rev. Thomas): Stewarts of Kynachan and Stewarts of Ballechin. (In his *Family and genealogical sketches.* 1911.) *Inv. P.; Ab. P.; Edin. S.; Ab. U.; Dund. Q.; Edin. P.*

Stewart, Earl of Lennox

STUART (Andrew): Genealogical history of the Stewarts . . . London, 1798. *S.C.L.; Inv. P.; St.A. U.; Per. C.; Glas. Mit.; Nai. C.; Edin. S.; Dumb. P.; Kirkcud. C.; Glas. U.; Edin. P.; Dumf. C.; Edin. L.L.; Edin. Ant.*

WINGFIELD-STRATFORD (Esme): The Lords of Cobham Hall. London, 1959. *S.C.L.*

see also **Lennox,** Earldom of

Stewart of Massater, Orkney

STEWART (R. A. Clapperton): The Stewarts of Massater, Orkney. (In *Viking Soc., Old-lore misc. of Orkney & Shetland,* v. 6, 1913, pp. 202-208.) *Ork. C.; Zet. C.*

Stewart of Menteith

BURNETT (George): The Red book of Menteith reviewed. Edinburgh, 1881. *Ab. P.; Sti. C.; St.A. U.; Ab. U.; Dund. P.; Glas. Mit.*

FRASER (Sir William): The Red book of Menteith. 2 v. Edinburgh, 1880. *S.C.L.; St.A. U.; Glas. U.; Sti. P.; Dumb. P.; Moth. P.; Sti. C.; Ab. U.; Dund. P.; Edin. P.; Edin. S.*

HUTCHISON (Andrew F.): The Lake of Menteith . . . with historical accounts of . . . the earldom of Menteith. Stirling, 1899. *Ab. P.*

STEWART (J. K.): The Lake of Menteith and its feudal lords. 1923. (Repr. from *The Stewarts,* v. 4.) *Edin. Ant.*

Stewart in Orkney

STEUART (A. F.): Orkney news from the letter-bag of Mr. Charles Steuart. (In *Viking Soc., Old-lore misc. of Orkney & Shetland*, v. 6, 1913, pp. 41-49, 101-109.) *Ork. C.*

Stewart, Earl of Orkney, *see* **Orkney,** Earldom of

Stewart, Earl of Strathearn, *see* **Strathearn,** Earldom of

Stewart of Traquair

HENDERSON (C. Stewart): The Stuarts of Traquair. n.p., 1947. (From *The Stewarts*, v. 8, no. 1.) *Edin. P.*

PINE (Leslie Gilbert): The History of the Stuarts, Earls of Traquair, Barons Linton of Cabarston and Charles Edward Traquair Stuart-Linton. [London], 1940. *Edin. L.L.; Edin. Ant.*

Stewart-Mackenzie of Seaforth

REPRESENTATION of the family of Seaforth in 1829. Inverness, 1867. (*MS.*) *Inv. P.*

see also **Mackenzie,** Earl of Seaforth

Stirling

W[OODWARD] (W. H.): Sterlings of Stirlingshire, Ireland and London, 1500-1935. London, 1935. *Edin. S.*

Stirling, Earldom of

. . . AN ACCOUNT of the resumption of the titles by the present Earl of Stirling . . . with an epitome of the genealogy of . . . Alexander. London, 1826. *Edin. P.*

BANKS (Sir Thomas Christopher): An analytical statement of the case of Alexander, Earl of Stirling and Dovan . . . London, 1832. *Glas. Mit.*

HUMPHRYS (Alexander): Narrative of the oppressive law proceedings . . . also a genealogical account of the family of Alexander . . . Edinburgh, 1836. *Glas. U.; Edin. P.; Edin. S.; Glas. Mit.*

— Report of the trial of Alexander Humphrys or Alexander, claiming the title of Earl of Stirling . . . [Ed.] by Archibald Swinton. Edinburgh, 1839. *S.C.L.; Glas. U.; Edin. P.; Dund. P.; Glas. Mit.; Edin. L.L.*

— Stirling peerage, session and other papers. [*Binder's title.*] n.p., n.d. *Edin. P.; Edin. L.L.*

— The Stirling peerage: trial of Alex. Humphrys or Alexander, styling himself Earl of Stirling . . . ed. W. B. D. D. Turnbull. Edinburgh, 1839. *Glas. U.; Edin. P.*

LOCKHART (Ephraim): Genealogical account of the family of Alexander, Earls of Stirling, etc. Edinburgh, 1836. *Glas. U.; Edin. P.; Glas. Mit.*

see also **Alexander,** Earl of Stirling

Stirling of Cadder

STIRLING (Thomas Willing): The Stirlings of Cadder. An account of the original family of that name and of the family of the Stirlings of Drumpellier, with which the representation of the ancient house of Cadder now lies. [Ed. by G. H. Bushnell.] St. Andrews, 1933. *St.A. U.*

Stirling of Craigbernard & Glorat

BAIN (Joseph): The Stirlings of Craigbernard and Glorat. Edinburgh, 1883. *Dumb. P.; Inv. P.; Edin. U.; St.A. U.; Ab. U.; Glas. U.; Falk. P.; Edin. P.; Edin. S.; Glas. Mit.; Edin. L.L.*

Stirling of Drumpellier, *see* **Stirling** of Cadder

Stirling of Keir

FRASER (Sir William): The Stirlings of Keir and their family papers. Edinburgh, 1858. *S.C.L.; Per. C.; Ab. U.; Glas. U.; Glas. Mit.; Edin. P.; Edin. S.; Edin. L.L.; Edin. Ant.*

RIDDELL (John): Comments in refutation . . . of statements in "The Stirlings of Keir and their family papers". Edinburgh, 1860. *Per. C.; St.A. U.; Air. P.; Glas. U.; Glas. Mit.; Edin. P.; Edin. S.; Edin. L.L.*

A SELECTION of original charters and papers of the family of Stirling of Keir, commencing in the year 1338. [?Edinburgh], 1860. *Edin. S.; Edin. L.L.*

see also **Maxwell** of Pollok

Stirton

STIRTON (Rev. John): Stirton of the Stormont: a brief history of the family. Forfar, 1935. *Per. P.; St.A. U.; Ab. U.; Glas. U.; Edin. P.; Edin. S.; Edin. Ant.*

Stobo

BULLOCH (Joseph Gaston Baillie): History and genealogy of the families of Bulloch and Stobo and of Irvine of Cults. Washington, 1911. *Ab. P.; Edin. S.*

Strachan of Glenkindie

ALLARDICE (James): The Strachans of Glenkindie, 1357-1726. Aberdeen, 1899. *Ab. P.; Edin. P.; Edin. S.; Glas. Mit.; Edin. L.L.; Edin. Ant.*

Strachan of Thornton

ROGERS (Charles): Memorials of the Strachans, baronets of Thornton, Kincardineshire, and of the family of Wise of Hillbank, formerly Wyse of Lunan, in the county of Forfar. London, [1873]. *Inv. P.; St.A. U.; Glas. U.; Edin. P.; Edin. S.; Glas. Mit.; Edin. L.L.; Edin. Ant.*

— Memorials of the Scottish families of Strachan and Wise. [2nd ed.], Edinburgh, 1877. *Dunf. P.; Sti. P.; Ab. U.; St.A. U.; Forf. P.; Glas. U.; Edin. P.; Edin. L.L.; Edin. Ant.*

Strang of Balcaskie

MCTAGGART (William): Sketch of a history of the family of Strang or Strange, of Balcasky, in the county of Fife in Scotland. Edinburgh, 1798. *Edin. P.*

Strange

STRANGE (Nora Kathleen): Jacobean tapestry. London, [1947]. *S.C.L.; Ab. P.; Edin. P.; Pai. P.; Glas. Mit.*

Strathearn, Earldom of

COWAN (Samuel): Three Celtic earldoms: Atholl, Strathearn, Menteith. Edinburgh, 1909. *Sti. P.; Per. C.; Ab. P.; Per. P.; Dund. P.*

NICOLAS (Sir Nicholas Harris): History of the Earldoms of Strathern, Monteith and Airth; with a report of the proceedings . . . on the claim of Robert Barclay Allardice . . . London, 1842. *Dund. P.; Per. C.; Per. P.; St.A. U.; Ab. U.; Glas. U.; Edin. P.; Edin. S.; Glas. Mit.; Edin. L.L.*

Strathmore, Earldom of

MINUTES of Evidence [and Appendix] in the Strathmore peerage claim, 1821. n.p., 1821. *Forf. P.*

Straton of Lauriston

STRATON (Charles Henry), *ed.*: The Stratons of Lauriston and their offshoots. Exmouth, 1939. *Mont. P.; Edin. L.L.*

[PAPERS, letters, etc. dealing with the family, 1124-1933. 9 v.] *Mont. P.*

Stuart, *see* **Stewart; Sobieski-Stuart**

Stuart of Allanbank
> FORBES (Louisa Lillias): Stuart of Allanbank, 1643-1880. [Folding pedigree.] n.p., 1880. *Edin. P.; Edin. L.L.*

Stuart of Aubigny
> CUST (Lady Elizabeth): Some account of the Stuarts of Aubigny in France. London, 1891. *Ab. P.; Edin. P.; Edin. S.; Glas. Mit.; Edin. L.L.*
> STUART (Andrew): Genealogical history of the Stewarts . . . London, 1798. *S.C.L.; Per. C.; St.A. U.; Glas. Mit.; Nai. C.; Edin. S.; Dumb. P.; Kirkcud. C.; Glas. U.; Edin. P.; Dumf. C.; Edin. L.L.; Edin. Ant.; Inv. P.*

Stuart of Castlemilk
> ANSWERS for Mrs. Rae Crawfurd of Milton, to the petition of Sir John Stewart of Castlemilk, Bart., and Mrs. Stirling of Keir. 1794. *Glas. Mit.*
> . . . THE PETITION of Sir John Stuart of Castlemilk, Baronet, and of Mrs. Stirling of Keir. 1794. *Glas. Mit.*
> STATE of the evidence for proving that the present Sir John Stuart of Castlemilk is the lineal heir-male and representative of Sir William Stuart of Castlemilk who lived during part of the 14th and 15th centuries. n.p., 1794. *Ruth. P.; Edin. S.; Glas. Mit.*
> STUART (Andrew): Genealogical history of the Stewarts . . . London, 1798. *S.C.L.; Inv. P.; Per. C.; St.A. U.; Glas. Mit.; Nai. C.; Edin. S.; Dumb. P.; Kirkcud. C.; Glas. U.; Edin. P.; Dumf. C.; Edin. L.L.; Edin. Ant.*

Stuart of Castle Stuart
> STUART (Andrew Godfrey): A genealogical and historical sketch of the Stuarts of the House of Castle Stuart, in Ireland. Edinburgh, 1854. *Ab. U.; Edin. P.; Edin. L.L.*

Stuart in England
> HUISH (Marcus Bourne): An old Stuart genealogy: a paper read before *Ye Sette of Odd Volumes,* Feb. 5th, 1897. London, 1898. *Nai. C.; Edin. P.; Edin. S.*

Stuart of Kingston
> YOUNG (Archibald H.): Rev. John Stuart, D.D., of Kingston, U.C., and his family. Kingston, Ont., 1920. *Ab. U.*

Stuart-Menteth

MENTETH (Sir James Stuart): The Stuart-Menteth pedigree not doubtful. 1868. (From *The Herald and Genealogist,* v. 5, 1868.) *Ab. U.*

Sutherland

LOCH (James): Dates and documents relating to the family and property of Sutherland. [London], 1859. *Edin. L.L.*

ROSE (David Murray): Sutherlands of Duffus and Skelbo. 1900. (Repr. from the *Northern Times,* July, 1900.) *Ab. U.*

Sutherland, Duke of, *see* Leveson-Gower, Duke of Sutherland

Sutherland, Earldom of

[DALRYMPLE (Sir D.), *3rd Lord Hailes*]: The Additional case of Elisabeth, claiming the title and dignity of Countess of Sutherland, by her Guardians . . . [London, 1771.] *Inv. P.; Glas. U.; Edin. P.; Glas. Mit.; Edin. L.L.; Edin. Ant.*

FRASER (Sir William): The Sutherland book. 3 v. Edinburgh, 1892. *S.C.L.; Inv. P.; St.A. U.; Ab. U.; Glas. U.; Edin. P.; Edin. S.; Glas. Mit.; Edin. L.L.; Edin. Ant.*

GORDON (Sir Robert): A genealogical history of the Earldom of Sutherland from its origin to the year 1630; published from the original MS. (by H. Weber). Edinburgh, 1813. *S.C.L.; Suth. C.; Ab. P.; Elg. P.; Cai. C.; Inv. P.; Per. C.; Edin. P.; Ab. U.; Glas. U.; Glas. Mit.; Edin. S.; Edin. L.L.; Edin. Ant.*

GORDON (Sir Robert) of Gordonstoun: Case of Sir Robert Gordon claiming the title . . . Earl of Sutherland, etc. 1769. *Edin. L.L.*

— Appendix to the case of Sir Robert Gordon, Bt. (claiming the title and dignity of Earl of Sutherland). *Edin. Ant.*

— In the question concerning the peerage of Sutherland . . . n.p., 1771. *Inv. P.; Glas. U.; Edin. P.; Edin. L.L.; Edin. Ant.; Glas. Mit.*

— Supplemental case . . . and pedigree . . . and pedigree of George Sutherland of Forss. 1770. *Edin. L.L.*

— Sutherland. Peerage case. 1769. (*MS.*) *Inv. P.; Edin. P.*

JUDGMENT . . . [1771.] *Edin. Ant.*

MAIDMENT (James): Report of claims . . . to the House of Lords . . . of the Cassillis, Sutherland, Spynie and Glencairn peerages, 1760-1797. Edinburgh, 1882. *Glas. U.; Dund. P. (1840); Edin. P.; Edin. S.; Glas. Mit.; Edin. Ant.; Edin. L.L. (1840).*

SUTHERLAND (Elisabeth), *Countess of*: Case of Elisabeth claiming the title . . . of Countess of Sutherland, by her Guardians . . . 1769. *Edin. L.L.*

WEMYSS (Elisabeth): Case of . . . Lady Elisabeth . . . and the Hon. James Wemyss of Wemyss, her husband, etc. *Edin. L.L.*

Swinton

SWINTON (Archibald Campbell): The Swintons of that ilk, and their cadets. Edinburgh, 1883. *Ber. C.; Rox. C.; St.A. U.; Ab. U.; Glas. U.; Edin. P.; Edin. S.; Edin. L.L.; Edin. Ant.* (+MS. notes by Capt. Geo. Swinton).

SWINTON (Archibald Campbell) & SWINTON (J. L. Campbell): Concerning Swinton family records and portraits at Kimmerghame. Edinburgh, 1908. *Ber. C.; Edin. P.; Edin. S.*

Symington

PATON (Rev. Henry): Genealogy of the Symington family. Edinburgh, 1908. *Pee. C.; Ab. U.; Edin. P.; Glas. Mit.; Edin. L.L.; Edin. Ant.*

Symons

MITCHELL (Silas Weir): A brief history of two families. The Mitchells of Ayrshire and the Symons of Cornwall. Philadelphia, Penn., 1912. *S.C.L.* (microfilm); *Dumf. C.*

Tennant

T[ENNANT] (H[arold] J[ohn]): Sir Charles Tennant, his forbears and descendants. London, 1932. *Edin. P.; Edin. S.*

Thoms

SMITH (William McCombie): Memoir of the families of McCombie and Thoms. Edinburgh, 1890. *Dunf. P.; Ab. P.; Nai. C.; Zet. C.; Dumb. P.; Ab. C.; St. A. U.; Ab.U.; Dund. Q.; Glas. U.; Dund. P.; Pai. P.; Edin. P.; Edin. S.; Glas. Mit.; Edin. L.L.*

Thomson

DEUCHAR (Alexander), *comp.*: Genealogical collections relative to the family of Thomson. 183- (*MS. & newspaper cuttings.*) *Edin. P.*

THOMSON (David Couper): Thomson, Couper, Yule, Sinclair genealogical chart. Dundee, [1937]. *Dund. P.; Edin. L.L.* (1936); *Edin. Ant.* (1936).

Thomson of Corstorphine

THOMSON (Theodore Radford): A history of the family of Thomson of Corstorphine. Edinburgh, 1926. *St.A. U.; Ab. U.; Edin. U.; Edin. P.; Edin. S.; Glas. Mit.; Edin. L.L.; Edin. Ant.*

Thomson of Duddingston

[WOOD (John Philip)]: Thomson of Duddingston. (In his *Memorials of various families.* c. 1830 (*MS.*).) *Edin. P.*

Thomson in Glasgow

THOMSON (G. Graham): An old Glasgow family of Thomson: a paper. [Glasgow, 1903.] *Glas. Mit.*

Thomson, Marquhitter

THOMSON (Henry Morton) & THOMSON (Andrew Sherran): The Thomson family and its pedigree: descendants and other kindred of Alexander Thomson, Greens Marquhitter, Aberdeenshire, and Elizabeth Clark, his wife. Norwich, 1896. *Pet. P.; Ab. C.; Edin. P.* ([1897]).

Threipland

CHAMBERS (Robert): The Threiplands of Fingask: a family memoir. Edinburgh, 1880. *S.C.L.; Per. P.; St.A. U.; Ber. C.; Cai. C.; Ab. P.; Inv. P.; Per. C.; Ab. U.; Dund. Q.; Glas. U.; Dund. P.; Pai. P.; Edin. P.; Glas. Mit.; Edin. S.; Edin. L.L.*

Thurburn

THURBURN (F. A. V.): The Thurburns; with pedigrees of Thurbrand and Thurburn. London, 1864. *Edin. L.L.*

Tod of Findaty

TOD (T. M.): Genealogy and its concomitant connections of the Tod family, also other matters of varied interest in connection with Findaty, Brackley, etc. 1947. (*Typescript.*) *S.C.L.*

Tolmie

MACKENZIE (Hector Hugh): Mackenzies of Ballone . . . with genealogical account of the Tolmies of Uiginish, Skye. Inverness, 1941. *Inv. P.; Ab. P.; Edin. P.; Glas. Mit.; Edin. S.*

Touche

TOUCHE (George A.): Some notes on the Scottish surname of Touch or Touche. n.p., [1906]. *Ab. U.*

Traill

GUTHRIE (Charles John), *Lord Guthrie, comp.*: Genealogy of the descendants of the Rev. Thomas Guthrie . . . connected chiefly with the families of Chalmers and Trail . . . Edinburgh, 1902. *Arb. P.; Ab. P.; St.A. U.; Glas. U.; Edin. P.; Edin. S.; Glas. Mit.*

Traill of Blebe, Blebo

FAMILY tree of Trail of Blebe, 1390 to date-1957. 1957. (*MS.*) *Ab. P.*

A SHORT account of the family of Trails of Blebe and their descendants, copied from authentic family manuscripts. [1836.] (*Typescript.*) *Ab. P.; Edin. P.*

TRAILL (William): A genealogical account of the Traills of Orkney, with a pedigree table tracing their descent from the Traills of Blebo, in Fifeshire. Kirkwall, 1883. *Ork. C.; Edin. P.; Ab. U.; St.A. U.; Glas. Mit.; Edin. S.; Edin. L.L.*

Traill of Elsness, Orkney

MARWICK (Hugh), *ed.*: Merchant lairds of long ago. Pt. 1, Traill family letters. Kirkwall, 1936. *Ork. C.; Glas. Mit.*

[ORIGINAL family papers.] *Ork. C.*

Traill of Frotoft

[ORIGINAL family papers.] *Ork. C.*

TRAILL (Thomas W.): Genealogical sketches: the Frotoft branch of the Orkney Traills. n.p., 1902. *Edin. S.*

Trotter

[KERR (Archibald)]: The Genealogie of the Trotters of Mortoun-Hall and Charter-Hall. 1704. (*Typescript.*) *Edin. P.*

Tullibardine, Earl of, Marquess of, *see* **Murray,** Earl of, Marquess of, Duke of Atholl

Turing

TURING (Sir Robert Fraser): Claim for baronetcy—case of Sir Robert Fraser Turing, Bt., with pedigrees, tables and documents. Edinburgh, 1912. *Edin. S.*

McKENZIE (H.): The Lay of the Turings: a sketch of the family history, 1316-1849. n.p., [1850]. *Ab. P.; Glas. Mit.*

181

Turner

THOMSON (David Couper), *comp.*: [Genealogical chart of] McCulloch Turner, McCormick and Russell. Dundee, 1943. *Edin. L.L.; Edin. Ant.*

Tweedie

TWEEDIE (Michael Forbes): The History of the Tweedie, or Tweedy, family. London, 1902. *S.C.L.; Edin. U.; St.A. U.; Edin. S.; Edin. L.L.*

Tyrie

TYRIE (Andrew): The Tyries of Drumkilbo, Perthshire, Dunnideer, Aberdeenshire and Lunan, Forfarshire. Glasgow, 1893. *Ab. U.; Edin. S.*

Udny

GENEALOGICAL tree of the Udny family, 1350-1930. Aberdeen, [1930]. *Ab. U.*

UDNY of that ilk. (Repr. from *The Genealogist*, Aug./Sept. 1877, vol. II.) *Ab. U.; Ab. P.*

Urquhart

TAYLER (Henrietta): History of the family of Urquhart. Aberdeen, 1946. *S.C.L.; Inv. P.; Cai. C.; Ab. C.; Ayr P.; Ross C.; Edin. U.; Ab. U.; St.A. U.; Ab. P.; Glas. U.; Edin. P.; Edin. S.; Glas. Mit.; Edin. L.L.; Edin. Ant.*

URQUHART (Sir Thomas): Tracts relating to the descent of the family of Urquharts, from the creation of the world to 1774. Edinburgh, 1774. *Inv. P.; Glas. U.; Edin. P.; Edin. S.; Glas. Mit.; Edin. L.L.; Edin. Ant.*

Usher

[USHER (Charles Milne), *ed.*]: A history of the Usher family in Scotland. Edinburgh, 1956. *S.C.L.; Edin. P.; Edin. S.*

Vanrenen

BLAIR-IMRIE (William): The Family of General Vanrenen, with their war services. 1902. *Arb. P.*

Vans-Agnew, *see* **Vaus, Vaux**

Vass

CRANNA (William H.): The Surnames of Cranna and Vass. Aberdeen, 1926. (*Typescript.*) *Ab. P.*

Vaus, Vaux

AGNEW (Sir Andrew): History of the hereditary Sheriffs of Galloway. Edinburgh, 1864. *Kil. P.; Dumf. C.; Wig. C.; Kirkcud. C.; St.A. U.; Glas. U.; Edin. P.; Edin. S.; Glas. Mit.*

—— 2 v. 2nd ed. 1893. *Haw. P.; Wig. C.; Glas. U.; St.A. U.; Edin. P.; Edin. S.; Glas. Mit.*

[VANS AGNEW (Robert)]: Sketch of a genealogical and historical account of the family of Vaux, Vaus or De Vallibus, now represented in Scotland by Vans Agnew of Barnbarrow . . . Pembroke, 1800. *Edin. S.*

[AGNEW (Henry Stewart Vans)]: A short account of the family of De Vaux, Vaus or Vans of Barnbarroch. 1832. *Wig. C.*

ROYAL letters and other original documents addressed to the lairds of Barnbarroch, MDLIX-MDCXVIII (1559-1618). n.d. *Kirkcud. Bro.*

see also **Waus** of Barnbarroch

Veitch

EXTRACTS from the General Register of Sasines and also from various parish registers (Lyne, Manor, Peebles, etc.) and notes from the Particular Register (Roxburgh, Selkirk and Peebles), 17th and 18th century. (*MSS.*) *Edin. L.L.*

MAIDMENT (James): Genealogical fragments relating to the families of . . . Veitch . . . Berwick, 1855. *Inv. P.; Glas. U.; Edin. P.; Edin. S.; Glas. Mit.; Edin. Ant.*

Vipont, *see* **De Veteripont**

Walker

WHITE (Emma Siggins), *Mrs. White, of Kansas City*: Genealogy of the descendants of John Walker of Wigton, Scotland, with records of a few allied families. [Kansas City, Mo. 1902. *Wig. C.*

Walker in Aberdeen

GENEALOGICAL details of Walker family, shopkeepers in Aberdeen. n.p., n.d. *Ab. P.*

Wallace of Bathgate

CUTHBERT (Alex. A.), *comp.*: Genealogical chart of the Wallace family, Bathgate. n.p., [1905]. *Glas. Mit.*

Wallace of Elderslie

MITCHELL (John Oswald): . . . The Two Elderslies. Glasgow, 1884. (Repr. from the *Glasgow Herald* of 13th Sept. 1884.) *Glas. Mit.*

— The Wallaces of Elderslie. Glasgow, 1884. (Repr. from *Trans. Arch. Soc. of Glasgow*, 1884.) *Glas. Mit.; Edin. S.; Edin. L.L.*

ROGERS (Charles): The Book of Wallace: history and genealogy of the family. 2 v. Edinburgh, 1889. (Grampian Club, 22.) *S.C.L.; Ab. P.; Inv. P.; Sti. P.; Ayr P.; Glas. U.; Dunf. P.; Edin. P.; Glas. Mit.; Edin. S.; Edin. L.L.; Edin. Ant.*

WALLACE, of "Elderslie", Renfrewshire, Scotland, and "Elderslie", of King George and Stafford counties, Virginia. (In *Hayden (H. E.): Virginia genealogies.* Wilkes-Barre, Pa. 1891.) *Glas. Mit.*

Wardlaw

GIBSON (John C.): The Wardlaws in Scotland: a history of the Wardlaws of Wilton and Torrie and their cadets. Edinburgh, 1912. *Dunf. P.; Sti. C.; Ab. U.; St.A. U.; Haw. P.; Kirkcud. C.; Glas. U.; Edin. P.; Edin. S.; Glas. Mit.; Edin. L.L.*

Watson

WATSON (Angus): The Angus clan (years 1588 to 1950). Gateshead, 1955. *Edin. P.*

WATSON (Charles Brodie Boog): Traditions and genealogies of some members of the families of Boog, Heron, Leishman, Ross, Watson. Perth, 1908. *Edin. P.; Edin. S.; St.A. U.; Edin. L.L.; Edin. Ant.*

Watson of Damhead

[WOOD (John Philip)]: Some notes about . . . Watson of Damhead. (In his *Memorials of various families* . . . c. 1830. (*MS.*).) *Edin. P.*

Watson of Saughton

[WOOD (John Philip)]: Memorial respecting the family of Watson of Saughton . . . (In his *Memorials of various families*. . . . c. 1830 (*MS.*).) *Edin. P.*

Watt of Breckness

[ORIGINAL family papers.] *Ork. C.*

Watt of Greenock

WILLIAMSON (George): Letters respecting the Watt family. Greenock, 1840. *Gree. P.; Glas. Mit.*

— Memorials of the lineage . . . of James Watt. Edinburgh, 1856. *Glas. U.; Glas. Mit.; Edin. P.; Edin. S.*

Wauchope

PATERSON (James): Scottish surnames: a contribution to genealogy. Edinburgh, 1866. *Arb. P.; Glas. Mit.; Ab. P.; Dund. Q.*

WAUCHOPE (Gladys Mary), *ed*: The Ulster branch of the family of Wauchope, Wanhope, Wahab, Wanghop, etc. with notes of the main Scottish family and on branches in America and Australia. London, 1929. *St.A. U.; Edin. P.; Edin. S.*

Wauchope of Niddrie-Marischall

PATERSON (James): History and genealogy of the family of Wauchope of Niddrie-Marischall. Edinburgh, 1858. *Mid. C.; Edin. P.; Edin. S.; Edin. L.L.*

Waus of Barnbarroch

WAUS (Sir Patrick): Correspondence, 1540-1597; ed. by Robert Vans Agnew. Edinburgh, 1882. *Glas. Mit.* (+1887).

see also **Vaus, Vaux**

Wedderburn

DEUCHAR (A.): Genealogical collections relative to the family of Wedderburn. (*MS*.) *Glas. Mit.*

WEDDERBURN (Alexander): The Wedderburn book: a history of the Wedderburns in the counties of Berwick and Forfar. 2 v. n.p., 1898. *S.C.L.; Dund. P.; Ber. C.; Ab. U.; St.A. U.; Forf. P.; Dund. Q.; Edin. P.; Edin. S.; Glas. Mit.; Edin. L.L.*

see also **Scrymgeour-Wedderburn**

Wemyss

CUNNINGHAM (Andrew Storar): Randolph Gordon Erskine Wemyss: an appreciation. [With an account of the family.] Leven, [1909]. *Dunf. P.; Buck. P.*

WEMYSS (Lady Mary Constance): Family record. London, 1932. *Edin. P*

Wemyss of Wemyss

FRASER (Sir William): Memorials of the family of Wemyss of Wemyss. 3 v. Edinburgh, 1888. *S.C.L.; Dunf. P.; Fife C.; Moth. P.; Kir. P.; Ab. U.; St.A. U.; Glas. U.; Edin. P.; Edin. S.; Edin. L.L.*

White

WHITE (W. R.): The White family from Donald Bain of Aberdeen, 1640-1740. c. 1845. (*Typescript.*) *Ab. P.*

Whitelaw

WHITELAW (Harry Vincent): The House of Whitelaw . . . 1400-1900. Glasgow, 1928. *S.C.L.; Air. P.; Edin. P.; Edin. S.; Glas. Mit.; Edin. L.L.; Edin. Ant.*

Whittet

WHITTET (William) [*of Dundee*] & WHITTET (Robert) [*of Richmond, Va.*]: Whittet: a family record, 1657-1900. Richmond, Va. 1900. *Per. P.*

Wigtown, Earl of, *see* **Fleming,** Earl of Wigtown

Wilkie of Rathobyres

MCCALL (Hardy Bertram): Some old families: a contribution to the genealogical history of Scotland. Birmingham, 1890. *S.C.L.; Edin. P.; Edin. S.; Sel. P.; Edin. L.L.; Edin. Ant.*

Willison

BLACK (William George): A note on the family of Black of Over Abington, 1694-1924. With memoranda on . . . Willison of Redshaw . . . [2nd ed.] Glasgow, 1924. *Ab. P.; Edin. P.; Edin. S.; Glas. U.* (+1908)*; Glas. Mit.; Edin. Ant.; Edin. L.L.* (+1908).

Wilson

THE FAMILY of Wilson of Belltrees, Bannockburn, etc. (*Genealogical MSS.*) *Glas. Mit.*

WILSON (Alex.): Fragments that remain. [A family history of the Wilsons.] Stroud, Glos. 1950. *Dumf. C.*

Wilson in Banffshire

BROWN (Andrew Cassels): The Wilsons: a Banffshire family of factors. Edinburgh, 1936. *S.C.L.; Ab. P.; Ab. U.; Edin. P.; Glas. Mit.; Edin. S.*

Wilson of Beith

CADBURY (W. A.): Wilsons of Beith (Ayrshire). n.p., [1933]. *Edin. P.*

Wimberley

WIMBERLEY (Douglas): Memorials of four old families. 1894. *Ab. P.; Inv. P.; Edin. P.; Edin. S.; Glas. Mit.; Dund. Q.*

— Memorials of the family of Wimberley of South Witham, etc. Inverness, 1893. *St.A. U.; Ab. U.; Edin. L.L.*

Winton, Earldom of

EGLINTOUN (Archibald William Montgomerie), *13th Earl of*: Abstract of the evidence in support of the Earl's claim. *Edin. L.L.*

— Case for the Earl of Eglinton in his service as heir-male general and heir-male of provision to George, 4th Earl of Winton, Lord Seaton and Tranent. *Edin. L.L.*

— Claim for the Earl in the Service. *Edin. L.L.*

INDEX to the case and abstract of evidence. *Edin. L.L.*

PEDIGREE . . . [Edinburgh, 1840.] *Edin. L.L.*

VERDICT of jury. *Edin. L.L.*

see also **Montgomerie,** Earl of Eglinton

Wise

ROGERS (Charles): Memorials of the Strachans, baronets of Thornton and of the family of Wise of Hillbank, formerly Wyse of Lunan, in the county of Forfar. London, [1873]. *Edin. P.; Inv. P.; Glas. U.; St.A. U.; Glas. Mit.; Edin. S.; Edin. L.L.*

— Memorials of the Scottish families of Strachan and Wise. [2nd ed.] Edinburgh, 1877. *Dunf. P.; Sti. P.; Ab. U.; St.A. U.; Glas. U.; Edin. P.; Edin. S.; Forf. P.*

Wishart

ROGERS (Charles): Life of George Wishart . . . and a genealogical history of the family of Wishart. London, 1876. (Grampian Club, 11.) *Inv. P.; Ab. P.; Dund. P.; Edin. P.; Glas. Mit.; Edin. L.L.*

Wishart of Pittarrow

[WISHART (D.)]: Genealogical history of the Wisharts of Pittarrow and Logie Wishart. Perth, 1914. *Edin. S.*

Wood

MONTAGU (Mrs. Frances Mary): Pedigree of Colonel Sir Mark Wood. n.d. (*MS.*) *ST.A. U.*

Wood of Largo

MONTAGUE (Mrs. Frances Mary): Memorials of the family of Wood of Largo. n.p., 1863. *Kir. P.; St.A. U.; Edin. P.; Edin. S.; Glas. Mit.*

Wyllie

NOTES on the Wyllie Album. n.p., n.d. (*Photocopy.*) *S.C.L.; Glas. U.; Dumf. C.; Edin. P.*

Wyse, *see* **Wise**

Young

JOHNSTON (Alexander): Short memoir of James Young, merchant burgess of Aberdeen, and Rachel Cruickshank his spouse, and of their descendants. [Aberdeen], 1861. *Ab. P.; Ab. C.; Edin. P.; Edin. S.; Edin. L.L.*

— [New ed.] ed. by W. Johnston. Aberdeen, 1894. *Ab. P.; Edin. P.; Edin. S.; Edin. L.L.*

LANG (Patrick Sellar), *comp.*: The Langs of Selkirk, with some notes on other families. Melbourne, 1910. *Edin. P.; Edin. S.*

MCCALL (Hardy Bertram): Some old families: a contribution to the genealogical history of Scotland. Birmingham, 1890. *S.C.L.; Edin. P.; Edin. S.; Sel. P.; Edin. L.L.; Edin. Ant.*

Younger of Clackmannanshire

HALLEN (Arthur Washington Cornelius): An account of the family of Younger, co. of Clackmannan. Edinburgh, 1889. *Clack. C.; Dunf. P.*

Younger of Peebles-shire

HALLEN (Arthur Washington Cornelius): An account of the family of Younger, co. Peebles. Edinburgh, 1890. *Clack. C.*

Yuille of Darleith

WILLIAMSON (George): Old Cartsburn: a history of the estate. Appendix. Paisley, 1894. *S.C.L.*

Yule

THOMSON (David Coupar): Thomson, Couper, Yule, Sinclair genealogical charts. Dundee, [1937]. *Dund. P.*

APPENDIX

A SELECTION OF GENERAL WORKS DEALING WITH SCOTTISH FAMILY HISTORY

While no locations are shown for the books in this Appendix, the Scottish Central Library should in most cases be able to trace copies.

ADAM (Frank): Clans, septs and regiments of the Scottish highlands. Edinburgh, 1908 etc.

ALLARDYCE (Col. James): Story of a Donside estate [Culquoich]. [Aberdeen], 1900.

ANDERSON (William): The Scottish nation; or, the surnames, families, literature, honours, and biographical history of the people of Scotland. 3 v. Edinburgh, 1860-62 etc.

BAIN (Robert): The Clans and tartans of Scotland. London, 1938 etc.

BEATON (Donald): Genealogical bibliography of Caithness and Sutherland. 1928. (Viking Society for Northern Research.)

BROWNE (James): A history of the Highlands and of the Highland clans. 4 v. Glasgow, 1838 etc.

BULLOCH (Joseph Gaston Baillie): A history and genealogy of the families of Bayard, Houston of Georgia and the descent of the Bolton family from Assheton, Byron and Hulton. (With notes on some Highland families connected with them.) Washington, 1919.

BURKE (Ashworth P.): Family records. London, 1897.

BURKE'S genealogical and heraldic history of the landed gentry. London, 1833 etc.

BURKE'S genealogical and heraldic history of the peerage, baronetage and knightage. London, 1826 etc.

BURKE (John) and BURKE (Sir John Bernard): A genealogical and heraldic history of the extinct and dormant baronetcies of England, Ireland and Scotland. London, 1838 etc.

CAMPBELL (Lord Archibald): Records of Argyll. Legends, traditions and recollections of Argyll-shire Highlanders, etc. Edinburgh, 1885.

CHAMBERS (William): Stories of old families. Edinburgh, 1878.

189

CLOUSTON (J. Storer): The Odal families of Orkney. (In *Orkney and Shetland Misc. Old-lore ser. of the Viking Club*, V. 1 & 2, 1907-08, 1909.)

CLOUSTON (J. Storer): The origin of the Orkney chiefs. (In *Orkney Antiq. Soc. Proc.* V. 12, 1934.)

[COKAYNE (George Edward)], "*G.E.C.*": Complete baronetage, etc. 6 v. Exeter, 1900-9.

[COKAYNE (George Edward)]: Complete peerage of England, Scotland, Ireland, Great Britain and the U.K., extant, extinct or dormant. New ed. by ... V. Gibbs and H. A. Doubleday. Vols. 1-9, 13. London, 1910-40.

COUTTS (James): The Anglo-Norman peaceful invasion of Scotland, 1057-1200: origin of great Scottish families. Edinburgh, 1922.

CRAWFURD (George): The peerage of Scotland, etc. Edinburgh, 1716.

CUNNINGHAM (Audrey): The loyal clans. Cambridge, 1932.

DAVIDSON (Rev. John): Inverurie and the earldom of the Garioch ... with a genealogical appendix of Garioch families flourishing at the period of the Revolution settlement and still represented. Edinburgh, 1878.

DONNER (Otto): A brief sketch of the Scottish families in Finland and Sweden. Helsingfors, 1884.

DOUGLAS (Sir Robert): The baronage of Scotland, etc. Edinburgh, 1798.

DOUGLAS (Sir Robert): The peerage of Scotland, etc. Edinburgh, 1764, etc.

DOUGLAS (Wm.): The owners of Dirleton. Edinburgh, [1929.] (Repr. from *Hist. of Ber. Nat. Club*, Vol. XXVII, 1929.)

[DRUMMOND (Henry), M.P.,]: Histories of noble British families, etc. 2 v. London, 1846.

EYRE-TODD (George): Highland clans of Scotland: their history and traditions. 2 v. London, 1923.

FISCHER (Thomas Alfred), pseud. [i.e. Ernst Ludwig Fischer]: The Scots in Germany, etc. Edinburgh, 1902.

FISCHER (Thomas Alfred), pseud. [i.e. Ernst Ludwig Fischer]: The Scots in Sweden ... ed. ... by J. Kirkpatrick. Edinburgh, 1907.

FISCHER (Thomas Alfred), pseud. [i.e. Ernst Ludwig Fischer]: The Scots in Eastern and Western Prussia; a sequel, etc. Edinburgh, 1903.

[FORBES (Arthur)]: Don: a poem, with large notes giving an account of the ancient families, castles and curiosities, on Don and its branches by Charles Dawson. New ed. corr. & enl. Peterhead, 1819.

FOSTER (Joseph): Members of Parliament, Scotland . . . 1357-1882; with genealogical and biographical notices. London, 1882.

FRASER-MACKINTOSH (Charles): Antiquarian notes, historical genealogical and social. (2nd ser.): Inverness-shire, parish by parish. Inverness, 1897.

FRASER-MACKINTOSH (Charles): Antiquarian notes. A series of papers regarding families and places in the Highlands. Inverness, 1865 etc.

A GENEALOGIE of the barons in the Mearns of late memory deschending lineally unto the year of God 1578. (Copy of this MS. in *Misc. Third Spalding Club*, v. II, 1940.)

GIBSON (John C.): The baronies and owners of Sauchie and Bannockburn. A paper read to the Stirling Natural History and Arch. Society, 20th Feb. 1934. Stirling, 1934.

GIBSON (John C.): The lands and lairds of Dunipace. Stirling, 1903.

GIBSON (John C.): Lands and lairds of Larbert and Dunipace parishes. Glasgow, 1908.

GRANT (Sir Francis James): The County families of the Zetland Islands. Lerwick, 1893.

HARRISON (Howard Guy): A select bibliography of English genealogy; with brief lists for Wales, Scotland and Ireland. London, 1937.

HENDERSON (John), W.S.: Caithness family history. Edinburgh, 1884.

HISTORY of the Highland regiments, Highland clans, etc., from official and other authentic sources. 2 v. Edinburgh, 1887.

INNES (Sir Thomas) of Learney: The tartans of the clans and families of Scotland. Edinburgh, 1938 etc.

IONA CLUB. Collectanea de rebus albanicis: consisting of original papers and documents relating to the history of the Highlands and islands of Scotland. Edinburgh, 1847.

IRVING (Joseph) : History of Dunbartonshire . . . with genealogical notices of the principal families in the county . . . Dumbarton, 1857 etc.

JOHNSTON (Thomas): Our Scots noble families. Glasgow, 1913.

JOHNSTON (T. B.) and ROBERTSON (Col. James Alex.): The historical geography of the clans of Scotland. Edinburgh, 1872 etc.

JOHNSTONE (Catherine Laura): Historical families of Dumfriesshire and the Border Wars. Dumfries, 1888 etc.

KELLY'S handbook to the titled, landed and official classes. London, 1875 etc.

KELTIE (Sir John Scott), *ed.*: History of the Scottish highlands, highland clans, and highland regiments. New ed. by Wm. Melven. 5 v. London [18—].

KNOWLES (George Parker): A genealogical and heraldic account of the Coultharts of Coulthart . . . [to which are added the pedigrees of seven other . . . families]. London, 1855.

LANGHORNE (William Henry): Reminiscences connected chiefly with Inveresk and Musselburgh, and sketches of family histories. Edinburgh, 1893.

MACDOUGALL (Donald): Scots and Scots' descendants in America. Vol. I. [New York, 1917.]

MCDOWALL (J. Kevan): Carrick Gallovidian. Ayr, 1947.

MACFARLANE (Walter): Genealogical collections concerning families in Scotland, made by W. MacFarlane, 1750-1751; ed. by J. T. Clark. 2 v. (Scottish Hist. Soc. XXXIII, XXXIV.) 1900.

MCKERLIE (Peter Handyside): History of the lands and their owners in Galloway. 5 v. Edinburgh, 1870-79 etc.

MCKERRAL (Andrew): Kintyre in the 17th century. Edinburgh, 1948.

MACKIE (John Duncan): The Denmilne MSS. in the National Library of Scotland. Edinburgh, 1928.

MACLEAN (John) [*of Inverness*]: Historical and traditional sketches of highland families, and of the Highlands. Dingwall, 1848 etc.

MACLEAY (Kenneth), *the younger*: Highlanders of Scotland: portraits illus. of the principal clans and followings and the retainers of the Royal Household at Balmoral, 1868. London, [1872].

MACLEOD (Donald) [*of Garelochside*]: Historic families, notable people, and memorabilia, of the Lennox, etc. Dumbarton, 1891.

MACPHAIL (J. R. N.), *ed.*: Highland papers. 4 v. (Scottish Hist. Soc. 2nd ser. v. 5, 12, 20. 3rd ser. v. 22.) Edinburgh, 1914-1934.

MACP[HERSON] (J.) and S[CHACHT] (F. W.): Sketches of the clans of Scotland, with col. plates of tartans, by Clansmen—J. McP., F. W. S. Edinburgh, 1884.

[MAIDMENT (James)]: Collectanea genealogica. Edinburgh, 1883.

MARSHALL (David): Genealogical notes anent some ancient Scottish families . . . Perth, 1884.

[MARSHALL (George)]: A catalogue of pedigrees hitherto unindexed. London, 1867.

192

MARSHALL (George William): The genealogist's guide to printed pedigrees, etc. London, 1879 etc.

MORRIS (David B.): Robert Louis Stevenson and the Scottish Highlanders. Stirling, 1929.

NICOLSON (Alexander): History of Skye ... a record of the families ... etc. illus. with genealogical tables. Glasgow, 1930.

NISBETT (Hamilton More): Oxenfoord and its owners. Edinburgh, 1932.

NISBETT (Hamilton More) and AGNEW (Stair Carnegie): Cairnhill. Edinburgh, 1949.

ORCADIAN families. Photostat copy of typescript. *Cont.*
Louttit of Lyking.
Louttit of Mirkbuster.
Hourston.
Fea of Clestrain.

PATERSON (James) [*of Edinburgh*]: History of the County of Ayr, with a genealogical account of the families of Ayrshire. 2 v. Ayr, 1847-1852.

PAUL (Sir James Balfour), *ed.*: The Scots peerage. 9 v. Edinburgh, 1904-14.

THE PEDIGREE REGISTER, Vols. 1-2. 1907-13; ed. by George Sherwood.

PETER (David MacGregor): The baronage of Angus and Mearns. Edinburgh, 1856.

PICKEN (Andrew): Traditionary stories of old families and legendary illustrations of family history. 2 v. in 1. London, 1833.

PLAYFAIR (Wm.): British family antiquity ... v. 8: The Baronetage of Scotland. London, 1811.

REID (John Eaton) : History of the county of Bute and families connected therewith. Glasgow, 1864.

ROBERTSON (George) [*of Irvine*]: A genealogical account of the principal families in Ayrshire, more particularly in Cunninghame. 4 v. (3 v.+Suppl.) Irvine, 1823-27.

ROBERTSON (Wm.), *Deputy Keeper of the Records, Scotland*: Proceedings relating to the Peerage of Scotland from January 16th, 1707 to Apr. 29th, 1788. Edinburgh, 1790.

ROGERS (Charles), D.D.: Estimate of the Scottish nobility during the minority of James the Sixth, with preliminary observations. London, 1873. (Grampian Club.)

THE SCOTS COMPENDIUM, or, pocket peerage of Scotland. 2 v. Edinburgh, 1826.

Sinclair (Alexander), *1794-1877*: Historical, genealogical and miscellaneous tracts. 22 pts. [Edinburgh, 1860?]

Skene (William Forbes): History of the Highlanders of Scotland. Ed. by A. Macbain. 2 v. Edinburgh, 1837 etc.

Smibert (Thomas), *ed.*: The clans of the highlands of Scotland ... with delineations of their tartans and family arms. Edinburgh, 1850.

Smith (John Guthrie): Strathendrick and its inhabitants: an account of the parishes of Fintry, Balfron, Killearn, Drymen, Buchanan, and Kilmaronock. Glasgow, 1896.

Stuart (Margt.) and Paul (Sir James Balfour): Scottish family history: a guide to works of reference on the history and genealogy of Scottish families. Edinburgh, 1930.

Tancred (George): The annals of a border club (the Jedforest) and biog. notices of the families connected therewith. Jedburgh, 1899 etc.

Tayler (Alistair) and Tayler (Henrietta): Jacobites of Aberdeenshire and Banffshire in the Forty-Five. Aberdeen, 1928.

Taylor (James) [*of Glasgow*]: The great historic families of Scotland. 2 v. London, 1887 etc.

Temple (Rev. William): The thanage of Fermartyn . . . its proprietors, with genealogical deductions, etc. Aberdeen, 1894.

Thomson (Theodore R.): Catalogue of British family history. London, 1928.

Walford (Edward): County families of the United Kingdom. London, 1860 etc.

Wallace (George): The nature and descent of ancient peerages connected with the State of Scotland, the origin of tenures, the succession of fiefs and the constitution of parliament in that country. Edinburgh, 1783 etc.

Whitmore (J. B.), *comp.*: A genealogical guide: an index to British pedigrees in continuation of Marshall's genealogist's Guide. London, 1953.

Wood (John Philip): The ancient and modern state of the parish of Cramond, to which are added biographical and genealogical collections, respecting some of the most considerable families and individuals connected with the district. Edinburgh, 1794.

Young (Rev. R.): The Buccleuch book with especial reference to Allanhaugh: a paper read to the Hawick Archaeological Society, 13th June, 1882. (Appears in v. 25 of *Trans. Haw. Arch. Soc.*)

Printed in Great Britain
at Hopetoun Street, Edinburgh,
by T. and A. CONSTABLE LTD.
Printers to the University of Edinburgh.